OCE

90°W

35°

PALMER
PENINSULA

WEDDELL
SEA

ORST

*ATLANTIC
OCEAN*

QUEEN
MAUD
LAND

ANTARCTICA WITHOUT ICE
An artist's conception of the
continent's appearance prior
to its envelopment in ice
Based on IGY results
Dashed line shows present shoreline

Ken Fagg

GEO-PHYSICAL MAPS INC.

0

ASSAULT
on the
UNKNOWN

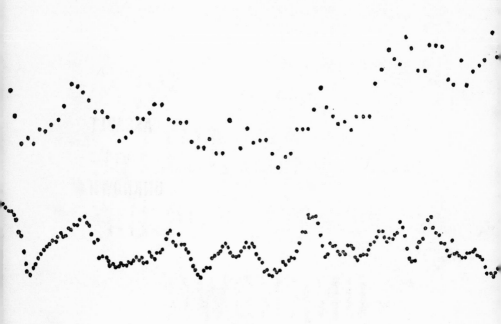

Books by Walter Sullivan
QUEST FOR A CONTINENT
ASSAULT ON THE UNKNOWN

Junior Book
WHITE LAND OF ADVENTURE

ASSAULT
on the
UNKNOWN

The International Geophysical Year

WALTER SULLIVAN

McGRAW-HILL BOOK COMPANY, INC. *New York   Toronto   London*

Library of Congress Catalog Card Number: 60-53222

First Edition

62337

To my wife, Mary,
and to our mutual hope that science
may help mankind find peace

PREFACE

This book has been written by a layman, for whom the International Geophysical Year was a scientific adventure of awesome dimensions, in the hope that the general reader will share the thrills of its discoveries and the promise that it holds for a peaceful future. The author has sought to lead the reader along the same path that he has followed, from the most elementary concepts to the wonders disclosed by the first earth satellites and the new reach of our exploration into the blackest ocean deeps, the turbulent atmosphere, and the perilous ice sheets.

Because no full account of Project Argus, the secret experiment that embraced the world, has been available to the public, it has been described in some detail. To season the scientific accounts with personal experience, the author has included a number of events that he witnessed and, because of this and the broad scope of the American program, more space has been devoted to the United States effort than to that of any other nation. Nevertheless the author has sought to bring out the international character of the IGY by including observations in many other lands.

Some believe that the chief importance of the IGY may have been its effect on relations between nations. It was directly responsible for the setting aside of an entire continent—Antarctica—as an international laboratory. The emergence of science as a potent force in international affairs has taken many by surprise. The subject has, in fact, been given scant attention by the historians although international scientific efforts have been gathering momentum for more than a century and a half. Several chapters have therefore been devoted to the history of such efforts and the way in which the IGY dealt with those problems thrust upon it by the "Cold War."

Scientifically this is, perforce, a bird's-eye view. Sixty-six nations carried out programs in one or more of the dozen sciences embraced by the IGY. It has been possible to touch upon only what seemed the more exciting aspects of the venture. Some participants will find their excellent work ignored or treated summarily. Although the author has sought to include the most important discoveries, he is aware that decades may pass before time and further discoveries give us sufficient perspective to decide which were, in fact, the most significant.

The footnotes, listed chapter by chapter in the back of the book, are primarily references to source material for the reader who wishes to pursue the subject matter further. A bibliography is to be included in the official *Annals of the International Geophysical Year,* being published in London by the Pergamon Press. An annotated bibliography of the IGY is also being prepared by the Library of Congress in Washington, D.C. In this book, for purposes of brevity, titles such as "doctor" and "professor," applicable to many of the individuals mentioned, have been omitted. Unless otherwise noted, statute miles and degrees Fahrenheit are used throughout.

ACKNOWLEDGMENTS

The author's foremost debt is to *The New York Times,* which regarded the IGY as of sufficient importance to assign one man to cover it full-time and which permitted him to draw extensively on his dispatches and their accompanying drawings in the preparation of this book. Special thanks are also due to the Carnegie Endowment for International Peace, which has allowed the author to use material from the issue of its publication, *International Conciliation,* that he wrote on the IGY.

Each of the chapters dealing with the scientific program has been reviewed by one or more specialists, although their assistance does not relieve the author of final responsibility for the accuracy of fact or interpretation. Those who have thus given generously of their time are: James K. Angell, Spencer Apollonio, Laurence J. Cahill, Jr., Gordon D. Cartwright, James B. Caskey, Jr., Talbot A. Chubb, Albert P. Crary, Charles L. Drake, William O. Field, Arnold W. Frutkin, Torrence H. MacDonald, Carl W. Gartlein, Kenneth L. Hunkins, Robert Jastrow, Lester Machta, John E. Nafe, Edward P. Ney, John A. O'Keefe, Jack Oliver, Donald K. Pack, Franklin E. Roach, Morton Rubin, Homer J. Stewart, Sidney Teweles, James A. Van Allen, Harry Wexler, and Walter A. Wood.

The following have kindly provided accounts of programs of which they had personal experience: D. E. Blackwell, Nicholas C. Christofilos, P. A. Day, F. R. Furth, Melvin B. Gottlieb, John P. Hagen, G. F. Harris, Gordon L. Harris, Victor F. Hess, George W. Hoover, Norman J. Oliver, Richard W. Porter, K. J. Salmon, John A. Simpson, S. F. Singer, James H. Smith, Jr., William G. Stroud, and Robert C. Truax.

It is not possible to list all the others who helped, but special mention must be made of Hugh Odishaw and his staff with the United States National Committee for the IGY, Lloyd V. Berkner and his assistants, as well as many at the National Aeronautics and Space

Administration, at the Naval Research Laboratory, and on the staff of the Navy's *Operation Deep Freeze*. Photographs and other material were furnished by a number of those mentioned above and were also provided by Hugo Benioff, Jan Hahn, V. P. Hessler, the High Altitude, Lockheed Solar, Sacramento Peak, and Smithsonian Astrophysical Observatories, the IGY Committee of the USSR Academy of Sciences, Edward R. La Chapelle, *Life* magazine, Sarah Lee Lippincott, Don J. Miller, the National Institute of Oceanography (Great Britain), the Soviet Embassy, Washington, D.C., Edward C. Thiel, and Don Tocher. Books for Pleasure, Ltd., has kindly given permission for use of the passages quoted from *Secrets of Soviet Science* by Lucien Barnier.

The book's maps and drawings are in great measure a tribute to the skill of Andrew Sabbatini. The endpapers were artistically done by Kenneth Fagg.

Patricia C. Wohlgemuth rendered valuable assistance with the footnotes. Olive M. Evans and Adele Szafranski did the extensive typing. Elizabeth H. Burpee helped in many ways. Finally, I believe my wife's skill and patience in editing helped significantly in making the text comprehensible to the layman.

CONTENTS

ILLUSTRATIONS

xiii

ASSAULT

on the

UNKNOWN

A five-stage Project Argus rocket rising from the USS Norton Sound. *In this shot, a month before the project's three atomic explosions were secretly fired in space, the bomb chamber in the rocket nose was empty. The Office of Naval Research kindly declassified this picture in time for publication in this book.*

CHAPTER 1
IMPACT

It was the evening of October 4, 1957, and the ballroom of the Soviet Embassy in Washington was crowded with Soviet, American and other specialists in rocket research. As they stood, glasses of vodka in hand, the sound of their mingled voices filled the ornate room. The Russians were playing host to those attending a conference in Washington to coordinate plans for the launching of rockets and earth satellites during the International Geophysical Year.

More than three months of the IGY already had passed, and much publicity had been given to United States plans for launching a satellite, but the first attempt was not expected for at least two more months.

At the conference, whose working sessions had come to an end that day, the Russians had said they would make no advance announcement of their first attempt. They told their American colleagues, almost in so many words, "We will not cackle until we have laid our egg."

As I stood in the ballroom with the scientists and a scattering of fellow newsmen, an official of the embassy said I was wanted on the telephone. It was *The New York Times'* Washington Bureau.

"Radio Moscow has just announced that the Russians have placed a satellite in orbit 900 kilometers above the earth," the news editor said. Heart pounding with excitement, I bounded up the great staircase to the ballroom and threaded my way across the floor to pass the news on to Lloyd V. Berkner, the American member of the international committee running the IGY. Whatever the Russians there may have known of their government's intentions, they could not have known that the launching was successful. The Americans could at least have the pleasure of making the announcement to the Russians in their own embassy.

1

Berkner clapped his hands loudly for silence and told the assembly of the launching. The reporters rushed in quest of telephones. Even though some of the Americans present had suspected that the Russians were about to launch a satellite (only a couple of hours earlier I had actually written a story to that effect which was now obsolete), the timing and the accomplished fact seemed almost incredible.

The impact on the American public was profound. Less than six weeks earlier Moscow had announced the successful firing of an intercontinental ballistic missile. The launching of a satellite more than eight times heavier than those being readied in the United States was dramatic proof that the Russians had such a missile and effective guidance for it. Furthermore—and most telling of all—the orbit of the final-stage rocket made it visible from virtually all inhabited areas of the earth. This rocket had given Sputnik I its final kick to orbiting speed and was now circling the earth on its own. It was so large and shiny that, when the observer was in darkness but the rocket was lighted by the rising or setting sun, it was brilliantly illuminated for all to see.

Until now the IGY had been something children heard about in the schoolroom, or the more scientifically inclined read about in selected newspapers or periodicals. Yet the effect of this launching was not to give a great boost to the IGY and its noble goals of international cooperation in science. Rather it sent a shudder through large parts of the world. The fact suddenly became inescapable that the largest nation in the world, geographically, was also the strongest in a field critical in war-making—rocketry.

A public conditioned to believe that such earlier Soviet achievements in science and technology as the hydrogen bomb were simply the fruits of espionage felt that again the Russians had somehow "put one over on us." The feeling of wonder and excitement at man's escape from the earth was largely lost in fear. The absence of advance warning, in humiliating contrast to elaborate publicity about American satellite plans, led to accusations that the Russians had not played the IGY game according to the rules.

The validity of this accusation will be discussed later, but once the United States had begun to launch its own space vehicles there was an improvement in American attitudes, a thrill at witnessing the inception of a new era. By now, references to the Space Age have become hackneyed, yet upon reflection it seems possible that, a thousand years hence, the year 1957 will be to the schoolchildren of the world what 1492 is to young Americans today. In 1492 the Old World opened the door to the New; in 1957 man opened the door to the solar system, and perhaps beyond.

CHAPTER 2
EXPERIMENTS IN CONCERT

The International Geophysical Year has been described by Hugh Odishaw, the man chiefly responsible for organizing the vast American effort, as "the single most significant peaceful activity of mankind since the Renaissance and the Copernican Revolution." The IGY involved about 60,000 scientists from sixty-six nations, working at thousands of stations, literally from pole to pole. Despite two small-scale predecessors in 1882 and 1932, there never had been anything like it before.

Francis Bacon, at the start of the seventeenth century, is said to have proposed "experiments in concert" as the most effective way in which to understand the world around us. The IGY marked the culmination of a growing awareness that only this sort of approach could bring substantial advances in a number of sciences.

Even though Pythagoras saw the world as a sphere as long ago as 500 B.C., man still finds it difficult, in his mind, to back off enough to see it as a whole. Yet, as the centuries passed, it became progressively more evident to the scientist that the destinies of men were governed by a multitude of events taking place beyond the observational range of any individual. A storm that flooded cities in Ohio or leveled crops in France was not an isolated phenomenon. It was a by-product of vast forces at work within the atmosphere. It was increasingly obvious that events in the ocean of air covering the earth moved and affected one another on a world-wide basis.

The oceans of water were no longer seen as separate entities, but as one great, mobile reservoir covering two-thirds of the globe and carrying, within its deep, slow currents, the seeds of latent climate change that might destroy existing civilizations and make possible new ones. The earth, in its flight through space, was dependent for its habitability on a balanced "diet" of radiation from the sun, but the composition and constancy of this diet were still little understood.

Attacks on such global problems obviously could not be confined within national boundaries. International science can be traced back to the ancients, who exchanged data to construct maps for their mutual benefit; it developed further as man gazed into space and sought to measure celestial distances. Nevertheless, not until the last century did coordinated observations by many men at many points come to be general practice.

This was a time when the area of scientific knowledge was small enough so that one genius could view all its frontiers and contribute to advances on a number of them. Such was Jean Baptiste Pierre Antoine de Monet, Chevalier de Lamarck, one of the first men to attempt systematic classification of plants and animals. Among Lamarck's contemporaries was Pierre Simon, Marquis de Laplace, a master of mathematical analysis, probability theory, and celestial mechanics. Another was Antoine Laurent Lavoisier, agronomist and expert on thunder, aurora, gunpowder, agriculture, and taxation; some consider him the father of modern chemistry. As the eighteenth century ended these three French scientists teamed up with others to study the weather, although in 1794 Lavoisier dropped out of the picture. Accused by the revolutionary firebrand, Marat, of suffocating Paris by promoting the erection of a "wall of toll stations" around the city, he went to the guillotine.

Under the auspices of the French scientists, a network of observing stations was established and publication of the assembled data began in 1800. In 1820 H. W. Brandes published a compilation of daily weather charts for the year 1783. His charts for major storms in later years showed how their movement across Europe was associated with the easterly migration of low-pressure areas. The work was of little value in forecasting weather since it took weeks, via stagecoach mail, to assemble the necessary data. But the many-talented scientists of that time were busy in a variety of fields and Laplace proposed a telegraph system based on twenty-six wires (one for each letter of the alphabet) with a magnet at the end of each. Samuel F. B. Morse, American painter and inventor, devised a more practical scheme that required only one wire and by 1851 fifty telegraph companies were in operation in the United States.

In the same year an American naval officer proposed a plan for coordinated, world-wide weather observations, both at sea and ashore. He was Matthew Fontaine Maury, who had been crippled when a stagecoach overturned. Forced by his disability to remain ashore, he presided over the birth of the United States Naval Observatory and the Navy's Hydrographic Office. Reportedly on the advice of British scientific friends, Commander Maury limited his initial effort to ship-based observations and obtained authority from the Secretary of the Navy to approach foreign embassies in Washington with his scheme. As a result, an international conference was held in Brussels in 1853 to discuss his plan. Represented were Belgium, Britain, Denmark, France, the Netherlands, Norway, Portugal, Russia, Sweden, and the United States. It was agreed that the warships of these nations would use standard forms to record weather and oceanic phenomena wherever they went, pooling the information for the good of mankind. The records were to be sacrosanct, even when such ships were captured in time of war.

> Rarely before [Maury wrote] has there been such a sublime spectacle presented to the scientific world: all nations agreeing to unite and cooperate in carrying out one system of philosophical research with regard to the sea. Though they may be enemies in all else, here they are to be friends.[1]

The Commander then proposed a second conference to map a program of international weather observations on land. The Crimean War (1853–55) helped doom this proposal, and his subsequent effort to organize a nation-wide weather service in the United States, taking advantage of the new telegraph nets, likewise failed. Not until 1870 was such a service established, under the Army Signal Service— a forerunner of the system operated by the present-day Weather Bureau. By then several European countries had already done likewise.

Meanwhile the Germans had begun to apply the same principles of observation to terrestrial magnetism, the force that orients the compass needle. One of the Europeans Maury befriended and greatly admired was Friedrich Heinrich Alexander, Baron von Humboldt, whose scientific interests were even more multiple than his name. They included subterranean vegetation, the nervous system, philosophy, exploration, climatology, and volcanoes, as well as magnetism. Humboldt has been described as the last man to encompass within his ken all the frontiers of science. His appeals to the Russians (in

1829) and to the British (in 1836) led to world-wide magnetic observations, scattered throughout the far-flung British and Russian Empires. The network extended as far as Peking, China, and Sitka, Alaska.

Comparison of the results showed that at the moment the compass needle moved erratically in Potsdam, near Berlin, it did so as well on the opposite side of the world and at scores of other places. Humboldt thus showed that the periodic fluctuations in the earth's magnetic field are integrated global phenomena; he called them "magnetic storms," a term still in use.

While Humboldt was at work, his friend Karl Friedrich Gauss had founded, with his co-worker Wilhelm Weber, the Magnetischer Verein (Magnetic Union) with headquarters in Göttingen, Germany. It soon grew from a German affair into an international organization that fixed, long in advance, special days for simultaneous recording of the earth's magnetism. Between 1835 and 1839 observations were carried out from the Netherlands to Sicily. Such was the impact of this work on the scientific world that, during the decades that followed, many observatories kept their clocks on Göttingen time to make it easier, later on, to compare the recorded data.

During the latter half of the nineteenth century, international science made rapid strides. One of the first steps was the formation of the International Association of Geodesy. In France, a century earlier, Alexis Claude Clairault had presented a theorem that fixed the equatorial bulge of the earth in terms of competition between the inward pull of gravity and the outward tug of centrifugal force. In part to test his theorem by widespread surveys and astronomical observations, the International Association of Geodesy was organized in 1864. It became what is regarded as the first long-lived international organization of scientists and its creation set in motion a slow chain reaction. It became apparent that successful measurements of the earth's shape were impossible unless the men from one country made observations in kilometers of precisely the same length as those from another nation; hence the International Bureau of Weights and Measures was formed in 1875.

Meanwhile the weather men had begun to band together. In 1872 they met in Leipzig and discussed formation of what became the International Meteorological Organization (IMO), forerunner of today's World Meteorological Organization (WMO). IMO was officially organized in 1878 and held its first congress at Rome in 1879.

In 1875 Karl Weyprecht, a lieutenant in the Austrian Navy who had distinguished himself in arctic exploration, presented to the German Scientific and Medical Association, meeting in Graz, a paper that set in motion the First Polar Year—grandfather of the IGY.[2] This was an era of extensive arctic exploration and Weyprecht had played a leading role in the discovery of one of its most important prizes, Franz Joseph Land, named for his emperor. This icy archipelago now forms part of the Soviet Union. The Austrian explorer argued that the quest for scientific knowledge was a far more important goal for such expeditions that the sighting of new capes, bays, and islands. He proposed that two rings of stations be established as close as possible to the Arctic and Antarctic Circles to take synchronized observations of weather, the earth's magnetism, the northern lights (aurora), and the polar ice. By the spring of 1877 a detailed program had been prepared by Weyprecht and Count Wilczek, his benefactor and co-worker, for presentation to the International Meteorological Congress, due to meet in Rome that September. The plan outlined a standard method of reporting weather and auroras, so that the observations of many expeditions could be compared. Göttingen Mean Time was to be used for the magnetic observations and the program said it was "extremely important" that they be made at exactly the same instant at each station, since magnetic variations were known to be very rapid.[3]

Although Weyprecht's plan was ready, the world was not. On April 24, 1877, Russia declared war on Turkey, and Europe, barely recovered from the Franco-Prussian War, feared a general conflagration. The Rome meeting of the International Meteorological Congress did not take place until April, 1879. Meanwhile, although Weyprecht did not live to see his dream fulfilled, it had been warmly received. Chancellor Bismarck had appointed a commission of leading scientists to study the plan and they commended it to the German Bundesrat. The Rome meeting likewise endorsed it and stressed the need for many countries to take part. An International Polar Conference was summoned to meet in Hamburg the following October. Scientists from eight countries attended and in August, 1880, at a follow-up conference in Berne, Heinrich von Wild, who presided, was made president of the International Polar Commission that ran the program.

It was decided that the coordinated observations would be carried out at fourteen especially established polar stations, to run for one year beginning in August, 1882. Previously established observatories in temperate latitudes were to join in making simultaneous observations, so that about forty stations in all were to take part. They included observatories in Los Angeles, Peking, Shanghai, and five points in what is now the USSR.

Expeditions were dispatched to set up the following stations:

Arctic

Jan Mayen in the Norwegian Sea	Austria-Hungary
Great Slave Lake, Canada	Britain
Godthaab, Greenland	Denmark
Sodankyla, Finland	Finland
Cumberland Sound, Baffin Island	Germany
Mouth of the Yenisei River, Siberia	Netherlands
Alten Fiord, Norway	Norway
Mouth of the Lena River, Siberia ⎫ Novaya Zemlya ⎭	Russia
Spitsbergen	Sweden
Point Barrow, Alaska ⎫ Lady Franklin Bay, Ellesmere Island ⎭	United States

Antarctic

Cape Horn	France
South Georgia	Germany

The ship in which the Dutch sought to reach the Yenisei River in northwestern Siberia was crushed by ice, but the men camped on the floes continued their scientific observations and finally crossed the ice to safety. The American expedition to Ellesmere Island was less fortunate; in fact it became one of the most terrible episodes in the history of the Arctic.

The Lady Franklin Bay Expedition was a military affair, organized and largely manned by the Signal Service of the United States Army. Its leader, Lieutenant Adolphus W. Greely, was under orders as acting signal officer in the Fifth Cavalry. Although one of the men had reached Greenland a year earlier, none was experienced in arctic work except two Eskimos who joined the expedition. Much of their equipment seems to have been standard Army issue. The expedition's budget was a mere $6000 for food, coal, dogs, instruments, and polar clothing.

The base was built near Lady Franklin Bay, one of the northernmost fiords in the world, in August, 1881. The following May, three months before the official start of the Polar Year, a sledging party followed the northern coast of Greenland to a point nearer the North Pole than any expedition up to that time. However, to the dismay of the twenty-five-man party, as the summer drew to an end, no relief ship made its way north through the icy sea between Greenland and Ellesmere Island. There was enough food for another winter, but when, after a second summer of hopeful waiting, no ship appeared, the party decided to make its own way south.

On August 9, 1883, they boarded their boats, one of which was a small steam launch. To preserve their hard-won scientific trophies they made duplicate records so that complete sets, safeguarded in waterproof containers, could be carried in separate boats. Included were two years of observation of auroral displays, magnetism, gravity, weather, geography, and biology. Also on board were their instruments so that they could continue the work, come what may.

The boats soon became trapped in the drifting ice of Kane Basin. All but one had to be abandoned, and the remaining craft was dragged tortuously over the ice with the records, instruments, and a limited amount of food. On two occasions, as the men neared land, gales drove the ice and themselves back into the middle of the sea. At length, after fifty-one days of travel over water and drifting ice, they set foot ashore, having covered 500 miles.

At Cape Sabine, on the Ellesmere Island side of the straits, they hoped to find a rescue ship. Instead there was a small cache of rations and a note telling them that the relief ship *Proteus* had been crushed by ice nine weeks earlier. Its thirty-seven men, after placing the cache, had fled by boat toward Greenland on the other side of the straits.

The winter that followed, their third in the Arctic, was one of incredible suffering for Greely and his men. Realizing that they might never be found, they erected a cairn on an island overlooking Smith Sound, where they felt sure it would be seen. The pendulum that had been used for gravity measurements was inserted so that its shaft jutted from the top of the cairn as a marker. Beneath was a box with the party's notebooks.

The expedition continued to record barometric pressures and other data long after the Polar Year had ended. The hunters found little game and the men, living on a starvation diet, gradually became too weak to keep more than the barest weather records. The first man died on January 18, 1884. In April death struck wholesale. Five died in the week beginning April 5. A four-man party, sent to bring in 144 pounds of beef at a distant cache, began to freeze. They abandoned the load and returned to camp. One of the group lost his hands and feet by natural amputation, yet survived until after the rescue.

A second pair of men went after the meat but could not find it; one of them died during the search. One of the Eskimos, desperately hunting for game, drowned when his kayak sank, and the expedition's best rifle was lost. Hundreds of pounds of shrimp were caught, but a breakup of the shore ice carried away the shrimping nets. Greely had brought with him his ceremonial sword, which they tried to shape into a harpoon head. Despite drastic cuts in rations, by mid-May, 1884, none were left. A bear appeared, but they were too weak to hunt it. More men died. The sealskin clothing was cooked, as were the thongs used to fasten the garments. Paperlike lichens were torn from the rocks and boiled. Some of the more demoralized men began pilfering from the others what they now regarded as food. One man, Private Charles B. Henry, was repeatedly charged with thefts of various sorts and finally, caught red-handed, he was ordered by Greely to be shot. It was a touchy business since, according to Greely, Henry was stronger than any two of the others. After the expedition surgeon, Dr. Pavy, and Private Bender had also died, another of the party wrote in his diary:

> Lots of seal-skin and thongs were found on the doctor and Bender both, which showed how dishonest they was. Although Henry has told before his death that I had eaten a lot of seal-skin, yet, although I am a dying man, I deny the assertion; I only ate my own boots and a part of an old pair of pants. I feel myself going fast, but I wish that it would go yet faster.[4]

On June 21 a gale partly flattened the tent, pinning three of the survivors in their sleeping bags. They were too weak to free themselves. Near midnight the next day they heard a ship's whistle. Of the twenty-five only eight were alive, and one of these was already comatose. Another died before reaching the United States. Greely himself lived to become head of the Army Signal Corps and a champion of military aviation even before the Wright brothers made their historic flight.

In the years that followed, the information won at such a terrible price was assembled and twenty or more volumes of Polar Year results were published. Using reports from ships as well as from land stations, weather charts were drawn for each day of the study period, covering North America and Europe and extending deep into the Arctic. Available to the researchers of all lands, the compilation formed the basis of a number of important studies in weather forecasting.

Likewise, the magnetic data made it possible to map the contours of the magnetic field, at the earth's surface, almost to the North Magnetic Pole, where all of the magnetic force is directed straight downward. Previous magnetic data had been of limited value since it had been collected over many years. The field not only changes progressively from year to year, but an expedition, taking only one reading at a given point, may come back with grossly deceptive information, since the reading may have coincided with a magnetic storm that twisted the compass needle several degrees.

The new magnetic information was also applicable to a communications problem. The first successful transatlantic cable had been laid in 1866, but it and the newer cable from England to India were repeatedly troubled with interference that coincided with magnetic storms. Greater understanding of these storms offered new hope of circumventing such interference.

The Second Polar Year, like the first, seems to have been conceived by a polar explorer.[5] The idea of carrying out such a program just fifty years after the first is said to have been proposed on November 23, 1927, by Johannes Georgi, a German meteorologist and explorer, who three years later suffered terrible hardships when he and two companions wintered in an ice cave at Eismitte, the German weather station established by the expedition of Alfred Wegener almost in the center of Greenland. Georgi presented his plan at a meeting of the Deutsche Seewarte, or hydrographic office, in Hamburg. It was taken up by Vice Admiral H. Dominik, president of the Seewarte, and the following June Dominik discussed it with the heads of various international scientific organizations who drafted a plan for its submission, in September, to the International Conference of Directors in Copenhagen. This was the group, consisting of the directors of all the national weather services, that had sponsored the First Polar Year.[6]

By September 16, 1928, when the conference opened in the palace of the Danish parliament at Christiansborg, the plan had already received wide support and grandiose plans were in the wind. Only twelve days before, the dirigible *Graf Zeppelin* had landed at Friedrichshafen, Germany, after carrying a score of passengers around the world via Russia, Asia, and the United States. One of the first items discussed was the trouble the German aviators had had with the multitude of weather codes they encountered on the voyage. Now new journeys were being planned for the dirigible. Some weeks earlier the dean of polar explorers, Fridtjof Nansen, had written to Admiral Dominik reporting that the *Graf Zeppelin* was to make three extended exploration trips into the Arctic to demonstrate the effectiveness of airships as a means of polar transport. Writing on behalf of Aeroarctic, the group in Germany that was sponsoring the ventures, Nansen urged that the voyages of the great dirigible be worked into the plan. Dominik's organization was enthusiastic. The dirigible, it said, could be used to set up drifting stations on large ice floes near the North Pole.

In a letter signed by Vladimir Y. Wiese (Vize), a polar specialist at the Central Geophysical Observatory in Leningrad, the Russians endorsed the plan and offered Soviet aid in establishing such a drifting station. It was likewise proposed that four stations be established at the opposite end of the world, in Antarctica—three on the coast and one in the interior—but the Russians said they could not take part in such an effort. Nevertheless there were high hopes for a many-pronged antarctic effort. Harald U. Sverdrup, the Norwegian scientist-explorer, reported that Norwegian whaling companies could carry several parties to the Antarctic and pick them up there once the Year was over.

Talk of the new Polar Year dominated the discussions at the conference and at the meetings of various specialized commissions held concurrently. The conference appointed a Commission for the Polar Year 1932–33, consisting of the presidents of three international research commissions plus four scientists from Canada, Denmark, Norway, and the Soviet Union. Dan Barfod la Cour, who was host to the conference as director of the Danish Meteorological Institute, was elected president of the commission and the Soviet Union invited it to hold its first meeting in Leningrad. At this conference, in August 1930, the Russians announced elaborate plans. Their observations were to be carried out not only by scientists but by workers from collective farms, state farms, factories, schools, transport systems, and social organizations. Some seventy arctic stations were listed, ten of them to be specially established for the Year.[7]

Meanwhile the commission had expanded its membership to include scientists from several other countries, including the United States. One of the Americans elected was John A. Fleming, head of the Department of Terrestrial Magnetism at the Carnegie Institution of Washington. His organization had contributed to the early planning of the Year and he was destined to wind up its affairs twenty years later.

The plan for the Year, as it emerged from the preparatory meetings, broke down into three main areas of study, to be carried out "for the earth as a whole," with emphasis on the polar regions only in that greater effort was needed to set up stations there. The three areas were weather, magnetism, and the aurora. Work was to be limited to those aspects of these phenomena "the study of which requires large scale collaboration throughout a network of stations for the comparatively limited time of one year." [8]

In many respects the methods applied to the study of our planet by scientists of the Second Polar Year anticipated those used on a far wider scale in the IGY. Some of the ideas, such as the use of "International Days" for simultaneous upper air observations, had been developing over a number of years. These Days were sponsored by the Commission for Exploration of the High Atmosphere and had been projected at a meeting held in Bergen, Norway, in 1921.[9] In Leipzig, Germany, this same commission drew up standard forms for reporting the results gleaned from unmanned balloons to be released simultaneously at all stations on each International Day. For the Second Polar Year it was agreed that there should be two kinds of days: On First Order International Days, falling on two successive days in the middle of the month, all balloon stations were to send up a balloon. On Second Order International Days only those stations that could spare the equipment would do so. In addition, during the eclipse of the sun on August 31, 1932, there were to be measurements of magnetism and earth currents similar to those called for on International Days.[10]

Another new technique was the use of cameras to record auroral displays, instead of having to depend on imprecise visual reports as had been the case a half-century earlier. Photographs taken of the same display at a number of points made it possible to trace the extent of a single curtain of light (often thousands of miles long) and to determine the height, both of its top and its bottom.

Perhaps the most important innovation since the First Polar Year was the development of radio. In 1902 Guglielmo Marconi, in Newfoundland, had been able to receive the letter S, transmitted from Poldhu, near Land's End in England. Although radio signals had been thought to travel only in a straight line, Marconi was able to send them around the curved earth. Two scientists proposed an explanation. There was, they said, a "mirror" about sixty miles up in the sky. It was given their names—the Kennelly-Heaviside Layer—and was thought to consist of air gases broken up by intense ultraviolet rays into electrified particles known as ions, making the layer highly conductive for electricity and an effective reflector of radio waves within a certain frequency range. The intensity of ultraviolet rays from the sun was apparently far greater at sixty miles' elevation than at the earth's surface. Sixty miles was not high enough to compensate for the transatlantic curvature of the earth, and so it was thought the radio waves bounced back and forth between this mirror and the ocean.[11]

High-frequency radio signals were not reflected by this layer and hence were thought unsuitable for long-range communications. They were assigned to amateur use, but soon it was discovered that the amateurs were able to reach across the oceans with only a small expenditure of power. The suspicion grew that there were other layers, as yet undiscovered.

Therefore one of the objectives of the Second Polar Year, as stated in its prospectus, was to study the "one or more electrically conducting layers at great heights, which are believed to be connected with the radiation from the sun and the phenomena of the aurora. The aurora in turn is in some way associated with the development of 'magnetic storms,' which form a fundamental problem in terrestrial magnetism." [12]

In 1926 Fleming's laboratory in Washington had succeeded in "sounding" the height of the known radio-reflecting layer by using photo-registration of wave pulses bounced off it. By the start of the Year this was being done on a routine basis, the signals transmitted in pulses by the Naval Research Laboratory both into the air and along a wire direct to the Department of Terrestrial Magnetism. This made possible a precise determination of the time lapse and therefore the height of reflection.

One of the more puzzling results was the discovery that the layer seemed to change its height by as much as fifty miles in a second. This seemed to be further evidence that there were actually two or more layers.

The region of man's interest was rising, and it was becoming clear that, to understand weather in the lower atmosphere, one should learn what goes on in the upper air. As a first step upward it was recommended at Leningrad that eighteen stations be placed on mountaintops in such northern areas as Greenland, Iceland, Norway, and the Soviet Union.

Another scheme, discussed at the 1929 Leipzig conference, anticipated one of the more ingenious experiments of the IGY—the recording at a circle of ground stations of the sound from explosions detonated at extremely high altitudes. Since the speed of sound through air of various temperatures was precisely known, it was thought that the time at which the sound reached the various stations could be used to calculate temperatures very high in the air.

The most exciting plan in man's new reach for the heavens was an American project for direct observation of conditions in the upper air, using rockets. In 1929 Charles A. Lindbergh, at a conference at which jet propulsion was one of the topics, learned of the work being done by a professor at Clark University in Worcester, Massachusetts. The famous flier went to visit him and was shown motion pictures of rocket flights achieved by using as fuel gasoline mixed with liquid oxygen. As a result of Lindburgh's intercession, Daniel Guggenheim, the industrialist, became patron of the work.

The professor was Robert H. Goddard, one of the fathers of modern rocketry. On January 27, 1932, Fleming told the House Foreign Affairs Committee of plans to use Goddard's rockets, during the Second Polar Year, to lift small payloads of instruments that would be parachuted to the ground from heights up to fifty miles. He said

Goddard had set up a rocket experiment station in New Mexico and that the work was progressing "very well." Asked by Representative Cyrenus Cole of Iowa how such seeming incredible heights were to be achieved, Fleming said, "by successive explosions." [13]

These hopeful schemes, and many others of the Second Polar Year, were dashed by economic depression. The Year was to run for thirteen months—from August 1, 1932, until the end of August, 1933. Before it began, Goddard's flight tests in New Mexico were cut short. His initial two-year arrangement with Guggenheim had expired and, though it was due to be renewed, his benefactor died and no other funds could be obtained. He had to return to his laboratory at Clark University.

The entire Polar Year almost foundered on the rocks of the depression. A strong move developed to delay it indefinitely; had it not been for the fight waged by La Cour as president of the commission preparing for it, this probably would have happened. He has been described by one of his close associates as a man of "obstinate energy, practically unlimited capacity for work, great expert knowledge and eminent organizational ability." [14]

In 1931 some of the members of the commission strongly urged postponement. It was pointed out that, with millions unemployed and suffering widespread, governments were reluctant to appropriate money for this sort of research. The plans for a ring of stations in the Antarctic seemed to be falling through entirely. There was also a scientific argument for postponement. It was expected that 1932–33 would be a time of minimum activity in the eleven-year sunspot cycle, hampering efforts to study the relationship between sunspots and magnetic storms on earth.

Nevertheless a subcommission, set up to study the question, advised against delaying the Year. Preparations were so advanced, it said, that it was too late to turn back. Once such an effort had been derailed, there might be difficulty in getting it back on the tracks again.[15]

La Cour's program was aided by a series of grants from the Rockefeller Foundation in New York. In February, 1932, a donation of $40,000 made it possible to obtain magnetic instruments and radiosondes for use by countries otherwise unable to obtain them. Radiosondes were the newly developed device for obtaining weather data aloft. They consisted of balloon-borne instrument packages which reported by radio as they ascended. Observation from the ground of the balloon's wandering in the course of its rise provided information on wind speed and direction at all levels until the balloon burst in the rarefied air. This use of radio to send back data from high in the sky anticipated the telemetering techniques upon which much IGY research was dependent.

La Cour designed the magnetic recording instruments massproduced during the final months before the start of the Year. He himself worked on their construction and in training the observers from many lands who were to use them.

When the Year began, fifty years to the day after the First Polar Year, forty-four nations had pledged themselves to take part. Special committees had been formed in sixteen countries; twenty-two undertook to send expeditions beyond their borders. The number of magnetic stations north of the 60th Parallel was increased from seven to thirty.

Thus the Second Polar Year ran its course, though on a considerably more modest scale than originally planned. Nevertheless, having weathered the storms of the depression, it was soon confronted with another calamity—World War II. As part of the allimportant task of digesting the results and making them useful, the Deutsche Seewarte, which had originally sponsored the Year, was given the job of compiling daily weather maps of the entire Northern Hemisphere for the thirteen months covered by the year. When Hitler marched into Poland in 1939, the maps covering all the days from August, 1932, to April, 1933, had been published and distributed to scientists throughout the world. Those for the following May and June had just come off the press; the remaining maps—for July and August, 1933—had been plotted but not yet published.

When the war ended, all of these maps were found except the manuscript maps for the last fifteen days of the Year. These, the fruit of painstaking observations by men in many lands, appear to have been lost forever.

La Cour had died during the war and when, in 1946, the International Meteorological Organization dissolved itself and its agencies in favor of the new World Meteorological Organization, a Temporary Commission on the Liquidation of the Polar Year 1932–33 was established with John A. Fleming as its president. Its headquarters was at the Danish Meteorological Institute, where La Cour had assembled as many reports on the Year's results as he could find, and it was given until December 31, 1950, to wind up its affairs. Although the Rockefeller Foundation had given $15,000 for "analysis and distribution" of Polar Year data in 1934, this was only a fraction of the sum needed and the war had virtually halted assembly of the material.[16]

It had been agreed in advance that the results of the Year should be available to the scientists of all lands, but this could not be achieved without assembling and cataloguing the data and publishing a bibliography. In 1947 the Rockefeller Foundation granted another $12,000 for this work.[17] Thousands of filmed records of magnetic changes, radio soundings of the upper air, and auroral displays were collected, but as a result of the war and the passage of many years much material seems to have been lost.

In 1951 the bibliography was published with the reports broken down on a national basis. They served as an indication of the various national efforts. The United States led, with 113 publications pertaining to the Year. Germany was second with 97, followed by the Soviet Union with 52 and Great Britain with 39.

It has been estimated that the knowledge gained during the Second Polar Year, as applied to radio communications alone, was worth hundreds of millions of dollars.[18]

CHAPTER 3
GLOBAL PLANS

Usually it is hard to pin down the time and place of an idea's birth, but it is generally agreed that the International Geophysical Year grew out of a conversation held in the Washington suburb of Silver Spring, Maryland, on the evening of April 5, 1950. James A. Van Allen had invited a group of American scientists concerned with upper-air research for an evening of talk with a visitor whom some regarded as the greatest living geophysicist—Sydney Chapman.

Chapman was then Sedleian Professor of Natural Philosophy at Queens College, Oxford, but to those present in the Van Allen living room he was the man who had constructed, in a manner magnificent and ingenious to his most sophisticated scientific colleagues, a "model" of the earth's atmosphere and the space surrounding it. It had long been suspected that some edifice of natural laws and phenomena, dependent upon outbursts from the sun, was responsible for the aurora, for magnetic storms, for the slight but persistent daily variations in compass direction, for the generation of electric currents in the earth, and for the various radio-reflecting regions of the atmosphere. Chapman, working with such men as V.C.A. Ferraro of England and Julius Bartels of Germany had built such an edifice, applying to the atmosphere and to the solar system the knowledge of physics gained in the laboratory.

His "model," seeking to explain the interrelationship of all these phenomena, was not intended to be the final answer, but rather a target at which other scientists could fire, in the hope that this would lead them closer to the truth.

If a stranger had walked into that living room, he would probably not have picked Chapman as the most distinguished member of the group. Despite his years—he was then sixty-two—he was almost boyish in his enthusiasm for scientific ideas. His energy was phenomenal. His favorite mode of transportation was a bicycle, and while he apparently did not use it to reach Silver Spring that evening, for twenty years he had cycled to and from his teaching post at Imperial College, London—a round-trip distance of fifteen miles. The general strike in 1926 had forced him to provide his own locomotion and he had become so wedded to this means of transport that on one occasion he is said to have arrived at a Royal Society soirée, resplendent in white tie and tails, firmly astride his wheel. He had become a fellow of the Royal Society at the unusually youthful age of thirty-one.

One of Chapman's early achievements had been to demonstrate that there was a tidal movement of the atmosphere comparable to that of the oceans. He had detected the pull of the moon on the atmosphere by studying 6457 hourly records of air pressure made at Greenwich, England. The large number of observations made it possible to average out the variations produced by weather, leaving clear evidence of the tides, which are estimated to cause the radio-reflecting region sixty miles aloft to move up and down one mile twice daily. This tidal motion provided Chapman with the "dynamo" that formed an integral part of his model. The movement of electrically charged particles across the earth's magnetic field generated currents that flowed in an earth-encircling pattern.

Another of the guests was Lloyd V. Berkner, who, when he spoke, was impressive both in his physical appearance (he is a solidly built six feet two and a half) and in his authoritative manner. Berkner had served as a radio technician on the First Byrd Antarctic Expedition and had been instrumental in developing the sounder which automatically charts the radio-reflecting layers of the atmosphere. The widespread use of such sounders had brought to light radical variations in these layers with time of day, time of year, and geographic location. Chapman's model was, in part, an attempt to explain these variations. Like Chapman and others who were to play leading roles in the IGY, Berkner had been active in the Second Polar Year, during which he had been head of the Section on Exploratory Geophysics of the Atmosphere in the Department of Terrestrial Magnetism of the Carnegie Institution of Washington. He was rising rapidly in the leadership of international scientific efforts and was soon to be elected president of the supreme nongovernmental scientific body, the International Council of Scientific Unions.

The host of the evening was almost unknown in world scientific circles, although today his name is associated with probably the most important discovery of the IGY. James Van Allen had worked for the United States Navy during the war and had helped develop the proximity fuse that detonated antiaircraft shells as they passed their targets, making a direct hit unnecessary. More recently he had turned to research with rockets.

During World War II, long-range missiles had emerged as standard weapons and, when the war was over, some sixty-nine captured V-2s were brought from Germany and fired by the United States Army from the New Mexico deserts. Aimed almost straight up, they carried instrument payloads to heights as great as 116 miles. The dreams of men like Goddard, who had seen in the rocket a means of obtaining direct evidence of what happens above the atmosphere, had been fulfilled. One of the first things scientists wished to "see" in space was the nature of cosmic rays in their virgin state, before they shatter themselves upon impact with the air. The attempt to capture some of these virgin rays with the V-2s had been Van Allen's job. On that evening in 1950, at thirty-five, he was head of the high-altitude research program at The Johns Hopkins University's Applied Physics Laboratory in Silver Spring. His reputation was as a doer rather than as a theoretician—a man of great ingenuity and resourcefulness in carrying out experiments on the forefront of upper-air research. His soft manner of speech gave an impression of quiet, competent purposefulness. His youthfulness was emphasized by a crew haircut.

Also in the Van Allen living room were three other geophysicists: J. Wallace Joyce, S. Fred Singer, and Ernest H. Vestine. The conversation turned to the present state of geophysics—the family of sciences involving the earth as whole: its oceans of air and water, its shape, the magnetism generated within it and outside it, and the role of such outside influences as the sun.

If the earth is thought of as the size of a schoolroom globe, the environment with which man, until then, had had direct contact was no thicker than a heavy coat of paint over that globe. The deepest penetration downward, a well drilled to a depth of almost five miles (25,340 feet) in Pecos County, Texas, would be, by the same measure, a mere pinprick. Until the development of the V-2, scientists had been unable to reach above the ocean of air overhead. From the ground, our view into space is hardly more enlightening than the view of the heavens obtained by a lobster on the ocean floor. We are little aware of what the air denies us, for our organs of sight have learned to "see" only a narrow spectrum of radiation that does get through—visible light. The drawing below shows what a small proportion this represents in the total breadth of electromagnetic radiation.

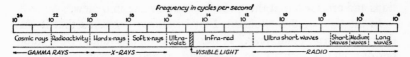

Electromagnetic radiation (Adapted from Massey & Boyd, 1959)

The tools available in 1950 made it possible to reach up through all, or most, of the atmosphere. In addition to the giant rockets, the war had produced many other scientific weapons. With radar, weather balloons could now be followed to the summit of their ascents, day or night, cloudy or clear. Gigantic polyethylene balloons, taller than a ten-story building, could lift instruments more than twenty miles and keep them floating for days on top of 99 per cent (by weight) of the atmosphere.

There were many other new "eyes" with which to peer into the mysteries of science. The growing family of optical instruments made it possible to record light spectra with great precision, whether from portions of the sun, from the aurora, or from the strange patches of light, invisible to the naked eye, that drift across the heavens at night —the so-called airglow. Analysis of light from the aurora and airglow at various levels of the atmosphere could increase understanding of the very nature of hydrogen, nitrogen, and oxygen—gases whose excitation produced the light.

In the observation of the sun it had once been necessary to wait for an eclipse to see the glowing plumes of light radiating from the sun—the corona. Now the coronagraph, mounted in a telescope, could to some extent produce the same effect. A method had also been found to chart the magnetic patterns of the sun. Because magnetism alters the light emanating from each region of the sun, Horace W. and Harold D. Babcock, in California, had developed an instrument that, by observing this so-called Zeeman effect, could map the sun's magnetism on a day-to-day basis. In the field of cosmic rays new recorders made it possible to observe the direction, intensity, and composition of those extremely high-energy particles. Finally, with new electronic techniques, there could be automatic, day-and-night recording of events in a manner hitherto unheard of. Spot observations had been of interest, but now, by watching complex phenomena continuously and digesting the results in automatic computers, it was possible to cut down the underbrush of random variations and errors so that the great panorama came into view.

In the light of this situation, Lloyd Berkner suggested that it was time for a new "polar year." It was agreed that advances on a number of scientific fronts were being held up by the lack of data which could be expected from world-wide observations using the new techniques. The assembled scientists were enthusiastic and it was agreed that Berkner and Chapman would present such a plan at the meeting of the Mixed Commission on the Ionosphere, to be held three months later in Brussels. The commission was one of several such bodies, designed to bring together men from various international scientific unions with a common area of interest. The Brussels meeting decided to commend the proposal to the scientific bodies represented in its membership, as well as to the International Council of Scientific Unions (ICSU), which embraced all such bodies.

ICSU was the third attempt to bring together, under a single umbrella, all international scientific unions. Because this represented the culmination of efforts to develop international science, it is worth while to glance briefly at its history. The first such organ, formed in 1900, was the International Association of Academies. By then the number of international scientific societies had grown to such proportions that they were treading on each other's toes, duplicating efforts in one area and leaving others untouched.

The banding together of the academies was carried out on the initiative of the Göttingen Academy of Sciences, and the preëminent role of Germany in the world of science was evident in the domination of the association by the academies of Berlin, Göttingen, Heidelberg, Leipzig, Munich, and also Vienna.[1]

This organization perished in the ruins of World War I and, in 1919, a new body emerged—the International Research Council—from which Germany and its allies were specifically excluded. The initiative for its founding came from the National Academy of Sciences in Washington, the Royal Society of London, and the Académie des Sciences in Paris. As the years passed the exclusion of scientists from the defeated countries was relaxed, but such was the heritage of bitterness that some of the academies refused to join when told they could do so. The situation was not resolved until, twelve years after its founding, the Council was replaced by ICSU.

The short life of the International Research Council has been attributed to two factors. First, its exclusions permitted political considerations to be injected into science. Second, its statutes provided that it should "initiate" and "direct" various international scientific programs. This led to resentment by the international unions formed under the Council by scientists in various fields, who are said to have felt that there was "an excessive control by the Council of their own affairs." [2]

The organization of ICSU was designed to avert such criticism. Federated within it are thirteen unions, divided into two categories with respect to voting power and representation. Their acronyms, in some cases based on the French titles, are well known in the scientific world but were clearly not chosen for their euphony:

General Unions

International Astronomical Union (IAU)
International Union of Geodesy and Geophysics (IUGG)
International Union of Pure and Applied Chemistry (IUPAC)
International Union of Pure and Applied Physics (IUPAP)
International Union of Biological Sciences (IUBS)
International Mathematical Union (IMU)

Specialized Unions

International Scientific Radio Union (URSI)
International Geographical Union (IGU)
International Union of Crystallography (IUCr)
International Union of Theoretical and Applied Mechanics (IUTAM)
International Union of History and Philosophy of Science (IUHPS)
International Union of Physiological Sciences (IUPS)
International Union of Biochemistry (IUB)

National academies of science or comparable bodies representing forty-five nations also participate.

Although some of these academies are governmental or quasi-governmental, ICSU is essentially a nongovernmental body. The formation after World War II of the United Nations Educational, Scientific and Cultural Organization (UNESCO) provided a parallel organ at the intergovernmental level. A formal agreement between the two organizations to define their areas of operation was made in 1947. Since then UNESCO has given ICSU about $180,000 a year to aid the latter's program of conferences, publication, and permanent services. ICSU, in turn, offers specialized advice when asked by UNESCO.

The plan for a new polar year was endorsed by the groups represented in the Mixed Commission on the Ionosphere (URSI, IAU, and IUGG), and in the fall of 1951 the ICSU Executive Board, representing all the unions, met in Washington and decided to create a special committee to work on plans for what was still being referred to as "the Third [International] Polar Year." [3]

The first invitation for participation in the new Year seems to have been that issued in London in May, 1952, by the ICSU Bureau, the eight-man executive body which runs that organization. It was addressed primarily to nations adhering to ICSU. The Soviet Union was not at that time a member, but the success of any program would obviously depend heavily on Soviet cooperation, since, to obtain a world picture, data were needed not only from the vast reaches of the USSR but also from other communist countries, particularly China. A separate invitation was therefore sent to the Academy of Sciences of the USSR. Despite its nonadherence to ICSU, the USSR belonged to an ICSU union, the IAU, and independent approaches were made through that organization and the World Meteorological Organization (WMO), to which the Soviet Union also belonged. The Russians were asked to renew the cooperation that had marked their participation in the first two polar years and were urged to encourage other nations to join.

As with its predecessor, the International Meteorological Organization, sponsor of the first two polar years, the WMO membership included virtually all nations of the world. When invited to take part in planning the Year, the WMO agreed, but responded that the program placed too much emphasis on the polar regions. This view was shared by two groups in the IUGG (the International Meteorological Association and the International Association of Terrestrial Magnetism and Electricity), which thought the studies should be worldwide.

Chapman proposed that the name be changed to International Geophysical Year, and this was approved at the ICSU General Assembly at Amsterdam in October, 1952. The Special Committee for the IGY (Comité Spécial de l'Année Géophysique Internationale, or CSAGI) met that month and again from June 30 to July 3, 1953. At the latter meeting Chapman was elected president of the committee, Lloyd Berkner was named vice-president, and Marcel Nicolet of Belgium secretary-general. This trio constituted the Bureau of CSAGI and, later augmented by two additional members, it ran the IGY. Brussels, the site of this organizational meeting, became its home, the headquarters being Nicolet's offices in the suburb of Uccle, where he directed the radiation department of Belgium's Royal Meteorological Institute. Nicolet was an authority on upper air chemistry.

It was decided that the IGY would run for eighteen months, from July 1, 1957, through December 31, 1958. This would coincide with an expected peak of sunspot activity as well as with several eclipses. The eighteen-month period was chosen simply because twelve months was not long enough to obtain an adequate sampling of data. The longer period would be more likely to span the full summit of the sunspot cycle and would give more time to overcome snags in the more complicated methods of observation (such as those dependent on satellites).

By the time of the CSAGI meeting in Brussels, more than a year after ICSU had issued its first call, twenty-two nations had formed IGY national committees, including all the major western countries plus Czechoslovakia and Yugoslavia. The independence of the Czechs in this respect is of interest, since it was another fifteen months before the Soviet Union led the rest of its allies into the IGY. Presumably this was because both the Czechs and Yugoslavs were members of URSI, one of the most active IGY sponsors.

May, 1954, was set as the deadline for submission of detailed national programs, in the hope that this schedule would make it possible to issue a master plan for the entire world in advance of the IGY. At an early stage the National Academy of Sciences in Washington persuaded the government that it should underwrite a major effort. The decision to do so, including the dispatch of a large-scale expedition to Antarctica, is said to have been made by the highest policy-making body, the National Security Council. Planning and direction of the scientific work were placed under the National Academy of Sciences–National Research Council, and the Department of Defense was told to furnish whatever support was necessary to place the scientists and their instruments in remote locations. Within the Academy, Joseph Kaplan, a specialist in upper-air research at the University of California at Los Angeles, was made chairman of the United States National Committee for the IGY. The function of the Committee was to make policy. The actual organization of the program was carried out by Hugh Odishaw, the Committee's executive director, with headquarters in Washington.

By March, 1954, the United States had outlined a massive program, based on suggestions from several hundred scientists in government agencies, universities, foundations, and private research institutions. Notably advanced were plans for rocket exploration of the upper air. The program, at that time, called for thirty-six Aerobee shots and thirty-seven launchings of rockoons. Both were research rockets in whose development Van Allen had played a leading role.

At this point, although the Soviet Union had not yet responded, many of the decisions that were to shape the IGY already had been made. A program of World Days and periodic ten-day Meteorological Intervals had been worked out by early 1954. The World Days were to occur at a rate of three per month to provide for intensive observation in many related sciences. During the following summer there were meetings of URSI, IUPAP, IUGG, WMO, and MCI to develop coordinated plans for presentation to the plenary CSAGI meeting in Rome, from September 30 to October 4. The absence of the Russians from early planning of the IGY was probably due in part to the fact that they did not then belong to the sponsoring organization (ICSU). By contrast, in the Second Polar Year, as members of the International Meteorological Committee, they participated in the planning to a greater extent than did the United States. However, at the opening of the CSAGI Assembly in Rome, the Russian Embassy in that city sent notification that the Soviet Academy of Sciences would participate. Stalin had died nineteen months earlier, and since then Soviet scientists had begun to venture more boldly into the international arena. They had been invited to the IUGG Assembly held in Rome immediately before the CSAGI meeting, and had accepted. During the following year they formally joined both IUGG and ICSU.

Vladimir V. Beloussov, who had led the Soviet scientists at the IUGG Assembly, was chief delegate at the CSAGI meeting. Chapman welcomed the Russians and, at the end of the conference, gave Beloussov a chance to speak.

Beloussov was becoming widely known for his work in geotectonics —the study of the forces which shape the crust of the earth, building mountains, producing earthquakes, and dividing the continents from the seas. As the IGY progressed it became evident that he was not one of those who, when speaking with westerners, seems to be looking over his shoulder for guidance. He was not inhibited about conversing in his somewhat faltering English and, when confronted by the western press, he nimbly talked his way around embarrassing questions. He did so, not with a glower, but with a twinkle in his eye. His broad face, heavy frame, sandy hair, and bushy eyebrows were suggestive of strength and seriousness.

When he mounted the rostrum at Rome Beloussov proposed that countries of vast area, such as China, India, and the Soviet Union, be included in CSAGI. Chapman replied that from the start it had been hoped that the USSR would take part and that its nationals could serve in the central planning group as representatives of one or both of the participating unions to which Moscow adhered (IAU and WMO). However, efforts by IAU and WMO to achieve this had heretofore proved fruitless. He added that it might still be possible to include Soviet nationals in CSAGI, but pointed out that its membership consisted of representatives from scientific unions—not from nations. Ultimately two Soviet scientists—Beloussov and N. V. Pushkov, a geomagnetist—were included as representatives of IUGG.

The Soviet Union eventually gave the highest priority to its IGY projects. A Joint Committee for the Implementation of the IGY was formed in 1955 under the Academy of Sciences of the USSR, and on November 2, 1956, the Academy issued a decree stating that, to guarantee prompt and successful fulfillment of the Soviet commitments, IGY projects were to have priority in the allocation of workers, facilities, and instruments. (It is possible that this resulted in an even more extensive and intensive effort than that under way in the United States.) To ensure that this directive was carried out and that IGY funds allocated to the various institutions were properly used, the Academy, on January 10, 1957, created a temporary "Consultative Committee for Preparing for and Implementing the International Geophysical Year at Establishments of the Academy of

Sciences, USSR." Its chairman was A. G. Kalashnikov and one of its tasks was to undertake "an extensive propaganda programme" to excite popular interest in the program. By early 1957, twenty-eight institutes, observatories, committees, and societies of the Academy were preparing for the IGY.[4]

In a sense, the IGY was a scientific club. To gain admittance—that is, to be included in the IGY program—a scientific project had to be concerned with "specific planetary problems of the earth," defined by the Rome conference as follows:

> a) Problems requiring concurrent synoptic observations at many points involving co-operative observations by many stations.
>
> b) Problems of branches of the geophysical sciences whose solutions will be aided by the availability of synoptic or other concentrated work during the International Geophysical Year in other geophysical sciences.
>
> c) Observation of all major geophysical phenomena in relatively inaccessible regions of the Earth that can be occupied during the International Geophysical Year because of the extraordinary effort during that interval, in order to augment our basic knowledge of the Earth and the solar and other influences acting upon it.
>
> d) Epochal observations of slowly varying terrestrial phenomena; to establish basic information for subsequent comparison at later epochs.[5]

Scientists of today would regard as priceless reliable information on ocean levels, weather patterns, the distribution of glacier ice, and other such phenomena in past centuries. Category *d* was designed to provide such data for future generations.

Where choice was necessary, priority was to be given to programs in category *a,* those dependent upon simultaneous coordinated observations at many points.

The Rome conference also set in motion efforts to explore the two great regions that mid-twentieth-century technology had brought within the reach of man: the Antarctic and outer space.

The assault on Antarctica, as stated in the conference report, was to be "the first really thorough world effort" to uncover the geophysical secrets of the continent at the bottom of the world. The Antarctic represents, it said,

> ... a region of almost unparalleled interest to the fields of geophysics and geography alike. In geophysics, Antarctica has many significant, unexplored aspects: for example, the influence of this huge ice mass on global weather; the influence of the ice mass on atmospheric and oceanographic dynamics; the nature and extent of aurora australis, for, although the aurora borealis has received considerable attention in recent years, the detailed characteristics of Antarctic aurora remain largely unknown; the possibility of conducting original ionospheric experiments northward from the South Polar Plateau during the long total-night season to determine the physical characteristics of the ionosphere during prolonged absence of sunlight. These and similar scientific considerations lead the CSAGI to recognize that Antarctica represents a most significant portion of the earth for intensive study during the International Geophysical Year.[6]

Five other areas were singled out for special attention: the Arctic, the equatorial region, and three pole-to-pole meridians along which a maximum number of observations were to be made. The latter were designed to obtain complete north-south profiles of such phenomena as air circulation, the electrified layers of air above the weather, and the earth's magnetic field still farther out in space. The north-south zones were chosen to take maximum advantage of existing observatories: Longitudes 70° to 80° West (east coast of North America, west coast of South America), 10° East (Europe and West Africa), and 140° East (Siberia, Japan, Australia).

The second major objective was the exploration of outer space. The idea of launching earth satellites had been promoted for several years by a small group of scientists in both East and West. In 1948 Van Allen sent a paper to the IUGG meeting in Oslo that said, in summarizing the current American rocket program: "Serious consideration is being given to the development of a satellite missile which will continuously orbit around the earth at a distance of, say, 1,000 kilometers." In November, 1953, A. N. Nesmeyanov, president of the Academy of Sciences of the USSR, told the World Peace

Council in Vienna: "Science has reached a state when it is feasible . . . to create an artificial satellite of the earth." [7]

In September, 1954, URSI met at The Hague and heard a proposal that satellite-launchings be included in the IGY. It was made by a twenty-nine-year-old physicist named Fred Singer, who had been in the Van Allen living room when the idea for the IGY was born. Born in Vienna and raised in the United States, he later joined the faculty of the University of Maryland. A resolution was passed, stressing "the extreme importance" of continuous observations of the radiation reaching the earth above the lower, or E region of the ionosphere. This would be especially important, it added, during the IGY. It drew attention to the fact that

> an extension of present isolated rocket observations by means of instrument earth satellite vehicles would allow the continuous monitoring of solar ultraviolet and X radiation intensity and its effects on the ionosphere, particularly during solar flares, thereby greatly enhancing our scientific knowledge of the outer atmosphere. [8]

A similar resolution was passed later that month by the IUGG General Assembly in Rome, and two weeks afterward CSAGI followed suit, recommending that "in view of the advanced state of present rocket techniques" consideration should be given "to the launching of small satellite vehicles, to their scientific instrumentation, and to the new problems associated with satellite experiments, such as power supply, telemetering, and orientation of the vehicle." [9]

The core of the IGY administration, the Bureau of CSAGI, was originally a three-man body consisting of Chapman, Berkner and Nicolet, but was later expanded to include Beloussov of the Soviet Union and Jean Coulomb of France. As finally constituted, therefore, it included citizens of the four great powers: France, the Soviet Union, the United Kingdom, and the United States.

The number of nations signing up for the IGY was growing rapidly and it seemed advisable that some agency be formed to give them a voice in IGY affairs. Hence, in March, 1955, ICSU recommended the creation of an Advisory Council, made up of representatives from all the participating nations, to advise and assist CSAGI on general IGY questions. From September 8 to 14 of that year there was a plenary CSAGI meeting in Brussels, and the newly formed Advisory Council held parallel sessions, with some thirty national delegations participating. From then on the Advisory Council met in conjunction with each plenary meeting of CSAGI.

Among other decisions made at the conference was the starting time of the IGY—zero hours Universal (Greenwich) Time, July 1, 1957. A new pole-to-pole band of stations was also discussed, in addition to the three already decided upon. It would lie along Longitude 110° East, passing directly through the Chinese People's Republic, which had just joined the program.

The final months before the start of the IGY were marked by a series of conferences dealing with regional problems or specific areas of IGY work. One of these, held in Stockholm from May 22 to 25 to coordinate arctic research plans of nations bordering on that region, led to a startling proposal. A problem in studying the drifting ice that covers the Arctic Ocean is the absence of information regarding the total distribution of this ice. Unlike the South Pole, which lies near the heart of a mountainous continent, the North Pole is in the midst of an ocean. (This was dramatically illustrated when the United States submarine *Skate,* on its twelve-day voyage to the North Pole, in March, 1959, was able to surface nine times, punching up through the ice even near the Pole itself.) The arctic ice moves constantly; one week it hugs the Alaskan coast, the next it shifts against Siberia, leaving Alaskan waters ice-free. During the conference, the United States delegates proposed to the Soviet delegates a joint program of aerial photographic mapping of the ice, with exchange of the results to make possible a composite picture of the pack-ice patterns.

According to the delegates from the United States, the Russians responded with a suggestion that photo-reconnaisance planes of both countries shuttle back and forth between Murmansk, USSR, and Fairbanks, Alaska, making use of each other's airfields. These two points are located at opposite ends of the long axis of the Arctic Ocean. Hence, through varying digressions from a straight line between them, it would be possible to cover the entire ocean. This would have set an important precedent for a disarmament program which, like President Eisenhower's "open skies" proposal, depended on aerial inspection.

A resolution adopted at the end of the conference read:

The CSAGI Arctic Conference recommends that regular aerial photographic traverses of the Arctic Basin be carried out with the objective of securing comprehensive data on sea ice distribution, lead patterns, and degrees of ice concentration.[10]

In Washington, however, there apparently were misgivings about the Soviet suggestion of flying into Fairbanks. Soviet ferry pilots had landed there regularly during the war to pick up United States planes, but since then two important Air Force bases had been built near by. In September, four months after the Stockholm conference, a note was delivered to the Soviet Embassy in Washington proposing that Soviet planes land at Nome (which is almost within sight of Siberia) rather than at Fairbanks.

During the weeks that followed—with the world preoccupied by the Hungarian and Suez crises—the Soviet government made its first official pronouncement on the ice-survey plan. In a note delivered on November 21, it said in effect that no help was needed by the Soviet Air Force in aerial photography of the ice on the Soviet side of the Pole and that if the United States Air Force was unable to do the job on its side, Moscow might consider helping out. This effectively killed the joint scheme, even though the Russians did extensive ice photography on their own, as did the United States to a more limited extent. It will never be known what might have happened had no world crisis arisen at just that moment and if the negotiations had been kept on a scientific level.

Another conference, held in Uccle, Belgium, from April 1 to 4, 1957, dealt with the question upon which the success of all aspects of the IGY hinged—data exchange. Without free movement across all national boundaries of the results of the observations there would be no point in having an IGY. This was reflected in a resolution of the 1955 Brussels conference that began: "The CSAGI resolves that all observational data to be exchanged in accordance with the IGY program shall be available to scientists and scientific institutions in all countries." [11] At these meetings it was agreed that the data should be presented, as far as possible, in a form suitable for machine processing, but it was left up to working groups in each field of research to agree on just what data were to be exchanged.

The United States and Soviet Union both offered to set up and finance archives for all of the IGY sciences, and offers to do so for individual sciences were received from other nations. The final decision was to establish three World Data Centers, each to house a complete set of IGY data. This, according to the resolutions of the Uccle meeting, was designed (1) to insure against catastrophic destruction of a single center and (2) to meet the geographic convenience of workers in different parts of the world. World Data Center A was to be in the United States, where it would be subdivided into about a dozen archives at institutions concerned with the various sciences. World Data Center B was to be in the Soviet Union, where it would be divided between Moscow and Novosibirsk, Siberia. World Data Center C was to be subdivided among countries in western Europe, Australia, and Japan. The chief weather archive was to be at WMO headquarters in Geneva.

In 1956 the CSAGI Bureau appointed Vice Admiral Sir Archibald Day, who had just retired as Hydrographer of Britain's Royal Navy, as IGY Coordinator. It was Day's task to see that the data centers were established and that the information reached them. Promptness was recognized as an important element of the program, and it was decided that each WDC must send copies of all incoming data to the other two centers within two months of receipt, at no cost, unless the other centers had already received the same material. Actually, during the IGY, many participating institutions sent their results to all three centers, obviating the need for later duplication. Finally, to insure that the fruits of the IGY be available to all, the Uccle conference provided that Data Centers, within three months, must satisfy requests for material from scientists in "any country," charging them no more than the cost of copying and mailing, and that researchers should have direct access to the material "by arrangement" with the authority responsible for the Center.[12] It was envisaged that the collection of all data would be completed by the end of 1960, allowing time for expeditions to return and process their results.

During June, 1957, dress rehearsals were held in many IGY programs, and a world-wide communications network to alert participants to flares on the sun was tested. All was set for what Chapman described as "the greatest example of world-wide scientific cooperation in the history of our race." [13] But a political crisis threatened the program which had sought with such determination to remain nonpolitical.

CHAPTER 4
CHINA AND THE KICKOFF

The crisis that marred final preparations for the IGY concerned the participation of the world's most populous nation, the Chinese People's Republic.

On September 12, 1955, Sydney Chapman, president of CSAGI, reported to the CSAGI conference in Brussels on an exchange of telegrams with the Academia Sinica in Peking. This was China's national scientific academy, which had held a world-wide reputation for scholarship since long before the Communists came into power. The Chinese, Chapman announced, had begun to form an IGY committee headed by Chu Cho-ching, a vice-president of the Academia with a doctor's degree from Harvard University. He was one of China's leading meteorologists and for a time headed the greatly expanded Institute of Geography at Nanking.

The message from Peking said that participation of the Chinese People's Republic was conditional on nonacceptance of the Chinese Nationalists as participants. This did not appear to be an obstacle since, three years after the initial invitation to participate in the IGY, no response had been received from Taiwan (Formosa).

Following the lead of the Soviet Union, the Chinese People's Republic took advantage of the IGY to carry out manifold expansion of its observations in the fields of weather, geomagnetism, and seismology. A list of IGY stations, issued by CSAGI as of March 24, 1957, showed some twenty-seven planned observation posts on the Chinese mainland, ranging from the coastal cities to Lhasa, Tibet, and Urumchi (Tihwa) in Sinkiang.

Scientists from Peking took part in the IGY regional conference for eastern Europe and Asia, held in Moscow from August 20 to 25, 1956. The following month delegations from China and the USSR went to the land ruled by an archenemy of communism, Francisco Franco, for the CSAGI conference in Barcelona.

The participation of scientists from Communist China in the Barcelona conference seems to have brought home to the Nationalists what was happening. About three months after the meeting a letter was received by Marcel Nicolet, secretary-general of CSAGI, from Chu Chia-hua, who identified himself as president of the Academia Sinica. The letter was postmarked Taipei, Taiwan. Thus there were two rival Academia Sinicas, represented by two Chus—one in Peking and one in Taipei. The latter said in his letter that the Republic of China (on Taiwan) was a member of ICSU and protested the admittance to the Barcelona conference of "three agents" from the Chinese People's Republic:

> It is needless to say that there is no independent scientific institute in any country behind the iron curtain, and that it has been the manifest intention of the communist rulers to turn every international gathering, scientific or cultural, into an arena of transmitting malicious propaganda and a battle ground for waging cold war. . . . It is impossible to expect scientists from Free China to sit face to face with the so-called representatives sent by a regime which is responsible for the wholesale massacre of some 15–20 millions of their innocent fellow countrymen.[1]

Chu Chia-hua claimed that no communication from CSAGI had been received in Taiwan since CSAGI had been formed. He said scientists in Taiwan were willing to cooperate in the IGY effort, but demanded deletion of the People's Republic of China from the official list of IGY participants.

Some of the IGY leaders expressed concern at this letter, since they felt that the Chinese Nationalists, having ignored the IGY for more than four years, had been induced to apply only by the news that the Chinese Communists were taking part. Every effort had been made to keep politics out of the IGY and, in the various preparatory conferences, the many political rivals had assiduously stuck to science. The letter from Taiwan raised an issue that, many feared, might open a Pandora's box of East-West hostility. The result might be the wrecking of the IGY.

Therefore, in January, 1957, Nicolet reminded Chu Chia-hua in Taiwan that his academy had been invited to join the IGY as early as 1952, and added:

You will realize that the International Geophysical Year organization functions through the initiative of individual scientists acting through committees, and that it is not organized through government action. Furthermore, it is the basic policy of the CSAGI, as formulated at its very inception, that participation in its program has no political significance.

On February 5, 1957, a message from Taiwan to CSAGI requested an invitation to a regional conference to be held in Tokyo, starting February 25, to coordinate IGY plans for the western Pacific. It made no mention of Chinese Communist participation, although a delegation from Peking obviously would attend. However, the host Japanese National Committee for the IGY received a message from Peking, saying in part, "Will send delegates on the condition Taiwan not invited." The Nationalists, not yet listed as IGY participants, had not been sent an invitation. The Japanese notified Peking to that effect.

On February 6 Nicolet asked Taiwan by cable to transmit the membership of its IGY committee and a description of its scientific program—standard preliminaries in adhering to the IGY. Late the next afternoon the Nationalist Chinese Embassy in Brussels phoned IGY headquarters and asked why this message had been sent instead of an invitation to the Tokyo meeting. The Embassy was notified that no invitation was possible until the widely scattered members of the CSAGI Bureau could make a decision. On February 8, after making three urgent phone calls, a representative of the Embassy called in person at Nicolet's headquarters to press Nationalist China's case. Consultations among some of the western members of the CSAGI Bureau showed a strong feeling that, before an invitation was sent, Taiwan should be required to give assurance that it would send scientists—not government representatives—and would not raise political questions.

On February 10 the Nationalists cabled to CSAGI the list of their IGY committee and the sciences in which observations were planned. This was followed by a letter ten days later from the committee chairman, Kenneth T. C. Cheng, giving details of the program and again requesting an invitation to Tokyo. Neither communication made reference to the barring of delegates from Peking, and it was thus hoped that a compromise might be effected.

During this crisis Chapman was in Göttingen, and he consulted by telephone with others of the CSAGI Bureau, including Vladimir Beloussov in Moscow. On February 12 he sent a letter to the chargé d'affaires of the People's Republic of China in London, requesting that its contents be passed on to the Academia Sinica in Peking. He noted the Academia's statement that adherence to the IGY was conditional on the exclusion of Taiwan.

> Up to that time [Chapman wrote] no such stipulation had formally been made by any nation as a condition of its participation. It was incompatible with the principles of CSAGI and the IGY, in which the cooperation of all countries is invited, regardless of political issues. Whatever disputes there may be as to the legitimacy of governments and rights to territory, CSAGI can only rely on the work of the scientists serving the governments actually administering the different parts of the earth: only they can make the geophysical observations needed for the IGY.

Participation of Peking had been welcomed, he added, "but without reference to the restrictive condition, which at the time was inoperative," since Taiwan, three years after being sent an invitation, had not accepted.

Chapman told Peking of the two communications from Taiwan— the November letter expressing unwillingness to sit with the delegates from Peking and the February message that did not mention Peking:

> CSAGI is now faced with this problem. Taiwan has at long last given its adherence, invited in 1952, to the IGY. After seeking to have China excluded from participation—a request that CSAGI would not consider—and after indicating that its scientists could not confer with yours, it has requested an invitation to the Tokyo conference. As Taiwan is a member of ICSU, and it alone can organize geophysical observations in Taiwan, the principles of CSAGI require that its adherence to the IGY be welcomed and an invitation sent to Taiwan to attend the Tokyo conference. To do this, however, as matters now stand, would seem to involve the loss of the participation by your country in the IGY and in the Tokyo conference. CSAGI would deeply regret such

a loss. The potential contribution by your country to the IGY is obviously much greater than that of Taiwan can be, especially in view of the very late adherence of Taiwan to the IGY.

Chapman, on behalf of CSAGI, proposed a compromise. The Nationalists, in view of their expressed hostility toward Peking, would be asked to pledge that they would send only geophysicists to Tokyo and would not raise political issues. If such a pledge were given, then Taiwan would be invited.

Chapman indicated reluctance to request such a pledge, however, until he had assurance from Peking of a similar withdrawal of its condition for going to Tokyo. It would be "most regrettable," he wrote, if Peking withdrew from the Tokyo conference after Taiwan had been asked and had agreed to drop its own political conditions for attendance. He noted that more than fifty nations had joined the IGY "in a harmonious spirit, regardless of political issues." For example, both parts of divided Germany were represented.

He emphasized that his letter was sent in the name of all five members of the CSAGI Bureau. Beloussov, he said, "agrees with the view that it is desirable to make this appeal in order to avoid the possible loss of China's cooperation in the IGY."

Meanwhile, the Nationalists persisted. On February 18 a representative of the Embassy in Brussels again delivered a message asking for an early decision on the invitation to Tokyo. This was relayed to Chapman in Göttingen and, on February 22, he wrote to the Nationalist chargé d'affaires in Brussels, calling attention to the last-minute nature of the Chinese Nationalist bid. Although welcome, despite its tardiness, it was accompanied, he said, "by requests of a nature contrary to the principles of CSAGI and the IGY." This was partly responsible for the delay in the original CSAGI reply and also presented "difficulties" in replying to the request for an invitation to the Tokyo conference. The making of a decision had been further complicated by the absence from Brussels of two of the five CSAGI Bureau members. Hence he doubted that the question could be resolved before the Tokyo meeting, due to begin in only three days.

On the day that it did open (with a Peking delegation in attendance), the chargé d'affaires in Brussels, R. H. Ouang, asked Chapman if Chinese Nationalist scientists could attend as observers. Chapman replied, in effect, that he could make no such arrangement on his own authority.

Meanwhile, on February 18, a message had reached Brussels from Peking as follows:

> Learned CSAGI intends admit Taiwan to IGY. This directly violates our previous understanding. China will join IGY only on condition Taiwan should not be admitted. Otherwise China will withdraw from IGY.
>
> Chu Choching Chairman CN IGY

This was probably in response to a summary of Chapman's letter, cabled to Peking by the Chinese mission in London. According to Chu, he did not see the full text until the end of March, when he returned from a trip. In a letter to Nicolet dated April 8, and one to Chapman two days later, he rejected their compromise plan:

> We Chinese are very apprehensive of the effort certain powers are making to create two Chinas to the detriment of their fatherland [he wrote]. The Chinese on the continent, and among them the Chinese scientists, therefore will recognize only one Chinese nation, i.e., the People's Republic of China, in existence in any international dealings and enterprises. We do not object [to] scientists from Taiwan coming to the IGY gatherings ... as long as they agree to this stipulation, implicitly or explicitly.

He described the late adherence of Taiwan as a political move, "for they knew fully well that we would walk out as soon as they were officially admitted." The participation of the two Germanys, he argued, could not be compared to the Chinese situation, for Germany had been divided on the basis of international agreements growing out of World War II, while "in 1949 the Chinese people overthrew the old corrupt regime and established their own government" and "only owing to foreign intervention ... there is the present temporary abnormal situation of Taiwan." Any qualified Chinese geophysicist would be welcomed as a member of the Chinese National Committee, he added, whether or not he resided on the mainland.

He noted that scientists from Peking had already taken part in three IGY conferences and had considerably enlarged their observation network, as requested by various conference resolutions. In a separate letter on April 8 Chu said that Peking would contribute $7500 in gold to the CSAGI budget for each of the next three years.

No more IGY conferences involving the Chinese were scheduled before the start of the Year, and the Bureau had begun to hope that a showdown could be avoided. However, in his letter to Nicolet, Chu said flatly that Peking would take part in the IGY only "on condition . . . that there should not be two National Committees of China."

This proved to be the insurmountable difficulty. All the Bureau members, with the possible exception of Beloussov, agreed that acceptance of Taiwan could no longer be deferred. In a message to CSAGI on May 2 the Taiwan scientists denied that their November letter implied political conditions and again asked that their admittance be expedited. This was elaborated in a letter two weeks later.

The CSAGI Bureau, meeting in Uccle from June 16 to 19, 1957, decided to make one final compromise attempt. Taiwan was quietly accepted, but at the same time it was announced to all IGY participants—without any stated reference to the Chinese problem—that henceforth no IGY committees would be listed in CSAGI documents as national.[2] Letters explaining the situation were sent to both Taiwan and Peking. Chapman, writing to Peking on June 17, thanked Chu Cho-ching for his letter of April 10 and explained that a reply had been delayed until the Bureau could meet and discuss the problems that it had raised and that arose from a letter from Taiwan:

> It appears to the Bureau that there will be IGY participation organized under the Academia Sinica, Taipei, which we must and do welcome. It cannot but be organized by a committee of scientists; this must be recognized in our list of participating IGY committees. As a whole these committees have been called national, for brevity, though we recognize that this term is not appropriate in all cases; the USSR IGY committee, for example, does not use the term national in its own title, because of the multinational character of the USSR. As regards Chinese IGY participation the Bureau has decided to include, in the list of participating IGY committees, two consecutive entries as follows:
>
> Chinese IGY Committee: Peking
> Chinese IGY Committee: Taipei

The General Secretary will try to avoid the use of the word national in specific references to these two committees. . . . In view of your references, which I was glad to see, to the IGY participation of overseas Chinese geophysicists, I sincerely hope that you will at least tacitly accept this course of action.

Dr. Chapman asserted that the inclusion of two Chinese committees had no political implications and concluded by saying: "The injection of political questions might even at this stage threaten serious dangers to the great IGY enterprise, in which so many geophysicists everywhere are eager peacefully to cooperate." The next day, Nicolet sent a letter along the same lines to Cheng, chairman of the IGY committee in Taiwan. The Year was due to start in less than two weeks.

The Chinese Nationalists apparently objected to the compromise listing of two Chinese committees. The second secretary of the Nationalist Embassy in Brussels asked, on June 19, for an appointment with Nicolet to discuss "the participation of the National Committee of the Republic of China in the IGY program." The CSAGI Bureau turned down this request, stating that it could not discuss political problems with government representatives.

On June 29, eve of the IGY, a cablegram arrived from Chu Choching in Peking stating that Taiwan was an integral part of China and could not take part as a country separate from the People's Republic of China. He demanded that CSAGI revoke its acceptance of Taiwan; until such action was taken, he said, Peking was withdrawing from CSAGI and all its activities.

Thus when the IGY began, at midnight the following day, the nation whose area ranks third in the world was officially not a participant. Nevertheless, China seems to have carried out all or most of the program originally planned. Satellite-tracking stations were set up across the country, from Sinkiang to the coast. The new observatories went to work and, according to Chinese press reports, the number of people working in the geophysical sciences was expanded from 40—most of them weather men—to 10,000. The roster of weather stations grew more than twentyfold to a total of 1000. Geomagnetic and seismic networks were established and an oceanographic research vessel fitted out.[3] While the Chinese were obviously feeding their satellite observations into Moscow,[4] it was not clear to what extent their general geophysical data would be made available to the world. Meanwhile, through at least the first half of the IGY, hope lingered that mainland China could be brought back into the enterprise.

> If there is any feasible step consistent with the principles that bind us, that could enable us to retain your participation [Chapman wrote to Chu], we should very much like to have an indication thereof from you.
>
> ... We hope you will continue to execute the IGY program you had planned, and we wish to aid you in this by the supply of the IGY Manuals and in any other ways that may be helpful to you. Should you not rejoin us officially at this time, we wish to state that our doors will always be open to welcome your return should this be desired by you.
>
> We wish, in any case, that your country may share in the benefits later to be reaped from our great enterprise.

Nevertheless, when the IGY came to an end, the Chinese People's Republic was still not a member, the one nation among sixty-seven to withdraw. It was the only case in which the IGY was significantly affected by political considerations.

Of all those concerned with the problem of Chinese participation, none was in a more delicate position than Beloussov. Technically his role in the CSAGI Bureau was as a representative of IUGG, rather than of the Soviet Union, and when he acted with other members of the Bureau he theoretically did so on his own and, in fact, appears to have had considerable independence of action. Like the head of the Soviet IGY program, Ivan Bardin, Beloussov was a member of the scientific elite whose role in Soviet affairs, as brought out during the IGY, was more influential than many outsiders had realized.

At the appointed hour on July 1, 1957, the great scientific adventure that was the IGY began. The crisis over China did not visibly dampen the enthusiasm of the IGY leaders, and few others knew of it—even, apparently, in China. Around the world, at zero hours, Greenwich time, scientists turned on recording instruments or checked their operation (many of the observations had begun on June 1 as a dress rehearsal). The sun was shining on the central Pacific and, as anticipated seven years before, was nearing peak activity. A twenty-four-hour watch on its spot-marked face had begun and was to continue, unbroken so far as weather allowed, for the next eighteen months. The task was shared by observatories in Alaska, Japan, Australia, the Soviet Union, western Europe, and the United States, so spaced around the world that the sun was always over one or more of them.

The IGY roster at that time included sixty-four countries. Scientists at an estimated 4000 stations were taking part. In preparation for this day observers had been placed in the most remote parts of the earth—at the South Pole, on drifting floes near the North Pole, in huts perilously perched on mountaintops from Haut de Stalin, Bulgaria, to Mount Eva Peron, Argentina. (The tides of fortune had made both names politically obsolete, but they remained on IGY station lists.) Other scientists were on Mount Norikura, Japan; at Tunchuan, in the mountains of southwest China; and on Sacramento Peak, New Mexico. Some IGY investigators went down instead of up, seeking knowledge of the earth's shape and interior. Many of those studying day-to-day shifts in the force and direction of gravity were underground: Americans in a tunnel at Dalton Canyon in California, Germans in a potash mine, and Italians in a grotto near Trieste.

Those observing the strange changes in ocean level, which range from shifts every few minutes to seasonal variations, were installed on remote islands, sometimes mere patches of white coral with no other inhabitants than a multitude of sea birds. Research vessels from virtually all the large maritime nations were at sea or preparing for long voyages.

The sun, whose eruptions set in motion so many of the events to be observed during the IGY, gave the Year a blazing send-off and tested the newly formed observing nets. Three days before the start of the IGY the observatory at Krasnaya Pakhra, twenty miles south of Moscow, observed on the sun the burgeoning ultraviolet light of a major flare. In accordance with the plan worked out in advance, Krasnaya Pakhra sent a specially coded dispatch to the newly created World Warning Agency in Fort Belvoir, Virginia, which recommended the calling of an Alert.

This would be preliminary to the calling of a Special World Interval—a period for particularly expensive or difficult observations, for rocket shots, and for a redoubling of regular observations to obtain a detailed picture of the flare's effect on the earth.

The World Warning Agency was not as imposing in appearance as in name. It consisted of a cluster of shedlike structures on the edge of a lonely Virginia cow pasture, where technicians of the National Bureau of Standards made forecasts of radio propagation conditions. Since solar flares often cause radio blackouts, these men were experienced at deciding what kind of flare was likely to produce auroral fireworks and other manifestations on earth.

They were not entirely dependent on visual sightings. Solar flares produce bursts of radio noise that can be heard, even on cloudy days. Likewise a large flare causes sudden, intense ionization below the radio-reflecting layers of the ionosphere, swallowing up signals from distant points. By keeping track of signal strengths from stations in various directions and by vertical soundings of the ionosphere with radio signals, it is possible to detect the appearance of an absorption layer formed abruptly at the moment that light from a flare reaches the earth.

Besides an ionospheric sounder, the forecaster had before him a large globe whose surface was a blackboard. On it, in ten imposing clusters, were sunspots as reported from around the world during the sun's own rotation. Since the sun is gaseous, it does not rotate uniformly like a solid sphere. Sunspots near its equator make the trip around a few days faster than those at higher latitudes. The true nature of these spots is still a mystery, although it is known that their number fluctuates in an eleven-year cycle. They are dark only by contrast with the rest of the solar disk. The solar flares that produce dramatic effects on earth usually erupt in the vicinity of sunspots.

When the sun came over the Virginia horizon, after the message from Krasnaya Pakhra, it was, indeed, remarkably pocked with spots and other manifestations of activity. Piecing together all available bits of information, the forecaster on duty, whose responsibility it was to decide, carried out the recommendation of the Soviet observatory and punched a message on perforated tape, which he inserted in four teletype machines. At 4 P.M. Universal (Greenwich) Time on June 28 he threw the switches and the four machines jumped into action. One carried the alarm to the communications networks of the World Meteorological Organization, serving all national weather services; another carried it, via United States Army Signal Corps circuits, to Alaska, Antarctica, Australia, Canada, and Japan. The other machines, via commercial links, serviced western Europe, Moscow, and Latin America. From Moscow the word was passed to eastern Europe and China; Tokyo relayed it to other Far Eastern stations. As a backstop the two time-signal radio stations of the

United States National Bureau of Standards, WWV in Washington and WWVH in Hawaii, broadcast the warning twice an hour. Britain's BBC carried it once a day on its Home Service.

The decision to call an Alert had been wise, for within seventeen hours the particles ejected by the flare began showering on the earth's atmosphere. The first Special World Interval of the IGY was proclaimed, to begin at one minute after midnight the morning of June 30. Four hours later world-wide communications were severely disrupted and there were radical fluctuations in the earth's magnetic field. After another hour, at 5 A.M. Universal Time, Weather Bureau observers and volunteers, gazing skyward from coast to coast of the United States and Canada, saw a magnificent auroral display. Most of some thirteen all-sky cameras, spaced across the United States to span the sky over the entire width of the continent, went into action. When the hundreds of visual reports were pieced together in the IGY Auroral Data Center at Cornell University (Ithaca, N.Y.), there emerged the picture of twin arcs of auroral light spanning the entire continent in a sweeping curve several thousand miles long.

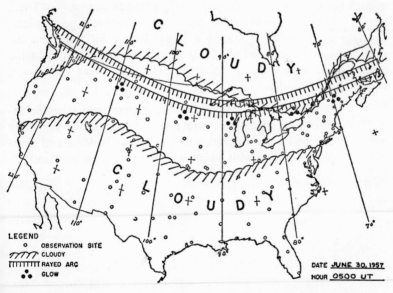

The aurora that inaugurated the IGY as mapped by the Data Center at Cornell. The arcs could be plotted over cloudy areas from observations made by those, farther south, who could see over the clouds.

On the second day of the IGY the magnetic storm subsided. As had been feared, many projects were not ready for the kickoff, and so some aspects of the storm were not seen at all. This was true in particular of direct observations high in the sky, using rockets, balloons, and earth satellites.

Thus the IGY began, carried forward by a seemingly irresistible tide of scientific enthusiasm. Many saw in it a great hope for mankind, setting a pattern of cooperation that could lead to permanent peace. In a television lecture on IGY eve, Prince Philip, Duke of Edinburgh, said:

> The IGY is the world studying itself. It is seldom that this world of ours acts together. . . . Yet, for the next eighteen months, East and West, North and South, will unite in the greatest assault in history on the secrets of the earth. . . . At the same time, it may well help to solve the real problem—the conflict of ideas.[5]

Joseph Kaplan, chairman of the United States IGY committee, suggested that, by gazing more intently beyond his narrow environment, man might be persuaded that his conflicts are petty. "These large views which are characteristic of astronomy and geophysics," he said, "have given the IGY a role which may far transcend the gathering of data and the observing of physical processes." [6] In the Soviet Union, Ivan Bardin, chairman of the Soviet IGY committee, said the Year would

> demonstrate once again that the cultural and scientific interests of all nations have a common base and that only international cooperation will solve the intricate and complex problems with which science today presents man.[7]

CHAPTER 5
MOSKVA—SPUTNIK

The July, 1957, issue of *Radio,* Soviet magazine for amateur radio operators, carried this announcement:

NOTICE TO RADIO AMATEURS

The Institute of Radio Engineering and Electronics of the USSR, Academy of Sciences asks radio amateurs to report on the preparation for the reception of signals from satellites launched in the USSR, to send a description of the radio equipment, and after observation of the satellite, to report the radio signal data and to forward the magnetic tapes with the recorded signals to the address: Moscow, K-9, Makhovaya ul., 11, IRE AN SSSR.

The notice then listed thirteen items to be included in the reports. It concluded:

Immediately at the end of reception of the signals please report briefly by telegram the place of reception, the date, the time (Moscow), and the signal frequency to the address: Moskva-Sputnik.[1]

Three months passed before *sputnik,* the Russian word for satellite, was dramatically added to all languages, but the *Radio* announcement and other warning signs had been ignored. Except for the Japanese attack on Pearl Harbor, probably no event has taken the American people quite so much by surprise as the launching of the first Soviet earth satellite.

The surprise came, as with Pearl Harbor, because so little attention had been paid to the evidence of what was coming. Few in the West were aware of the swift Soviet advances in science and technology that had taken place in the four or five years before the launching of the first Sputnik. The name Konstantin Edouardovich Tsiolkovsky was virtually unknown in the United States, although now it is acknowledged that his work on the principles of rocketry at the turn of the century made him "father of . . . the science of astronautics." [2] The extent of Russian rocketry research between the world wars and the heavy dependence of the Red Army on tactical rockets during World War II were likewise generally unfamiliar. Finally the limited information on the Soviet earth satellite program published in Russia was ignored until the Russians were ready to shoot.

Actually the idea of placing an object in orbit around the earth is almost three centuries old. It goes back to Sir Isaac Newton, who first worked out the laws of motion. By demonstrating mathematically the combined effect upon moving bodies of their tendency to fly in a straight line (centrifugal force) and the pull of gravity, he showed why the planets remain in orbit. His classic *Principia,* first published in 1687 and revised in 1713, described the launching of an artificial earth satellite to illustrate his principles. Except during the few minutes of acceleration at their launching, the satellites now in orbit are unpowered. They coast about 375,000 miles daily without falling to earth. What keeps them up there? The satellites keep going, in part, because there is almost no air to slow them; but the principles which hold them in orbit are best described in Newton's words, using the drawing from *Principia:*

> The manner in which planets are held in fixed orbits by gravitational forces can be understood from the motions of projectiles. When a stone is thrown, it is deflected from a straight line by its own weight and, describing a curve in the air, it finally falls to earth. If it is projected with greater speed, it goes further. It is possible, by increasing the velocity, to cause it to describe an arc, of one, two, five, ten, 100, 1,000 miles, until finally, continuing beyond the ends of the earth, it would no longer fall to earth.
>
> Let AFB designate the surface of the earth. C its center & VD, VE, VF the trajectories described by a projectile thrown horizontally, with successively increasing velocities, from the vertex V on the peak of a very high mountain. To avoid taking into account air resistance, which hardly retards the motion of celestial bodies, let us ignore it, or assume that it offers no resistance. Then the same law that

causes a body with a low velocity to describe the smaller
arc VD; and, with a greater velocity, the greater arc VE;
and, with a still greater velocity, causes it to reach F; and
further to G; will cause the body, if the velocity continues
to increase, to go beyond the entire circumference of the
earth and return to the top, whence it was projected. . . .
Moreover, maintaining its velocity, it will continue by the
same law to revolve over and over. Now let us imagine
bodies projected horizontally from greater heights. Take,

DE MUNDI SYSTE

projiciatur, pergit longiùs. Augendo vel
ut arcum defcriberet miłliaris unius, duoı
centum, mille; ac tandem ut, pergendo
non amplius in terram caderet. Defignet A

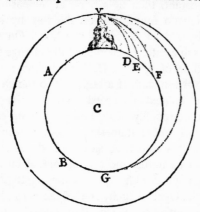

c centrum e
neas curvas, ı
tis præalti v
neas horizon
velocitatis g
miffum defc
fiftentia, qu
retardantur,
fingamus h
faltem nil re
tione quâ cc

defcribit arcum minorem vD, & majore ɛ
auctâ adhuc velocitate pergit longiùs ad F,
tandem, fi augeatur femper velocitas, fı
ambitum, & redibit ad montem, unde fue
que area, quam, radio ad centrum terræ d
Prop. I. Lib. 1. Princip. Math.) proportior
ejus in reditu ad montem non minor erit

Facsimile of Newton's illustration with a fragment of the original text.

for example, points five, ten, 100, 1,000 or more miles in height, or even as high as several semidiameters of the earth. Depending upon the velocity of the bodies and the force of gravity at each of the heights, the bodies would describe arcs which were either concentric to the earth, or were eccentric in various ways.[3]

The chief impediment to a demonstration of this idea was the impossibility of firing a gun at an altitude high enough to encounter no air resistance. Another was the difficulty of achieving the necessary speed. The muzzle velocity of the newest high-velocity rifles is 3000 miles an hour; that necessary for an orbit above the atmosphere is roughly 18,000 miles an hour.

Newton's laws also made it possible to calculate two other critical velocities: that necessary for complete escape from the earth's gravity and that needed to escape the pull of the sun. If a stone is thrown up, it slows, pauses an instant, then falls back at increasing speed. Disregarding air drag, Newton found that on the way up its speed decreased each second by almost 22 miles per hour. On the way down it increased at the same rate. In each case the change in speed was a measure of the force of gravity. Halfway to the moon, this force would be far less, Newton said. If a body fell to the earth from an infinite distance, he calculated, its speed on impact (again disregarding air drag) would be roughly 25,000 miles an hour. If a body were shot upward at slightly more than that speed, it would never fall back. The earth's gravity would keep slowing it down until, past the moon, its speed would be hardly more than that of an airplane. But gravity, nibbling at its speed with ever-lessening strength, would be fighting a hopeless battle. Once virtually free of the earth, however, the object would still be a captive of the sun. Before leaving the earth, it was already orbiting the sun at some 66,600 miles per hour. Once its motion away from the earth dwindled to almost zero, it would still have this far greater speed, in terms of the sun. To escape from this orbit, and hence from the solar system, it would need another 28,000 miles per hour.

The laws governing gravity and the movements of bodies in space, as set forth by Newton and Johann Kepler in the seventeenth century, were well known to the father of science fiction, Jules Verne. Shortly after the American Civil War, according to an account by this French author, an artificial satellite containing three men and two dogs was fired into an orbit around the moon. Ironically, this fictitious feat was the fruit of American inventive genius heavily subsidized by Moscow. His account, which appeared in 1865 in two volumes, entitled *From the Earth to the Moon* and *Round the Moon,* reflected Verne's admiration for American inventiveness. "The Yankees, the first mechanicians in the world, are engineers," he wrote, "just as the Italians are musicians and the Germans are metaphysicians—by right of birth."

When foreign aid was sought to help in financing the proposed shot to the moon, Verne said, Russia contributed 368,733 rubles, an act he attributed to "the scientific taste of the Russians and the impetus which they have given to astronomical studies."

As with many of Verne's dreams, this one had striking parallels to what later came to pass. He chose "Tampa Town" in central Florida as his launching site. The first American satellites and moon probes actually were launched from Cape Canaveral, across the peninsula on the Atlantic. The computation of the flight trajectory and the proper time and angle of fire in his account were made by the observatory in Cambridge, Massachusetts, where, as it turned out, American orbital studies of the first real earth satellites were carried out. Verne's space vehicle missed the moon and went into orbit around it. To escape from this, its passengers ignited what today are known as retro-rockets—small rockets for slowing a space vehicle. This kicked them back toward the earth and the vehicle fell, flaming like a meteor, into the Pacific, where it bobbed to the surface and its passengers, unhurt because of heavy shielding, were rescued.

Verne was not the only nineteenth-century novelist who was aware of satellite possibilities. Dostoevsky, in *The Brothers Karamazov,* described a nightmare in which the Devil tells one of the brothers how he could throw an axe into space so that it would orbit the earth. Astronomers, he said, would then keep track of its rising and setting, just like nature's moon.

With Tsiolkovsky's studies at the end of the century, the fictions of the past began to become fact. About 1909, six years after Tsiolkovsky published his first important treatise, Robert Hutchings Goddard began his rocket research in the United States. Probably the first application of his study was in the development of better pyrotechnic signals for the Navy. To achieve the heights needed for exploration of the upper air (and ultimately, he hoped, the moon), Goddard decided that rockets would have to be propelled by liquid fuel; solid-fueled rockets had been in use since the Chinese began making them in the ninth century. In 1926 Goddard achieved the world's first flight by a liquid-fueled rocket, but he worked quietly, apparently fearful that if publicized his serious studies would be confused with the "Buck Rogers" treatment space travel was getting at that time.

In Europe, on the other hand, competent men did not hesitate to band together and publicly devote their talents to such problems. In 1927 the Verein für Raumschiffahrt (Society for Space Navigation) was founded. This set in motion a growing program of German research on the subject, aided by Hermann Oberth, a pioneer in rocket theory who, although of German extraction, had been born in what is now Romania. In 1931 one of the Verein members achieved the first European flight of a liquid-fueled rocket (several hundred feet) and by the end of that year nearly a hundred rockets had been flown. Although the Verein was killed by the depression, the German Army had recognized the potentialities of its work, particularly since rocketry seemed to offer a loophole in the Versailles Treaty limitation on German development of heavy artillery. In 1933 Captain (later Major General) Walter R. Dornberger was placed in charge of the army's rocket project; for an assistant he selected one of the former directors of the Verein, a twenty-one-year-old student named Wernher von Braun.

In the years that followed, larger and larger rockets were developed—the A-1, the A-2, and the A-3, a modification of which, the A-5, reached a height of seven miles. As their range increased, it was necessary to fire over water and hence the project moved to Peenemünde, where the missiles could be fired over the Baltic. By the outbreak of World War II the A-4 had been projected. This was a monster forty-seven feet long that weighed twelve tons on the pad, and included an explosive charge of almost a ton plus nine tons of propellant (all of it burned up in the first minute of flight).[4]

The first attempt to fire the A-4 was a fizzle. On the next attempt it broke apart after forty-five seconds in the air. The third shot, on October 3, 1942, was successful. It soared to a height of 53 miles and landed more than 118 miles down the range. Two years later the first A-4 was fired on London; the Nazis christened it *Vergeltungs-*

waffe II—"Retaliation Weapon II." It soon came to be known in England as the V-2, and in the six months of the war that remained 3600 of them were hurled at London and Antwerp, Belgium. Before the war ended, the Germans discussed plans for a multistage missile that could cross the Atlantic and hit New York City.

Although the Russians apparently were not interested in long-range rockets until after the war, their early work in rocketry and jet propulsion was not far behind that of the Germans. In 1929, two years after the founding of the Verein für Raumschiffahrt, they formed GIRD, acronym in Russian for Groups for the Study of Reactive Motion. In a study undertaken for the United States Air Force and published in 1957–58, F. J. Krieger of the Rand Corporation wrote that the research papers produced by GIRD "contain a wealth of evidence of native competence in the various aspects of rocketry and space flight and clearly indicate that the Russians possessed a relatively high degree of technical sophistication more than two decades ago." [5]

During World War II it was the Soviet Union—not Germany—that pioneered in the use of tactical rockets on the battlefield.[6] As the Red Army advanced into Germany, Von Braun and some 400 of his co-workers fled westward from Peenemünde and thus the cream of German rocket talent fell into American hands. Some 120 of the Peenemünde group ended up at the United States Army's Redstone Arsenal in Huntsville, Alabama, with Von Braun at their head. He became director of the Development Operations Division of the Army Ballistic Missile Agency and on April 14, 1955, he and 102 of his colleagues and their families became United States citizens.

The Russians came home with truckloads of German research reports, but, so far as personnel was concerned, their haul consisted largely of lower-level German technicians. The Russians put them to work on isolated research projects, keeping them completely apart from the central stream of Soviet rocketry development.

Von Braun himself sought to debunk the American notion that Soviet space achievements were the work of Germans. He told a congressional hearing of the "debriefing" of returning German rocket men by western intelligence agencies in West Berlin and West Germany. These technicians, he said, "were obviously not even aware of the large and extensive ballistic missile program that was going on inside Soviet Russia." [7]

As an answer to the construction of United States Air Force bases facing the various Soviet frontiers, Moscow had ordered a crash program for the development of a missile that could menace the American homeland. While such intelligence devices as the American missile-tracking radar in Turkey gave western governments clues to what was going on in Russia, the outcome of the Soviet effort came as a complete surprise to the American public.

This shock was the more profound because so little publicity had been given to Soviet preparations. On April 16, 1955, six months after CSAGI, meeting in Rome, had urged the launching of satellites (and three months before the White House announced the American intention to do so), the Moscow evening newspaper *Vechernyaya Moskva* told of Soviet plans to launch such a vehicle. The article described the formation of a permanent Interdepartmental Commission on Interplanetary Communications under the Academy of Sciences of the USSR, with Leonid I. Sedov as chairman.

Among the twenty-seven members of this commission were some of the Soviet Union's best-known scientists.[8] They included such men as Ambartsumyan, one of the world's leading astronomers; Kapitsa, who once headed an atomic research laboratory at Cambridge University; and Bogolyubov, who turned his mathematical genius to the study of the atom. The inclusion of men of this stature showed that the Russians meant business in their space program. No such organ was formed in the United States until 1958, when the Space Science Board was created under the National Academy of Sciences, with Lloyd Berkner as chairman.

The April, 1955, report in *Vechernyaya Moskva* said that "one of the immediate tasks" of the newly formed commission was "to organize work" on construction of a scientific earth satellite. Among the tasks of the satellite were to be the biological study of weightlessness, observation of ultraviolet light and X rays from the sun and stars, study of the effect of the ionosphere on radio signals from the satellite, and photo-reconnaissance of polar ice floes and cloud cover. No timetable was given and there was no mention of the IGY.[9]

This report indicates that a living passenger, such as the dog carried on Sputnik II, was being contemplated more than two and a half years before the actual firing. Biological research had nothing to do with the IGY, but the inclusion of a passenger would have obvious advantages, both as a first step toward space travel by man and for its dramatic impact. The Moscow newspaper account was virtually ignored by the rest of the world, whereas the White House announcement of July 29, 1955, created a sensation and was followed by publication of a growing mass of detail on the American plans. Four days after the announcement in Washington, Sedov, in Copenhagen for an astronautical congress, held a press conference at the Soviet legation. He noted the United States announcement and said that "much consideration" had recently been given in the Soviet Union to research on satellite launchings.

> In my opinion [he declared], it will be possible to launch an artificial earth satellite within the next two years. . . . From a technical point of view, it is possible to create a satellite of larger dimensions than that reported in the newspapers which we had the opportunity of scanning today. The realization of the Soviet project can be expected in the comparatively near future. . . . It seems to me that the time has come when it is possible to direct all forces and means toward mutual efforts for creating an artificial satellite and to switch the military potential in the technology of rockets to the peaceful and noble purposes of developing cosmic flights. I think that such work would be an important contribution to the cause of eliminating the cold war and would serve the cause of consolidating peace.[10]

An official announcement was made about a year later, at the CSAGI Barcelona conference, by Ivan Pavlovich Bardin, chairman of the Soviet IGY committee. Bardin was Russia's leading metallurgist. His face looked like a block of granite and, although at seventy-three he was approaching retirement, those who had to keep pace with him found it hard to believe he was that old.

> The USSR [Bardin said] intends to launch a satellite by means of which measurements of atmospheric pressure and temperature, as well as observations of cosmic rays, micrometeorites, the geomagnetic field and solar radiation will be conducted. The preparations for launching the satellite are presently being made. . . . Since the question of USSR participation in the IGY Rocket-Satellite observations was

decided quite recently the detailed program of these investigations is not yet elaborated.[11]

During the Barcelona conference, Bardin took part in a sixteen-man Working Group on Rockets and Satellites which included eight scientists from the United States, two from the United Kingdom, and one each from Australia, the Chinese People's Republic, France, Switzerland, and the Union of South Africa. Bardin was the only Soviet representative. Among the resolutions adopted by the group, and ultimately by the full CSAGI, were three that imposed specific obligations on satellite-launching countries. They required each nation launching satellites to provide to any country requesting it "full technical information on optical and radio tracking equipment—and on telemetry equipment as appropriate." Likewise to be furnished was "scheduling and planning information as is essential for the preparation for and execution of optical and radio observations." Finally it was recommended that the radio systems of all IGY satellites be "compatible" with those announced by the United States at that meeting, "in order that the same ground-based receiving equipment can be used throughout." [12]

Those in attendance reported that Bardin did not seem familiar with satellite problems and acceded to the various western proposals without argument.

During the months that followed, IGY leaders were anxious to receive details of the Soviet satellite program so that documents could be prepared for the use of the many nations that planned to take part in tracking. Finally, after a number of appeals to Moscow, a long document was received from Bardin on June 16, 1957, dated six days earlier. It discussed at length the scientific problems to be attacked in the Soviet rocket and satellite firings but gave little information on the firing schedule itself.

The communication said the "satellites" would be launched from within the USSR in an almost north-south orbit, so that they would pass over all parts of the earth except the central areas of the Arctic and Antarctic. Rockets were to be fired from three "zones":

1. Franz Joseph Land in the Arctic (25 launchings in 1958).
2. "Middle latitudes of the USSR, 50°–60° North" (30 launchings in 1957; 40 in 1958).
3. Antarctica, mainly near Mirny (30 launchings in 1957–58).

Some of the instruments in the rockets were to be housed in containers in the nose, which would be jettisoned at an elevation of about 125 miles and recovered.

Meanwhile, in the same month, the Soviet magazine *Radio* printed two articles which revealed:

1. The satellites would transmit radio-telegraph signals ("beeps") alternately on 20 and 40 megacycles. When a beep was being sent on one frequency, the other would be silent.

2. Signals from the "first satellites" would telemeter (radio) data on the environment in which their transmitters were operating, to facilitate "further work in designing radio apparatus for artificial satellites."

3. This data would be encoded by varying the length of the beeps on each frequency and the pauses between them. The duration of the beeps was to range from .05 to .7 seconds, depending on environmental conditions within the satellite. The changes in the beeps would be "easily distinguished even . . . by ear."

4. The radiated power of the transmitters was to be one watt (100 times that planned for the first American satellites).

Much space was given to satellite tracking by means of doppler— a method particularly suitable for amateurs, since all they had to do was make tape recordings in a specified way. Doppler is the change in wavelength due to motion of the wave source toward or away from the observer. The classic example is the drop in pitch of a train whistle as it passes a listener. As the train approaches, its speed shortens the sound waves, making the note higher. Once the train has passed, its speed elongates the waves, making the pitch suddenly lower.

The closer the observer stands to the tracks, the more abrupt is the change. If he is several blocks away, the change in pitch is more gradual. A scientist could thus use a recording of the whistle of a passing train to tell both how near it had passed and at what time. This principle, applied to the frequency of radio signals, was the essence of the Soviet plan for amateur radio tracking. At a frequency of 40 megacycles the total expected change was about 2000 cycles, the magazine said. To establish the exact time of the observations, it noted, the tape recording should also include radio time signals. The magazine noted that "highly qualified radio amateurs and radio clubs" could build equipment to observe a passing satellite continuously.

The next issue of *Radio* described the American Minitrack II system, designed to enable amateurs to follow a satellite with comparatively inexpensive equipment. This was a modification of the complex, high-precision Minitrack system developed by the Naval Research Laboratory in Washington for use along a north-south "fence" of tracking stations. Minitrack antennas are strung out over the ground in pairs, each connected with electronic equipment that can analyze radio waves. The moment at which a particular phase of a radio wave arrives at each antenna is dependent on the direction of the transmitter. If the satellite is due east, on the horizon, a particular phase of each wave would reach the easternmost antenna before it reached the westernmost, the interval being equal to the speed of light over the distance between the antennas. With the satellite directly overhead, the arrival time of a particular wave phase would be simultaneous at all the antennas. Thus, by phase comparison, using what are known as interferometers, it was expected that Minitrack could pinpoint the direction of a signal to within three minutes of arc under normal conditions, and within twenty seconds of arc under optimum conditions—at night or near the zenith. This was far more accurate than any data expected from doppler tracking, but the Russians also did rather precise observations with their missile-tracking radars.

The American plan to use 108 megacycles for satellite radio signals had been widely publicized since its announcement in September, 1956. The June, 1957, issue of *Radio* made no mention of this, but went into considerable detail on the advantage of using 20 and 40 megacycles in tandem. To understand what the Russians had in mind, it is necessary to review knowledge of the ionosphere at that time.

Due in large part to the work of Sir Edward Appleton and the observations of the Second Polar Year, it was now well established that there are a number of radio-reflecting layers in the atmosphere. It was believed that these are produced by ionization of the air, largely (if not entirely) by sunlight. Radiation in the X-ray and ultraviolet portions of the spectrum has the capacity to ionize the atoms and molecules of the air—that is, it can knock off their outer electrons. This fills the air with electrically charged particles: free electrons (negative) and positive ions (atoms and molecules whose electric neutrality has been upset by the loss of an electron). In their agitated movement free electrons may encounter positive ions, in which case they recombine, again forming neutral atoms or molecules. Some of the free electrons may attach themselves to neutral atoms or molecules, giving them a negative charge (negative ions).

Such ionization in the upper air gives it its name, the ionosphere. The degree of ionization is determined by a number of factors that vary with height, such as the intensity of the ionizing rays, the density of the atmosphere (the more particles per cubic inch, the greater likelihood that electrons will meet ions and recombine), and the composition of the atmosphere. The various combinations of these factors at different depths in the atmosphere determine the degree to which it is ionized. Up to thirty miles or more above the earth almost all atoms and molecules in the air are electrically neutral, but by forty miles, when the air is under the influence of sunlight, there is sufficient ionization to absorb some radio signals before they penetrate higher and are reflected to their destination. This is known as the D region. The absence of ionization there at night makes for better radio reception. When light from a solar flare strikes the D region, the ionization in the comparatively dense air at that level completely absorbs the waves used in long-distance communications, causing a radio blackout.

Above this, at about sixty-five miles, lies the E region. This is the lowest layer normally used for reflecting radio signals, but, as with other layers of the ionosphere, it is not a sharply defined mirror. Rather it is a region about six miles thick in which ionization (and hence electron density) reaches a level that is critical for certain radio wavelengths.

On top of this is the F region which, in daylight, divides into two layers: The F_1 is at about 100 miles and the F_2 may begin anywhere from 160 to 250 miles up. The F_2 is more than thirty miles thick. Each layer, progressing upward, has a greater concentration of electrons than those below it and hence reflects radio signals of shorter wavelength. The F layers are of the greatest value for long-range communications, but their height is the most variable. The heights of all the layers vary with latitude, time of day, season, and intensity of sunspot activity, but the F_2 layer changes to by far the greatest degree, complicating the task of those who must choose the best frequency to use at any particular time and place.

In radio probing of the ionosphere, the "critical" frequency of any layer is the maximum frequency which it reflects when the pulses are directed vertically. Since signals of higher frequency (shorter wavelength) pass on out into space and are not reflected, the structure of the ionosphere above the F_2 layer was unexplored; signals from a satellite offered a chance to look into this region for the first time.

Radio explained that during the sunspot maximum of the IGY the critical frequency of the F_2 layer was expected to reach 15 to 16 megacycles in winter, dropping to 10 megacycles in summer. Hence 20 megacycles had been chosen as the lowest satellite frequency that would surely penetrate the F_2 region and reach the earth. But such penetration was likely at 20 megacycles only when the satellite was near the zenith, since at a frequency so near the margin the signals must hit the ionosphere nearly at right angles. To penetrate at more oblique angles the frequency must be still higher.

The use of 20 and 40 megacycles, beeping alternately, therefore made possible a number of experiments. By using two frequencies, one marginal (20 megacycles) and the other well above the critical level (40 megacycles) it would be possible to "watch" the satellite on the higher frequency and observe at exactly what angle of elevation the 20 megacycle signals first broke through. To aid in such calculations, the amateurs were urged to monitor the exact moments when signals on each of the two frequencies became audible, and when each faded out.

Unfortunately the two articles in *Radio* were not translated and circulated in the West until a week or two before Sputnik I was launched. According to one CSAGI Bureau member, Moscow sent the same information to CSAGI by mail, but its processing was delayed because the addressee was absent on a trip.

On September 30, 1957, the conference to coordinate final rocket and satellite plans for the IGY met at the National Academy of Sciences on Constitution Avenue in Washington, D.C. Those attending represented nations taking part in rocket and satellite launchings (Australia, Britain, Canada, France, Japan, the Soviet Union, and the United States) and those with special tracking stations (Chile, Cuba, Ecuador, India, Iran, and Peru).

The plenary meetings were held in the domed hall of the Academy. In the adjoining library was an extensive exhibit on the American rocket program and Project Vanguard—the launching of American

IGY satellites. In one animated exhibit a miniature Vanguard sphere buzzed happily around a globe. There was a full-scale model of at least one of the proposed "moons." On the table was a sample of the stubby telescopes developed for the United States *Moonwatch* program. Teams of volunteer Moonwatch sky-gazers had been organized both at home and abroad to watch for the satellites when they would be visible. This would be during the hour or two before sunrise or after sunset, when the baby moon gleamed in sunlight, though the earth beneath it was dark. In such conditions the satellite would be visible great distances, much as a speck of dust can be seen as it drifts through a shaft of sunlight.

The Moonwatch teams, under supervision of the Smithsonian Astrophysical Observatory in Cambridge, Massachusetts, had been trained to sit along a north-south line, each person gazing into a scope aimed at a fixed portion of the meridian, or north-south arc of the heavens. When one person saw the satellite, he was to shout a signal just as it crossed the meridian, his voice being recorded against the time tick of the National Bureau of Standards radio signals. The chief value of these visual observations would be to keep track of a satellite, especially during the uncertain periods at the start and finish of its life.

Alongside the Moonwatch telescope was a similar one provided by the Soviet Union. Soviet teams had been organized in much the same way.

The three Soviet delegates to the conference were led by Anatoli A. Blagonravov, who had risen to lieutenant general of artillery before becoming involved in the Soviet space program. Now he was not only a full-fledged member of the Soviet Academy of Sciences, but also of the Interdepartmental Commission on Interplanetary Communications. In contrast to the two younger men with him, his shock of white hair gave him a professorial look. The inner intensity of the man came out occasionally, as he whispered earnestly to his countrymen, but much of the time he wore a thin smile and carried his Russian cigarette tipped upward at a rakish angle.

The afternoon of the first day of the conference the delegates assembled in the Academy lecture room to hear technical papers on the subject "Satellite Vehicles, Launching and Tracking." The first man on the program was John P. Hagen of the Naval Research Laboratory, who was in charge of Project Vanguard, the American

satellite program. He gave a detailed progress report. Next came
Sergei M. Poloskov of the Soviet Union, a man with black hair
brushed straight across his forehead. He looked as though he rarely
ventured forth from his laboratory. The western rocket men were
hushed and hopeful that at last they would learn details of the Soviet
satellite project.

Most of those present had just heard of the Soviet plan to use 20
and 40 megacycles. The Americans were particularly disturbed, since
their whole radio tracking system was tuned to the projected 108-
megacycle output of the American satellites. They felt that the proposed Soviet frequencies were not "compatible" with the United
States equipment in the sense of the Barcelona resolutions. Furthermore, they regarded 108 megacycles as better for tracking because
such high frequencies are less subject to bending during passage
through the ionosphere.

Poloskov argued that such bending was useful, rather than an
impediment. Comparison of the greater effect on 20 megacycles with
that on 40 megacycles, he said, would reveal the density of electrons
along the signal paths. Since the high and low points of the expected
orbits would lie above and below the F_2 layer, correlation of results
from these two types of passes would indicate electron densities in
the unknown region above the F_2.

In his paper, Poloskov described the doppler tracking system which
had been set forth previously in *Radio*. When he returned to his seat
with the other Russians on the far left, the floor was thrown open to
questions. Hagen, on the right, stood up and pointed out that the
Soviet frequencies required modification of the American tracking
stations. Would there be enough advance warning of a shot, he asked,
for the shift to be made?

While the question was being translated, Wernher von Braun,
seated in the center, leaned forward in eager anticipation of the answer. Poloskov's reply, when translated, gave the impression that a
firing was imminent. He added, however, that the lifetime of the
satellite would make possible such a shift after its launching. Then,
perhaps feeling he had gone too far, he rephrased his reply in a
manner that toned down the imminence of the shot.

As the conference progressed, the United States delegation of
some eighteen scientists presented a series of papers on the American
rocket and satellite program which were voluminous in their detail.

Neither the research rockets, nor the Vanguard rocket combination being prepared for the satellite launchings, were of military design and hence there were few secrets. Even the composition of the various fuels was given, one of the few items withheld being the nature of the solid fuel used in the third and final stage of the Vanguard.

In contrast to Bardin at the Barcelona conference, the Russians here were specialists in space research. Poloskov described a Soviet method of obtaining upper-air samples free of rocket gas contamination through ejection from the rocket of a sample-collecting canister which parachuted to earth. A. M. Kasatkin, a jovial man with the build of a wrestler, astonished the western scientists by giving extensive details on operation of the Soviet "Meteo" rocket. It represented an early stage of postwar Soviet rocketry, but even so, the willingness of the Russians to tell anything at all about their rockets was a radically new development and encouraged the belief that during the IGY they would be more candid about such matters than they had been in the past.

At this conference there began in earnest the discussion of a problem that, because of its political and military overtones, introduced the only discordant note in the exchange of IGY data. It centered on the wording of the rocket and satellite chapter of the *CSAGI Guide to IGY World Data Centers*. The *Guide* was the rule-book of the IGY, setting forth the doctrine governing dissemination of data in each of the IGY sciences. It defined what data were to be submitted, and when.

On November 29 of the previous year, Vice Admiral Sir Archibald Day, IGY Coordinator, had sent to the "reporters" coordinating plans in each science a series of skeletal chapters for the *Guide*. He described each as "little more than an introductory stage" and asked every reporter to submit a detailed version. The person in the key position of Reporter for Rockets and Satellites was Lloyd Berkner, president of ICSU. On December 19, 1956, he circulated to all concerned, including Dr. Bardin, his redraft of the chapter sent to him by Sir Archibald. It proposed that the launching country be required to submit such information as: the launching sites of both rockets and satellites; rocket firing schedules and information as to the "approximate period" of satellite launchings to enable ground stations to make the necessary preparations; announcement of each satellite launching within an hour, with a report on its success within three hours (it would take about a hundred minutes to determine whether or not the first orbit had been completed). Precision orbital data was to be issued within five months and "a complete tabulation of the reduced, calibrated, and corrected data" radioed from the satellite was to be made public within eight months. The nation launching the vehicle would keep its recordings of the satellite signal, but they were to be accessible to other scientists "for assurance against misinterpretations."

At the end of June, 1957, this draft was made public by the CSAGI Bureau, with the statement that it had called a rocket and satellite conference for the next fall at which the manual on this subject would be finally revised. At the fall meeting in Washington, the Soviet delegates insisted on a number of changes, and some were apparently suggested by other delegates, too. Principal among the alterations was deletion of the requirement that the satellite launching site be identified. Only successful launchings had to be announced, and the deadline was increased from one to two hours.

Remaining key provisions of the proposed draft were accepted unanimously, including the provision for delivery to the World Data Centers of complete tabulations of the satellite data. The atmosphere of the talks was cordial and the resolutions seemed to presage a prolonged period of cooperation in rocket and satellite research. They provided for: exchange of rocket equipment and satellite instruments among participating nations; a compromise recommendation that all nations concerned prepare to monitor satellites on both the United States and Soviet radio frequencies; a special world rocket shoot to be held on June 18, 1958; and rapid dissemination of data on satellite orbits. Most important of all, the resolutions foresaw the creation of a permanent ICSU organ to "direct" space exploration. The conference recommended that the international scientific unions and ICSU develop suitable means "in the same general manner as initiated under the IGY."

During this week-long conference the American scientists, as tactfully as they could, made their Russian colleagues aware of their disappointment at the lack of information which the Russians had produced on their satellite program. The Russians, in turn, made it clear that they thought it unseemly for scientists to "boast" about their experiments until they were done.

Later, after the fact, there was much criticism at home of the build-up given to Vanguard, making the failures all the more humiliating. But the Russians were more sensitive to the possibility of failure than the Americans. On August 11 they had announced to a somewhat skeptical world that they had successfully fired an intercontinental ballistic missile. The Russian leaders apparently felt that they could not tolerate a public failure on their first satellite-launching attempt. In fact they admitted to no failures in the launching of their first three satellites, although doubts were expressed in the West, particularly in view of the difficulties at Cape Canaveral. However, their achievement of the first launching three months after the tracking notice in *Radio* suggests that, if there were any misfires on the first shot, they were few.

The timing of that shot, on the eve of the final day of the conference in Washington, was no less dramatic than the Soviet bull's-eye on the moon on the eve of Khrushchev's first visit to the United States. Both implied that Russian rocketeers were able to call the shots when they wished.

For the Russian delegates, the final day of the Washington conference was one of pent-up excitement released. As western scientists crowded around to congratulate him, Blagonravov intimated that, when he and his companions had left Moscow, they were aware that preparations were virtually complete for a launching but did not know the date. In the Academy library the model of the American Vanguard buzzed bravely, but a bit forlornly, around the globe. The closing session had been expected to be a routine endorsement of resolutions already agreed upon by the various working groups. Instead it provided Blagonravov with an opportunity to talk about what he had kept secret all through the six-day meeting.

On a blackboard he sketched the newly launched satellite. Its four antennas, ranging in length from five to ten feet, were hinged so that, on release from the nose of the final stage rocket, they would spring out and lock in position (much like the design for the Vanguard satellites). The sphere, he said, was 58 centimeters (22.8 inches) in diameter and weighed 185 pounds, including seventy pounds of batteries which were expected to furnish power for about three weeks. (Actually the satellite signals stayed on the air for twenty-three days.)

This, he explained, was not an instrumented satellite of the type called for by the IGY. Rather it was a test vehicle designed to demonstrate the effectiveness of the launching system and also to report, in a crude way, on the environment which future satellites would encounter. The signaling, or telemetering, system resembled that described four months earlier in *Radio,* except that it provided for variations in radio frequency as well as in the length of the beeps

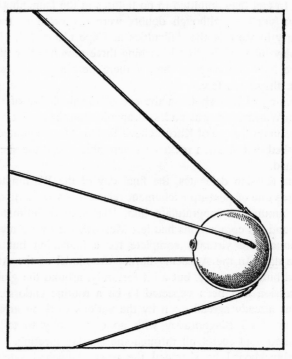

Sputnik I

and the pauses between them.[13] These variations reflected changes within the satellite of temperature and "other" elements. In the course of each orbit the sphere would spend part of its time in a scorching bath of naked sunlight and part in the frigid shadow of the earth. It was hoped that the internal temperature would be kept even enough so that equipment on future vehicles would work reliably. The airtight shell was made of aluminum alloys, but was given radiation characteristics designed to keep the temperature relatively uniform. It was also filled with nitrogen gas which was circulated as a sort of air-conditioning system.

If the sphere was pricked by striking a meteoric particle in its 18,000-mile-an-hour flight, the gas would squirt out into the near-vacuum at that elevation. This presumably would produce a rise in internal temperature which could not otherwise be explained and which, in turn, would indicate that meteoric particles presented a danger to future space flights. Blagonravov said the sphere was polished to mirrorlike reflectivity, so that at dawn and dusk it would shine in the lofty sunlight and be visible at distances of 600 miles or more.

At the end of his talk he asked if arrangements could be made for members of the Soviet delegation to hear signals from the newly launched vehicle. John Hagen of Project Vanguard stepped to the stage and pressed a button on a tape recorder. In a moment the hall was resounding to a chirping beep (recorded during one of the four passes already observed by the Naval Research Laboratory).

Blagonravov's reserve vanished. He displayed the excitement of a father seeing his son for the first time. "That is its voice!" he cried, and his countrymen beamed happily.

The conference closed with a carefully worded speech by Sydney Chapman, head of the IGY, in which he hinted at what some others were saying privately—that the launching of the Sputnik without advance warning had taken tracking systems in the West unaware and hence had reduced the amount of scientific observations that could be made. In congratulating the Russians on their "magnificent achievement," Chapman noted in his gentle, British way that news of the launching had been "indirectly received."

"Thus is settled," he continued, "the identity of the first winner in this grand cooperative race to enrich geophysical knowledge by means of earth satellites." Speaking of the two contestants, he said: "They have worked in their different ways—on the one hand keeping the world informed of much of their plans, their progress and setbacks—on the other hand, in silence until and unless their declared aim had been accomplished."

> Our USSR colleagues calculate a long life for a satellite in so high an orbit as this is announced to have [he continued]. We hope its life will be long enough to enable other nations to share in gathering the harvest of knowl-

edge that a satellite can provide.... We trust that our resolutions concerning timely announcements and adequate information will be fully observed, so that the best possible results may be gained from the vast effort, skill and expense devoted to these satellites.

As Chapman spoke, American tracking stations were working feverishly to modify their equipment for observation of the Soviet vehicle. It was a comparatively simple matter to shift the receivers, so that the Sputnik signal could be recorded, but precision tracking required relocation and resurvey of the antenna fields, which took weeks.

The Moonwatch visual observing stations were set up with their scopes aimed along the north-south meridian of the heavens. This was designed for satellites in generally east-west orbits, but since the Sputnik orbit was more north-south, some of its passes within sight of a Moonwatch station did not cross the scanned arc at all. Hence word was sent to about 150 stations suggesting realignment of the scopes so they would cover arcs sure to span each anticipated pass.

Of the twelve mammoth tracking cameras being built by the United States for a world-circling net of optical stations, only one was completed. Nor was it at its planned site at Organ Pass, New Mexico. Nevertheless, it swung into action in a yard in Pasadena, California, and began taking pictures of the satellite and its rocket. Actually, so far as tracking cameras were concerned, the Russians do not seem to have been very well off themselves. Their photo-tracking plan called for twenty-four specially made cameras, but only a limited number were in operation.[14]

The period that followed the launching of Sputnik I was one of dismay and confusion in the United States. There was a rash of reports from radio amateurs—and professionals—that all kinds of undecipherable code messages were being sent out by the satellite. Some suspected that, somehow, it was spying on the United States. On the basis of later experience with our own satellites, it seems that all or most of these "code" signals were either from other sources or were due to pulsing distortions produced by spinning of the satellite and by passage of its radio beams through a "wavy" ionosphere.

Nevertheless, with what Moscow had published on the nature of the telemetering system, it was not possible to decode the signals. For

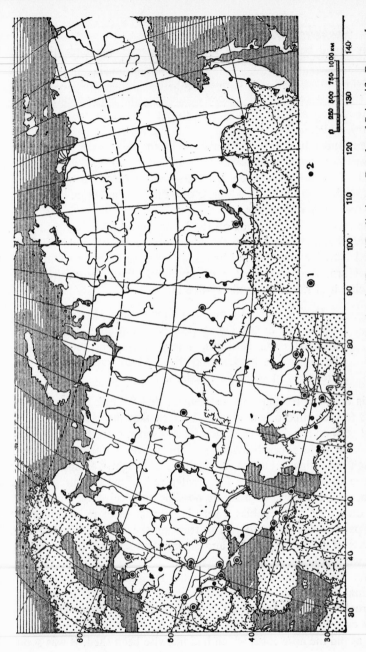

SOVIET SATELLITE TRACKING STATIONS: 1. photographic; 2. visual. (From "Preliminary Results of Scientific Researches on the First Soviet Artificial Earth Satellites and Rockets," Academy of Sciences USSR, Moscow, 1958, p. 7)

71

this it would be necessary to know the precise characteristics and calibrations of the equipment being carried. Therefore the IGY planners had decided that it was impractical for anyone to decipher such signals except the laboratory conducting the experiment. Everyone recording satellite signals was to send them to the launching country, which would ultimately publish the results. Moscow was not obliged, under IGY rules, to make public the key to the signals, but this was not generally understood in the West and, furthermore, the dearth of other information from Moscow fostered a widespread belief, at least in the United States, that the Russians were not living up to their IGY obligations.

The Moscow communiqué on the launching of Sputnik I said that its orbit was inclined 65° to the plane of the earth's equator. This carried it as far north as Fairbanks, Alaska, and farther south than Cape Horn. According to the communiqué, the sphere completed each circuit of the earth in ninety-five minutes.

> During the International Geophysical Year [Moscow added] the Soviet Union proposes launching several more artificial earth satellites. These subsequent satellites will be larger and heavier and they will be used to carry out programs of scientific research.

This bore out Blagonravov's statement that Sputnik I was not designed for scientific observations. The idea that the next one would be "larger and heavier" was somewhat awesome, since Sputnik I was more than eight times heavier than the planned Vanguard moons (though only slightly larger). Its far greater weight was due in large measure to heavier batteries for greater radio power. This was designed, said Moscow, to make it possible to receive the signals at great distances, "and enables a very large number of radio amateurs in all parts of the world to join in tracking the satellite." [15] The advantages of using frequencies and signal strengths within the reach of all were political as well as scientific.

After the launching of Sputnik I, the Russians were notably uncommunicative about the final-stage rocket that placed it in orbit. The rocket, having developed orbital speed and direction before gently casting loose its Sputnik payload, itself perforce remained in orbit, as did the nose cone, which had likewise been shed. It was soon obvious to western observers that the rocket was far more easily seen than the little satellite. Sightings of the latter by casual observers rarely if ever occurred. It was the rocket which, in its flight over virtually all inhabited areas of the world, proclaimed the Soviet achievement for all to see.

The Russians had announced enough about the characteristics of Sputnik I to make possible the use of its flight to revise the estimates of air density at the highest levels of the atmosphere. At the perigee, or low point of its orbit, the satellite dipped sufficiently into the upper traces of atmosphere to lose a slight amount of its energy. This was expected with all the IGY satellites. It would cause a steady lowering of the orbit—primarily at its apogee, or high point—and would ultimately cause the satellite to fall back into the denser atmosphere and disintegrate from friction. By careful observation of its orbital "decay" it would be possible to make comparatively precise estimates of air density at the perigee levels.

The rocket was better suited to such studies than the satellite, because of its greater visibility, but these could not be carried out without knowing its weight and dimensions. Nevertheless, G. F. Schilling and J. S. Rinehart, at the Smithsonian Astrophysical Observatory in Cambridge, Massachusetts, took the air density indicated by Sputnik I (whose characteristics were largely known) and applied that information to the decay of the rocket orbit. They calculated how much weight was necessary to keep the rocket orbiting as long as it did. The maximum weight, they said, was 2690 kilograms (5918 pounds).

This estimate, they emphasized, was based on "speculative, unconfirmed assumptions." The air density estimates were still uncertain by more than 50 per cent, they said, more firm conclusions being dependent on Soviet announcement of the rocket characteristics. "Since the Sputnik launchings were part of the International Geophysical Year Program," they wrote in their internationally circulated report, "we expect that these rocket parameters will be made available soon." [16] They still had not been published by 1960.

On October 9, five days after Sputnik I had been hurled into orbit, *Pravda* said that, in preparation for space flight by man, it was important to study the effect of such flight on other living creatures. The Soviet Union, it added, "will launch a satellite having animals on board as passengers, and detailed observations of their behavior and the course of their physiological processes will be conducted." [17]

This advance notice did not diminish the impact of the news, on November 3, that a satellite carrying a payload of 1118 pounds, including a dog, had been placed in orbit. This time the payload remained attached to the final-stage rocket, making it easier by optical observations to determine the precise path of the vehicle and hence where its instruments were in space at any given instant.

The largest American radars began detecting something else in orbit and eventually Moscow announced that Sputnik II had cast loose a nose cone which had protected the instruments during their soaring flight through the atmosphere.[18] When added to the three components launched with Sputnik I (the satellite, nose cone, and rocket) this meant there were now five pieces of hardware circling the earth, all put up there by the USSR.

In contrast to Sputnik I, the new satellite was loaded with scientific experiments. At the forward end, mounted within a frame in the rocket nose, were three instruments for measuring radiation from the sun. They were aimed sideways in three directions to increase the frequency with which one would be pointing toward the sun. In front of each was a wheel bearing filters which, as the wheel turned, were successively held over the scope. These, in turn, permitted sunlight in a number of wavelengths invisible to the human eye to penetrate the recorder (the Lyman-alpha line of ultraviolet and several portions of the X-ray spectrum). The intensity of the light in each of these parts of the spectrum was radioed to earth. To save power, this apparatus was switched on only when activated by sunlight.

Behind this instrument package was a sphere which was in effect a replica of Sputnik I. It contained radio transmitters, batteries, heat regulators, and instruments for recording temperature and "other" physical qualities (including pressure). Behind that, likewise within the nose frame, was the airtight, cylindrical tank containing Laika, the little trained dog, whose pulse, breathing, and blood pressure were recorded and fed into the radio telemetering system, as was the output of an apparatus similar to that used to obtain electrocardiograms of heart patients. There were devices to provide the passenger with food, water, and fresh air of proper humidity. The animal wore a sack to hold its waste products. Since gravity within the satellite had

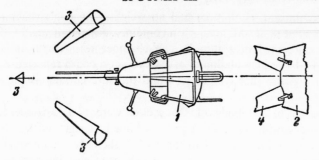

THE FIVE PIECES LAUNCHED

1. Sputnik III
2. carrier rocket
3. nose-cone sections
4. shields attached to rocket

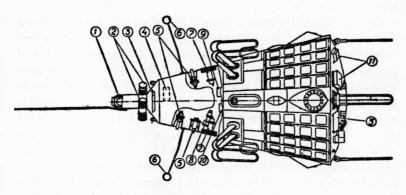

THE SATELLITE'S INSTRUMENTATION

1. Magnetometer, to measure intensity of the earth's magnetism
2. Photomultipliers to record solar radiation
3. Solar batteries
4. Cosmic ray photon recorder
5. Magnetic and ionization manometers
6. Ion traps
7. Fluxmeters to measure the electrostatic charge of the vehicle and nearby space
8. Mass spectrometer to analyze composition of the upper air
9. Cosmic ray heavy nuclei recorder
10. Primary cosmic ray intensity recorder
11. Micrometeorite recorders

been neutralized, substances had no weight. The dog's water could therefore not be served in an open container. Instead, it was furnished by a compressed-air system.[19] The chamber was temperature-controlled by forced circulation of gas. Devices on board reported via the satellite signals what temperature and pressure conditions prevailed within it.

Attached to the body of the rocket were two instruments for measuring cosmic rays, the detectors aimed at right angles to one another. Likewise attached to the rocket shell were additional batteries and telemetering equipment which broadcast instrument data "periodically according to a special programmed arrangement."

Although signals from the vehicle indicated that the dog's heart pounded during the acceleration of take-off, Moscow reported that subsequently its heartbeat and respiration were normal. It died after a week, probably due to exhaustion of its air supply or of electric power needed to keep the conditions livable. The satellite radios went dead after seven days.

On May 15, 1958, Sputnik III was launched with a payload more than double that of Sputnik II. The scientists at Smithsonian had calculated the total weight of Sputnik II at 3200 kilograms (7040 pounds), including the burned-out rocket and the announced payload of 508 kilograms (1118 pounds).[20] Sputnik III, cast loose in orbit as Sputnik I had been, weighed 1327 kilograms (2925 pounds), which made it as heavy as a sports car. In view of its elaborate instrumentation, the Russians spoke of it as "an automatic scientific space station." [21] According to the official announcements from Moscow this was the first Soviet satellite to use "memory" devices to store the data collected on each trip around the world, then spew it out rapidly upon radio command from a ground station.[22] Another innovation, for the Russians, was the use of batteries powered by sunlight. The apparatus on board is shown in the drawing on the preceding page.

Again the American public was struck by the increasing Sputnik weights, but the reaction in the United States was less frantic than it had been on the first two Soviet shots, for at last there were three American satellites in orbit.

CHAPTER 6
VANGUARD BRINGS UP THE REAR

After Lloyd Berkner had made his historic announcement in the ballroom of the Soviet Embassy, one of the American scientists present—a man deeply involved in the Vanguard satellite project—remarked:

"Well, at least the pressure is off. Now we can concentrate on doing a good job."

At a press conference five days later, President Eisenhower said, "Every scientist that I have talked to since this occurred ... has spoken in most congratulatory terms about the capabilities of the Russian scientists in putting this thing in the air. They expressed themselves as pleased, rather than chagrined, because at least the Soviets have proved the first part of it—that this thing will successfully orbit." [1]

The public was not so generous. One of its first reactions seems to have been a search for scapegoats. *Life* magazine sent its men out to inquire of those who, it thought, might know why the United States had been beaten into space. The replies struck out in all directions: "Navy lobbies"; "Wilson's pigheadedness" (Charles A. Wilson had been Secretary of Defense); "Interservice competition"; "We started too late"; "We're a smug, arrogant people ... underestimating Russia." Others argued that American openness had enabled the Russians to copy United States satellite plans and then forge ahead. Representative James G. Fulton of Pennsylvania said, "There is a feeling in many quarters that it was like the canary that jumps on the eagle's back. When the eagle flies high as it can and then just as it reaches the top the canary jumps 30 feet higher and it has the record." [2] The Internal Security Subcommittee of the Senate said the Sputnik launching "more sharply highlighted the value of Soviet espionage than any recent happening." [3]

For a more realistic explanation it is necessary to glance over the history of Vanguard. Because the decisions that determined the American satellite timetable were made in secret, this history is only now beginning to emerge. As early as 1945 the Department of Defense studied an earth-satellite program, but it was rejected, reportedly as of insufficient military value.[4] Had the government seized the initiative then, it might have been possible to launch a satellite as early as 1955. This, at least, was the view of Clifford C. Furnas, Assistant Secretary of Defense for Research and Development during the critical period from December, 1955, until February, 1957.[5] Sporadic satellite proposals continued to appear and members of the American Rocket Society agitated for such a program.[6]

In 1953, at the congress of the International Astronautical Federation in Zurich, S. Fred Singer proposed his *Mouse*. This was the acronym of "Minimum Orbital Unmanned Satellite of the Earth." It was to be a sphere, instrumented to collect scientific data and, in many respects, it resembled the eventual Vanguard design. On July 25, 1954, Singer was present at a gathering at the Office of Naval Research (ONR) in Washington that included Wernher von Braun, Frederick C. Durant, president of the International Astronautical Federation and formerly a Navy rocket specialist, Fred L. Whipple, head of the Astronomy Department at Harvard, and Commander George W. Hoover from ONR.

Out of this meeting grew the plan for Project Orbiter: the launching of a five-pound satellite that would be inflated in flight, making it visible from the earth. It was to be launched within two or three years as a step toward the orbiting of a more sophisticated sphere, such as Singer's Mouse. The first stage of the launching vehicle was to be the Redstone, an early missile developed by Von Braun and his team at the Redstone Arsenal in Huntsville, Alabama. A direct successor to the German V-2, it was much larger, with more payload and greater range. On top of it were to be no less than thirty-seven Loki rockets, stacked in three upper stages (thirty in the second, six in the third, and one in the fourth). The Loki was a small, unguided rocket designed to be fired in great numbers at attacking aircraft. The launching site was originally to be an abandoned naval air station in the Galapagos Islands off Ecuador, but this was shifted to the Gilbert Islands in mid-Pacific. Orbiter was an Army-Navy venture. Army Ordnance was to furnish the rockets and Hoover talked ONR into putting up $88,000 for the necessary design work. He was eventually made project officer and in March, 1955, the Assistant Secretary of the Navy for Air requested formal approval for the proposal.

There was, however, another unit of the Navy that was involved in rocketry. This was the Naval Research Laboratory, which had carried out extensive exploration of the upper air, using, among others, a large rocket known as the Viking and a smaller one, the Aerobee. The Viking was a research vehicle, roughly half the weight of the V-2, that reached a height of around 150 miles. The Aerobee soared 100 miles and an improved version, the Aerobee-Hi, was expected to reach 150 miles or more. The Naval Research Laboratory proposed a three-stage launching with the Viking as first stage, and the Aerobee-Hi as the second.[7]

The request for approval of Orbiter brought to the attention of Secretary of Defense Wilson the fact that there were several rival schemes. On March 28 he told his Assistant Secretary for Research and Development, Donald A. Quarles, to coordinate the plans. He also instructed the three military departments not to commit funds for such projects without Quarles' approval. Quarles put his scientific coordinating committee, representing the three services, to work on the problem. It recommended a triple approach:

1. Project Orbiter.
2. The plan of the Naval Research Laboratory, using the Viking rocket as the first stage of a three-stage vehicle.
3. An Air Force plan, with the engine of the Atlas intercontinental ballistic missile as booster and the Aerobee-Hi rocket as the second and final stage.

Meanwhile, Singer's proposal that satellite launchings be attempted during the IGY had been endorsed, the previous fall, by the CSAGI conference in Rome. This gave a new stimulus to the proposals brewing in the Pentagon. The committee within the National Academy of Sciences that was planning the American IGY program felt the United States should attempt a launching, even though the cost would dwarf any other item in the IGY budget. Since the Department of Defense was the only agency capable of carrying out such a project, the White House ordered that it undertake the job. There was, however, a strong feeling that nothing should hinder the desperate rush to perfect an intercontinental ballistic missile. The United States had begun its ICBM program several years after the Soviet Union had done so and was racing to catch up. Hence the fateful decision was made by the nation's highest policy-making body, the National Security Council, not to allow the satellite project to interfere in any way with ICBM development.[8] Instructions to this effect were given to the Pentagon.

The Kremlin, on the other hand, decided to rely on its still nonexistent ICBM as satellite launcher. The Soviet Union thus appears to have made a triple gamble. The United States waited until development of a compact nuclear warhead had been proved feasible before beginning work on a missile to deliver it. The Russians experimented with both at the same time and likewise made their satellite program dependent on the success of their ICBM.[9]

On July 29, 1955, the White House made public a joint announcement by the National Academy of Sciences and the National Science Foundation that the United States intended to launch an IGY satellite. The disclosure was dramatized by a White House briefing presided over by the President's press secretary, James C. Hagerty. On the same day the United States presented to Sydney Chapman, senior international officer of the IGY, a letter which said the American program "now includes definite plans for the launching of small satellites during the International Geophysical Year." No information was given on launching plans—for, in fact, they were still unsettled. The letter to Chapman emphasized the scientific objectives. "The United States National Committee believes," it said, "that significant scientific data may be gathered as a result of this program in such fields as geodesy, atmospheric physics, ionospheric physics, auroral physics and solar radiations." [10]

One of the three projects recommended by the Pentagon's scientific coordinating committee had to be selected as the IGY satellite launcher; to aid in making this choice, a committee of eight civilian specialists was convened by the Department of Defense in April. Two members each were nominated by the Army, Navy, and Air Force and another two were named by Quarles. Known as the Advisory Group on Special Capabilities, it had to make what proved later to be a historic decision. Its chairman was Homer J. Stewart of the California Institute of Technology, and among its members were Clifford C. Furnas, who later succeeded Quarles, and Richard W.

Porter, soon to be named chairman of the Technical Panel on Earth Satellites of the United States IGY Committee.

During an intensive week, early in July, the group heard presentations from proponents of each of the schemes. It visited the Naval Research Laboratory on the Potomac in southeast Washington and the Martin plant (which made the Viking) near Baltimore. It flew from there to Huntsville, Alabama, home of the Redstone, and to the Los Angeles area, where it visited the Rand Corporation, the Jet Propulsion Laboratory of the California Institute of Technology, and the Ballistic Missile Division of the Air Force.

The advisory group was somewhat limited in its selection by the requirement that the satellite program not interfere with missile development. Its membership consisted primarily of university professors who felt they were not competent to decide whether or not the use of the Air Force's Atlas ICBM for satellite launchings would interfere with its development as a weapon. In evaluating the two other alternatives the group was divided. Of the seven participating in the report, five were for the NRL Viking plan, the other two (Furnas and Stewart) for Orbiter.

The majority felt that the Viking offered better performance and required less logistic support than the Redstone, to be used in Project Orbiter. Being nonmilitary, it would eliminate the need for security limitations. Thus, it would be in keeping with the spirit of the IGY, and also would not compete with weapons projects. The group was reportedly told that Martin, maker of the Viking, would not be given the contract for development of the Titan ICBM (although it did, in fact, ultimately receive it). Most of the group's members believed that the many rocket stages involved in Orbiter multiplied the chances of failure, and they may also have been skeptical of the seemingly wild plan for overcoming the lack of upper-stage guidance. This was to set the second, third, and fourth stages spinning before the vehicle left the launching pad—in effect, like trying to overcome the absence of rifling in a gun barrel by spinning the bullet before pulling the trigger. Furthermore, the majority was impressed by NRL's postwar record of rocket research.

The two dissenters argued that the Redstone had greater flexibility as a satellite launcher and was therefore preferable, in view of the "unforeseen development difficulties" likely to beset the NRL plan in the rush job necessary to complete it in time for the IGY.[11] Thus they anticipated some of the troubles that hindered Project Vanguard, as the NRL plan came to be called, and forced revival of the Orbiter project.

For Von Braun the recommendation against using his Redstone must have been bitter news. Ever since his teens he had dreamed of ushering in the era of space travel. Nevertheless, despite his enthusiasm, he did not make a good impression on at least some of the committee members. In the words of one man in the advisory group he offered "more salesmanship than facts" on the Redstone's performance, whereas the team from NRL was ready with performance figures on all three of the proposed stages of its satellite launcher. It has also been speculated that the majority may have been reluctant to recommend, as the first American satellite launcher, a vehicle developed by the men who built Hitler's V-2.

Von Braun himself said later that his 1954 proposal for launching a "minimum" satellite was dismissed as "nothing but a stunt." [12] This feeling may have pervaded the advisory group since, in view of the IGY commitment, the success of the project in the long run would stand or fall on its scientific achievements.

In any case, when the group made its report on August 4, 1955, the Army reacted swiftly. In a memorandum sent to the group on August 15, 1955, the Assistant Chief of Army Ordnance for Research and Development said he wished to clarify what he regarded as the group's misinformation. By replacing Loki rockets with Sergeants, he asserted, the Redstone combination could place eighteen pounds in an orbit with a minimum altitude of 216 miles.

> The first orbital flight for this configuration [he wrote] can be scheduled for January 1957 if an immediate approval is granted. Since this is the date by which the U.S.S.R. may well be ready to launch, U.S. prestige dictates that every effort should be made to launch the first U.S. satellite at that time.[13]

By August, 1957, he said, a larger motor would be available, increasing to 162 pounds the amount which could be orbited. Since Redstone was going into industrial production at the Chrysler Corporation, its use would not interfere with the Army's missile research, he added.

When the Army was given a second hearing, NRL asked for one too, but these return performances did not substantially alter the views of the advisory group, which passed on its majority and minority recommendations to the Pentagon's Research and Development Policy Council, made up of some eight assistant secretaries of defense or of the armed services, plus an assortment of generals and admirals. Within the Policy Council the case made by the Army group evoked a more sympathetic response and it looked as though Von Braun's project was going to win after all, when James E. Smith, Jr., Assistant Secretary of the Navy for Air, stepped into the breach.

Since the previous November, when he had presented his views in a speech before the American Legion, Smith had been promoting the development of a missile that could be launched from a submerged submarine. Lindbergh had told him of German research on such a weapon during World War II. On September 3, 1955, when the Pentagon debate was at its height, Smith sent a memorandum to the Secretary of the Navy and the Navy's other high-ranking policymakers in which he argued that winning the satellite job would help the Navy in its fight for permission to develop a medium-range missile. To avoid duplication in missile programs, there was an inclination in the Department of Defense to limit missiles to the Air Force and Army, with the latter developing nothing larger than weapons of medium range.

It may be that Smith's intervention was decisive, for the Policy Council, with its Army members in dissent, backed the majority view of the Advisory Group and on September 9 the directive was issued that set Project Vanguard in motion.[14] The Navy was allowed to develop a submarine missile as a joint project with the Army, but eventually it became a purely Navy affair, resulting in the Polaris, a deadly weapon that proved, in large measure, to be the Navy's answer to the obsolescence of the battleship.

In the meantime Von Braun and the Army had by no means given up on Orbiter. It became known, among missile contractors, that Redstone Arsenal in Alabama was continuing to order components that were clearly designed for a satellite launching. On September 20, 1956, the Army fired a Redstone missile from Cape Canaveral, Florida, with two stages above it consisting of scaled-down solid-fueled Sergeant rockets that threw an eighty-four pound payload 3300 miles down the range. The upper stages were set spinning before launch and, far from proving a crackpot idea, the scheme worked. If the payload had consisted of a small rocket, Von Braun said, it could have injected itself into a satellite orbit. On the basis of this, he later maintained that the Army could have launched a satellite as early as 1956.[15]

With this shot as a trump card, the Army again sought permission to try a launching. Lieutenant General James M. Gavin, who had been deputy chief of the Army's Office of Research and Development, told a congressional committee that he addressed "a half dozen" memoranda to the Department of Defense, seeking authority for an attempt.[16] The Army was specifically told not to do so. Von Braun was asked by a congressman whether or not it was true that, to make sure the Army did not use its Redstone for a launching, "people came down [to Cape Canaveral] to see to it that certain parts of it were not activated."

He replied: "Yes, sir." [17]

Meanwhile, as supporters of the Army plan had feared, development of the Vanguard was plagued with difficulties. It is likely that they were no more severe than those encountered in any other pioneering rocket development, but outside circumstances made them critical. Rather than make minor modifications to the Viking to serve as a first stage, it was decided to build an entirely new rocket with about 50 per cent more weight, a new engine, a new autopilot (mounted in the second stage) and new propellants. In contrast to the massive ballistic missiles, the Vanguard was to be a slender vehicle seven stories tall and only forty-five inches in diameter at its base, the three stages fitted together in the clean lines of an elongated rifle bullet. The first two stages would be liquid-fueled; the third would burn a solid fuel. There were no tail fins. Initial guidance would be by slight adjustments in the aim of the first- and second-stage rocket engines, each of which was mounted in gimbals. Roll, during the initial flight trajectory, was to be controlled by distribution of the turbine exhaust thrust.

In the first 140 seconds after lift-off the first stage was to push the vehicle to a height of about thirty-five miles—above all but a trace of atmosphere—at the same time arching toward the east until, at burn-out, it was tipped 45 degrees from the vertical. It would then be cast off and the second stage would ignite. The latter, modeled after the tried-and-true Aerobee, was to carry the most important guidance equipment. Once above the atmosphere the nose cone would be shed, exposing the third-stage rocket and the delicate satellite sphere in front of it. When the second stage had burned out, it would coast until it reached the crest of its trajectory, automatically making refined adjustments of its aim by an array of gas jets. As it neared the crest, it would set the third stage spinning, to stabilize its aim before casting it loose. The third stage would burn up its fuel in thirty seconds, achieving a horizontal speed well above the minimum required velocity of 17,069 miles an hour, then gently cast loose its satellite burden.

To produce such a complex vehicle, test it, and correct its deficiencies, all within two years, was a formidable task. It was doubly difficult since priority had been given to the missile program. When it needed parts, help, or money, Vanguard had to go to the end of the line. Since the Defense Department had been given the task of launching the satellites, Furnas, as Assistant Secretary of Defense for Research and Development, was responsible for getting them off the ground. He wrote later that the project "never did receive the high-priority status it would have needed to get it into its orbit before the Russian Sputnik." He placed much of the onus on Defense Secretary Wilson who, he said, regarded the satellite as "a nice scientific trick" which had no military value and therefore should not drain the Pentagon's budget.[18]

On several occasions the Pentagon was asked to furnish back-up facilities which would have eliminated placing all the satellite eggs in one basket.[19] The Advisory Group on Special Capabilities recommended a back-up program; the Office of Naval Research requested an additional launch pad and six more satellite-launching vehicles; a similar plan was put forth early in 1956 by the U.S. National Committee for the IGY. Any of these steps would have greatly increased the chances of success. The additional pad would have been particularly helpful since it would have meant that, for any firing, a back-up vehicle could be standing by in an advanced state of preparation. With only one pad it took roughly a month to get ready for a new shot. All of these proposals were turned down on economy grounds.

As it was, the Pentagon was somewhat disgusted with the increasing cost of the Vanguard project. It had been conceived as a comparatively inexpensive program costing between $20 and $30 million. By the end of the IGY $111,085,000 had been spent or committed.

The original estimates had not included such extras as the charge by the Air Force for use of its facilities at Cape Canaveral and for the use of the missile range reaching out across the Atlantic. The Air Force bill was $7,888,000. An additional $14,551,000 had to be spent on the Navy radio tracking system that extended from Maryland to Chile. The rockets and their flight operations cost $73,470,000. The bulk of this money had to be taken from the Department of Defense's emergency funds or other of its appropriations and the Pentagon was understandably reluctant to rob Peter to pay Paul.[20]

By February, 1957, an accumulation of troubles since the previous fall made necessary a five-month delay in the scheduled date for firing SLV-1, the first satellite-launching vehicle, which was to follow a series of six test shots. The difficulties applied to all sections of the vehicle and were typical of what had to be expected in such a stage of development. The performance of the first-stage engine, being built by General Electric, was below specifications. It was supposed to develop a thrust of 27,000 pounds, compared to 21,000 pounds in the original Viking rocket, but there were burn-outs and the injector had to be redesigned. A number of the second-stage engines being built by the Aerojet General Corporation in Azusa, California, had to be rejected because of "difficult component fabrication." Design changes had to be made. The third stage proved to be too heavy. "Certain aspects" of the reliability effort by the Martin Company, which as prime contractor was responsible for the over-all vehicle, were found to have been deficient. The Vanguard men at Canaveral said that components they received contained metal shavings, dirt, and other debris which meant they had to be laboriously dismantled, cleaned, and reassembled before firing. Above all, as reported in 1959 by a congressional staff investigation, "It was suspected that the structural design of the vehicle was inadequate to withstand the vibration loads. As a consequence, design and production were stopped completely for about one month until this problem was resolved." [21]

These setbacks were somewhat offset by the first test firing of the third stage, with a motor made by the Grand Central Rocket Company of Redlands, California. This rocket was a midget compared to the first two stages required to get it into space, and carried no guidance equipment. To keep it going in a straight line, it had to be set spinning by a mechanism in the nose of the second stage before being cast loose. To do this in midflight, after the wild vibrations and strains of the take-off, was a neat trick, to say the least.

On May 1, 1957, two months before the start of the IGY, this third-stage rocket and its spin mechanism were mounted on the last of the old Viking rockets and fired into space. The test was rated "highly successful" and, before the end of the month, it was decided to include, in the test shots which made use of all three stages, a four-pound satellite. These grapefruit-size spheres would carry little more than radio beacons and would have solar batteries to generate power from sunlight.

Their stated objective was to serve as a dress rehearsal, particularly in testing out the radio tracking system. Crystals for the two radio transmitters within the spheres were mounted in such a way that temperature changes would alter signal frequencies and thus reveal the success of the instrument packaging. One crystal was to be in the thermally insulated inner package; the other was to be mounted on the outer shell, subject to the variations in temperature due to the repeated passages between sunlight and shadow.

The little spheres may have had another mission. By now it was definitely known that the Russians, too, were planning to launch. The grapefruits would increase this country's chances of being the first into orbit. But, as 1957 progressed, more trouble developed with the second stage. It was found in ground tests that the aluminum combustion chamber eroded in a manner that cut down performance to the point where it would not generate the necessary velocity. By the time this problem was solved, in October, the projected launching dates were running eight to nine months behind the original schedule.

Reluctance to view the satellite program as a race was not limited to the Pentagon. The scientists taking part in the effort wished to keep it methodical and scientific. They also sought to prepare the public for possible failures. At the Washington conference that ended with the Sputnik launching, Hagen, puffing at his pipe, brought the delegates up to date on the American program and described the plan for including small spheres:

> It is relatively unlikely that any of these test spheres will actually go into a sustained orbit. In a three-stage vehicle of this kind, a great many components and pieces of equipment must work perfectly, all at the same time, in order for

the flight to be successful. The probability of such a complex system operating perfectly during the first few realistic tests is extremely small.[22]

When Sputnik I roared into space at the end of the conference, Vanguard could hardly have been caught more flatfooted. Neither of its first two stages had been test-flown. Those gazing wistfully at the Vanguard launch pad, near the beach at Cape Canaveral, could see a vehicle displaying the trim Vanguard configuration aimed boldly at the zenith, but actually its upper two stages were dummies. It was fired on October 23 as the initial test of General Electric's first-stage engine. As such, it was a spanking success.

This was just cause for the cheers of the launching crew, but the heat was on. The stepchild project was now under tremendous pressure to get a satellite into orbit. On October 9, five days after the Sputnik launching, President Eisenhower issued a statement designed to alleviate public distress at the United States' being in second place. "I consider our country's satellite program well designed and properly scheduled to achieve the scientific purposes for which it was initiated," he said. He cited the plan to launch small spheres during the testing period: "The first of these test vehicles is planned to be launched in December of this year." [23]

To the Vanguard team, this was a command performance. A number of measures were taken to cut corners and make up for lost time. The Martin Company, prime contractor for the whole vehicle, increased the tempo of its deliveries. It was decided to eliminate static firing tests of the second-stage engine at Cape Canaveral [24] (it later proved the least reliable of the three engines [25]). Work at the Cape was placed on a three-shift basis, which apparently did more harm than good. According to congressional investigators:

> The groups working on different shifts tended to work independently and strict control over the operations being performed became impossible.
>
> In the general hysteria which prevailed, work which should have been done in the hangar was left undone; and because of poor communication and lack of continuity of working forces, people working on the launch pad assumed the required operations had been performed in the hangar. This situation contributed to the adjustments which had

to be made during "checkout" procedures just prior to the launch attempt.

It should be noted that none of the people interviewed claimed that any vehicle was launched before it was thought to be ready. Some of them, however, felt that their judgment as to "readiness" was no doubt influenced by the pressure on the program to "get a satellite into orbit" so as to meet the expectations of the public.[26]

Preparations were rushed for the first attempt to fire the full Vanguard. By now the first and third stages had each had one firing test (both successful), but this would be the first flight test for the second stage.

Because this experimental shot would carry a small sphere in its nose, it quickly became, in the public eye, a bid to recover some of the prestige lost to Moscow. Newspapermen, not only from throughout the United States, but from abroad, gathered at Cocoa Beach, where there was an unobstructed view of the launching pads, several miles away across the water. The motels were jammed and binoculars became unobtainable. The pessimistic predictions of John Hagen were forgotten and the rising pitch of excitement was reflected in the page-one headlines of *The New York Times:* U.S. READY TO FIRE FIRST SATELLITE EARLY THIS WEEK (December 2) and . . . TEST DEVICE "PROBABLY" WILL ORBIT, SCIENTIST SAYS AT FLORIDA LAUNCHING SITE (December 4).

The next day the shot was postponed after the countdown had come within fifty minutes of firing. The trouble was with a valve at the point where liquid oxygen was being pumped into the rocket. The first-stage engine burned kerosene, mixed in flight with liquid oxygen. Since the maximum temperature of oxygen in liquid form is 298° below zero, its handling required special precautions, including a delay in pumping it into the rocket until the final part of the countdown. Even then, by the time of firing, the rocket was sheathed in ice, which it was expected to shed in the first moments of its thundering ascent.

The frigid valve was not working properly and was replaced. The new valve proved to be aligned improperly and hence the firing attempt was "scrubbed." The tanks had to be drained and cleaned for a new try the next day, December 6.

At 8:45 A.M. a large red ball was hoisted on a pole at the Cape—

a warning to all, including the Canaveral fishing fleet, that a firing was imminent. By 11 A.M. there were thousands on the beach, training telescopes, binoculars, and every kind of camera on the launching site. The Vanguard pad was easily distinguishable among the pads of the military missiles, for its gantry was distinctive—a tall, slender frame with a crane on top. The gantry was used to service all stages of the rocket. It rolled back on its widely spaced rails an hour before firing time and the Vanguard stood in lonely splendor, silhouetted against a blue sky streaked with a few clouds.

Inside the blockhouse next to the pad J. Paul Walsh, the Deputy Director of Vanguard, whose clean-cut, youthful appearance made him look like a college student, was linked by his headphones to his superior, John Hagen, in Washington. Another telephone line was kept open to the White House. The entire Cape, unified in tension by a public-address system, followed the announced progress of the countdown. Veterans who have gone through scores of these counts say they still cannot endure one without a thrill.

At thirty minutes before firing time roadblocks were set up at all approaches to the Vanguard site.

"T minus twenty-five and counting!" cried the announcer: twenty-five minutes to go.

"Clear all working areas!" Everyone took cover in the blockhouse or elsewhere except the specialists in pyrotechnics who install the rocket igniters.

"Cease all unnecessary conversation in the blockhouse. The smoking lamp is out!" (Navy jargon for "no smoking").

"T minus fifteen and counting!" Word came in that planes and ships were clear of the transoceanic line-of-fire.

"Minitrack system clear!"

"T minus seven!" Men in protective clothing cut the topping-off flow of liquid oxygen. Outside air supply to the blockhouse was closed.

"T minus three. All equipment on internal power!" Valves were opened, flooding water into the flame-deflector underneath the first-stage engine.

"Satellite clear to launch!" The helium connection, which had been building up fuel-injection pressure, was closed. The vehicle was on its own.

Then, inexorably, came the final seconds: "Nine! Eight! Seven!"
Walsh echoed the count over his phone:

"Three!"

"Two!"

"One!"

"Zero!"

"First ignition!"

"Explosion!"

That last word echoed around the world and disheartened an entire nation. On the beach there was a gasp of horror and disappointment as the onlookers saw the bullet-shaped vehicle rise a few feet,
then suddenly fall back to be enveloped in a cloud of flame and
smoke. The rocket pillar fell one way, its nose cone tipped drunkenly
the other. The miniature satellite fell to the pad, little damaged, but
ignominiously grounded.

The word that cropped up most frequently in news accounts the
next morning was *disaster*. To the Vanguard team, one of the most
distressing aspects of the situation was that the failure had occurred
too early in the firing sequence to provide any test of the untried
second stage and guidance system.

Another test shot was attempted on February 5, 1958, again with
a full-fledged Vanguard assembly. This time the great bullet roared
into the sky, but after sixty seconds its control system went awry.
The slender vehicle swerved so sharply that it broke apart. After
two attempts, there still had been no flight test of the second stage.

The weeks that followed were bitter for the men working day and
night at the Cape. Almost daily they read in the press of digs and jibes
at their efforts. Premier Khrushchev suggested that the project would
have been better named Rearguard. Berliners referred to it as Project
Spaetnik (*Spaet* is the German for "late").

At least once, as the men struggled in darkness to prepare their
vehicle, a flashing light sailed majestically over their heads, one of
the Sputnik rockets tumbling head-over-heels in its orbital flight
through lofty sunlight.

The daily reports of delays and difficulties became so irksome that
the press found itself in the unusual position of urging greater secrecy
on the government. *The New York Times,* on March 14, asked in
an editorial:

. . . Would it not be wiser—when malfunction and other obstacles are so likely and so frequent—to let the devoted men who are preparing Vanguard do their work in quiet? When Vanguard is fired is time enough for the world to know what has happened.

Meanwhile, the Army had been called to the rescue. On November 7, less than a week after the launching of Sputnik II, President Eisenhower had named James R. Killian, Jr., president of the Massachusetts Institute of Technology, to the newly created post of Special Assistant to the President for Science and Technology. At the same time administrative changes were announced whose avowed purpose was to eliminate interservice rivalry in rocket development.

The next day Neil H. McElroy, who had succeeded Wilson as Secretary of Defense, told the Army to go ahead and back up Vanguard with its own satellite launchings. This was the chance Von Braun and his men had been longing for, and it may not have been purely coincidental that they had a missile in partial readiness. It had gone through successful static firing tests and had been in storage at Huntsville for a year. The Army plan was essentially that which had been outlined to the Group on Special Capabilities almost two and a half years earlier, except that by now the Redstone, with clustered Sergeant rockets as upper stages, had been used in three long-range shots, two of them completely successful. Its chief mission was testing nose cones during re-entry into the atmosphere from prolonged flights in space. The cones, when perfected, were to be used on the more powerful Jupiter intermediate-range ballistic missile then in development; the combination of Redstone and solid-fueled rockets was known as the Jupiter-C, although it bore no resemblance to the Jupiter itself. In August, 1957, it carried a nose cone 1500 miles down the range from Canaveral and the cone, after recovery from the water, was displayed by President Eisenhower in a television broadcast designed to reassure the public after the second Sputnik launching.

The weird assemblage of Sergeants atop the Jupiter-C—key to the success of these shots—was, in essence, the arrangement proposed for the Orbiter project. It had been developed by the Jet Propulsion Laboratory (JPL) in Pasadena, California, by a group under the laboratory's director, William H. Pickering. The laboratory, administered by the California Institute of Technology, was the Army's chief contractor for developing new missile components. Pickering, born a New Zealander, had obtained his doctor's degree at Cal Tech in 1936, the year that institution began studying rocketry theory, and was now chairman of the working group on satellite tracking in the American IGY program.

For its satellite launching, the Redstone first stage was surmounted by a tapered section that contained the guidance equipment controlling all the stages. Atop this was a tub enclosing fourteen scaled-down Sergeant rockets, with a fifteenth rocket protruding on top like a slender hypodermic needle. Like lady fingers in a charlotte russe, eleven of the rockets in the tub were arranged in an outer ring to serve as the second stage; within them, three rockets were clustered as the third stage; the single rocket on top carried the instruments and was to serve both as fourth stage and satellite.

The firing sequence was to be as follows: About eleven minutes before lift-off, the tub would be set spinning by electric motors, so that by firing time it would be whirling at some 400 revolutions per minute. Since the upper three stages had no guidance system of their own, this would spin-stabilize their flight.

Once ignited, the massive Redstone would burn its propellants at 50 gallons per second, exhausting its tanks in about 156 seconds at an elevation of some 60 miles. Here the guidance compartment and upper stages would break free and coast upward, as a unit, to the summit of free flight, trailed by the coasting Redstone. Compressed-air jets in the guidance compartment were to make any necessary corrections in the flight path.

When signals from the vehicle and tracking data indicated to the men at the Cape that it was nearing the summit of its flight, someone would press a button, sending a radio signal into space that would fire the ring of second-stage rockets. What followed would be a rapid series of fireworks: The fiery ring would burn for six seconds, followed by a two-second coasting period. Then the inner cluster would ignite, yanking itself out of the ring of dead rockets, which would fall to the ocean while the inner trio of rockets burned six seconds. After another two-second pause, the single rocket would pull away, driving itself up to and beyond minimum orbiting speed. When burned out, this rocket would weigh thirteen pounds with an additional eighteen pounds of instruments and radio gear.

The system was vulnerable in several respects. The split-second decision on firing the second stage was a human one and its execution depended on the deft use of a finger. Likewise, if any of the rockets in the second or third stage fired a fraction of a second later than the others, this could knock the rocket assembly enough off course to ruin the shot. An error in aim of a few degrees could lower the perigee (low point of the orbit) sufficiently to cause the vehicle to burn up in the atmosphere. JPL had experimented with various systems for sure-fire simultaneous ignition and had finally installed electric matches in the motor case of each rocket, with parallel wiring as an added precaution.

Another problem concerned the spin of the tub. To keep itself on a true course it should be whirling at about 750 turns per minute, but the resonance characteristics of the fully fueled Redstone were such that this might shake it to pieces. Hence spin rate at launching was to be held down to 400 or 450 r.p.m. and built up during first-stage flight to 750 r.p.m. This could be done because, once empty of fuel, the Redstone could withstand higher frequency vibration.

While the launching vehicle was being prepared, the cosmic-ray package that Van Allen and his men at the State University of Iowa had been preparing for a full-size Vanguard sphere was quickly redesigned at the Jet Propulsion Laboratory for mounting in the nose of the topmost Sergeant rocket.

The Army gave its men eighty days in which to prepare. On December 20, forty-two days after the green light had been given, a hulking C-124 Globemaster set down on the airstrip that spans Cape Canaveral. The great doors beneath its nose swung open and its ramp was lowered, exposing a Redstone missile within the cavernous interior. By January 17 the rocket had been serviced and hoisted, its graphite tail vanes carefully oriented on the stand for correct aim into the planned trajectory. A week later installation of the upper stages began and by January 27 all was in readiness—except the weather. The winds, for a while, were among the highest ever observed at the Cape, but at last, eighty-four days after the order had been given, the countdown was in progress.

Night fell as the climax neared on January 31. Igniters were brought from the storage area in shielded containers and inserted in each of the fifteen Sergeants to ignite their solid fuel. During the ticklish period of their transfer from the containers to the rockets, radio transmitters in the area were ordered turned off. Half an hour before firing time the gantry rolled back and the great missile stood alone, shining in the cold blue light of searchlights focused on it from many directions—as were the eyes and hopes of thousands of onlookers. As its tanks were topped off, liquid oxygen vapor trailed from the side of the rocket in a cloud tinged lavender by the arc lights. The tub atop the main rocket began spinning. A pulsing red light nearby flashed a warning and the raucous sound of a klaxon resounded in the darkness.

The crucial moment came at 10:48 P.M. Eastern Standard Time, but for more than fifteen seconds afterward nothing was to be seen. The firing set in motion an automatic sequence of events which finally resulted in a burst of orange fire at the base of the missile. This grew into a blinding light and for miles around the earth shook with the roar as the towering rocket rose, first imperceptibly, then with gathering speed. The needlelike satellite at its top seemed aimed directly at the zenith. The vehicle punched through a thin overcast, then reappeared above it, now little more than a spark which seemed almost motionless in the sky, but its location, southeast of the zenith, showed that the vehicle was arching over in its long, high trajectory.

On the beaches some mistook the first burst of fire for an explosion, but gasps quickly gave way to cheers as the rocket soared. At the Cape, Ernst Stuhlinger and Walter Haeussermann, two of Von Braun's key men, were making hasty computations. At length Stuhlinger reached out deliberately and pressed the button that sent the critical radio impulse into space. The fireworks of the upper stages began and, a scant seven minutes after launch, north of the Windward Passage between Cuba and Haiti and about 225 miles in the sky, the final stage ignited and thrust itself into orbit. The receipt of its radio signals in California about 110 minutes later confirmed the success of the shot. In Huntsville, Alabama, home town of the Army missilemen, crowds appeared in the streets as though it were New Year's Eve. Police cars and fire trucks paraded, sirens howling, and placards appeared, reading OUR MISSILES NEVER MISS and MOVE OVER SPUTNIK, SPACE IS OURS.

Word was relayed to the President, on a golfing vacation in Georgia, and he joyously made the official announcement. The United States had a vehicle in space and it was christened Explorer I.

Explorer's launching relieved some of the pressure on Vanguard and, on March 17, the third attempt to fire a full Vanguard vehicle was gloriously successful. All three stages functioned perfectly and a small satellite sphere was injected into an orbit higher than that of any other vehicle launched by anyone during the IGY. Because it was above all but the merest traces of atmosphere, estimates of its

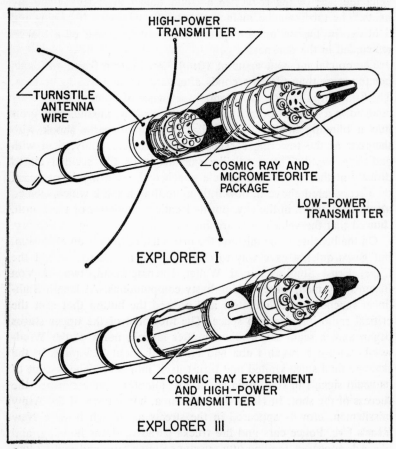

HIGH–POWER
TRANSMITTER

TURNSTILE
ANTENNA
WIRE

COSMIC RAY AND
MICROMETEORITE
PACKAGE

LOW–POWER
TRANSMITTER

EXPLORER I

COSMIC RAY EXPERIMENT
AND HIGH–POWER
TRANSMITTER

EXPLORER III

Explorer satellites (Jet Propulsion Laboratory)

lifetime ran as high as 1000 years. One of its transmitters was powered by sunlight and it even seemed possible that its little radio voice might still be whispering from the skies centuries hence.

Nevertheless, Vanguard was not out of the woods. A month later the first attempt was made to launch a full-scale Vanguard satellite.

On the night of April 24–25 newspaper correspondents and camera-
men, the author included, were hauled by bus to a lookout platform
on the roof of the Optics Building, about a mile from the launching
pad at the Air Force Missile Test Center on the Cape. Rough wooden
telephone cubicles lined the side of the platform away from the beach
so that we could stand, telephone in hand, and watch the launching.
During the final phase of the countdown I kept a line open to our
office in New York. The record of that count tells its own tale of
frustration. At T minus four (four minutes before firing time) the
announcer said:

"Recycling back to T minus seven. The count is at T minus seven
and holding." This meant that there was trouble and that the count
had been set back and suspended. A few minutes later came another
announcement:

"Recycling back to T minus thirty-five. The count is now T minus
thirty-five and counting."

The next time the count got up to T minus seven there was another
prolonged hold. Then the count resumed. Three minutes before firing
time the voice said:

"T minus three and holding momentarily." A few moments later:
"Recycling back to T minus seven."

Again the count began, but bogged down at T minus five. By now
it was past 1 A.M. and the rotation of the earth had carried Florida
into such a position that, if the launching were carried out, the
satellite orbit would be almost constantly in sunlight. The plan called
for an orbit which would put the sphere in the earth's shadow for
about a third of the time on each trip around, and its heat absorption
characteristics were designed for such a situation. If constantly in
sunlight, the instruments would be cooked. Also, the repeated delays
had allowed the rocket mechanisms to be so chilled by the liquid
oxygen that their proper function could no longer be relied upon.
Hence the impersonal voice on the loudspeakers finally said:

"The firing has been scrubbed." The delays were said later to have
been due to such troubles as a burned-out fuse, valve malfunctions,
and difficulty with a radio beacon.

When the shot did take place, on April 28, it was a thrilling sight
and looked completely successful. Shortly thereafter, however, it
was learned that the control system had failed to activate the third
stage, which had fallen into the middle Atlantic. The next try was

even more frustrating. On May 27 an improper second-stage cutoff produced too high an aim. The final stage roared into space in a high arc over Africa and plunged back into the atmosphere over the Indian Ocean.

After two more failures, the newly formed National Aeronautics and Space Administration, which had taken over responsibility for all the American IGY satellites, announced on November 18 that Vanguard attempts would be suspended, pending a study of ways to improve its reliability. The first successful launching of a full-sized Vanguard, therefore, did not take place until after the end of the IGY.

The congressional staff investigation of 1959 found some cases of mismanagement in the Vanguard program, but it reported that in general the Vanguard team had done a "commendable job," completing the development of a complex vehicle in less than half the time required for most missiles. The staff study group said that it was firmly convinced "that the VANGUARD project is not a failure if the rulebook used in creating it is also used in passing judgment on it." [27]

> The program was never allowed to complete its development test programs [the report said]. Instead, it was called upon to produce a satellite on its fourth test shot (the first vehicle to have orbiting capability), and since that time each VANGUARD rocket fired has been expected by the public to be successful, i.e., to produce an orbit. Because this has not been done, the program has been condemned by the news media as a failure. It has borne the brunt of a hurt national pride—hurt because Sputnik I was in orbit before any U.S. satellite and because Sputnik II was many times larger than the VANGUARD satellite.

In hindsight one might criticize those who ruled out the use of ballistic missiles and failed to give the satellite effort adequate priority, the report said. "These criticisms, however," it continued, "cannot fairly be the basis upon which to judge Project VANGUARD; they must be addressed to those who felt that the VANGUARD approach was adequate for our national needs and who set the course accordingly." [28]

Midway through the IGY, on March 27, 1958, Defense Secretary McElroy announced a program "to determine our capability of exploring space in the vicinity of the moon, to obtain useful data concerning the moon, and provide a close look at the moon." [29] The projected "lunar probes" included three Air Force shots, using as a first stage the Thor intermediate-range ballistic missile. The upper two stages were both taken, in toto or in part, from the upper stages designed for Vanguard, providing some comfort to the wounded pride of the Vanguard team. In addition, the Army was to be given one or two shots at the moon.

The government was still troubled with the problem of secrecy in a democracy. In joining in the announcement, Roy W. Johnson, director of the Pentagon's Advanced Research Projects Agency, said:

> We would prefer to announce these programs when we are sure of success rather than merely announcing that the work has been authorized.
>
> However, public interest in knowing more about the country's programs in space exploration is so high that it was decided to release this information and at the same time advise the public that it is impossible to put a time table on successful accomplishment of these efforts.[30]

Not until more than four months later was it announced that the lunar probes were being made a part of the United States IGY effort. Actually, such probes were not called for by the agreed IGY program, and these thrusts toward the moon before the United States was fully prepared for them may have been politically motivated. Nevertheless, their inclusion in the IGY was of historic importance in that it set a precedent for carrying out all space probes under international auspices, with exchange of the resulting data.

The Air Force plan was to hurl past the moon a top-shaped vehicle with a backward firing (retro) rocket through its center. This would be ignited by radio command from earth as the vehicle passed the moon, in the hope that it would slow the vehicle enough for the moon's gravity to hold it in a moon-circling orbit. This was a complicated scheme and it was no discredit to the Air Force that it did not succeed on any of the tries. Nevertheless, the second attempt, on October 11, reached up 71,300 miles, almost a third of the way to the moon, before the vehicle fell back and disintegrated in the atmosphere over the Pacific Ocean. As the Air Force prepared for its last try, one of the more romantic rocketeers remembered the lines from Tennyson:

> Launch your vessel
> And crowd your canvas,
> And, ere it vanishes
> Over the margin,
> After it, follow it,
> Follow the Gleam.

The last two lines he stenciled on the base of the Thor. It rose on a roaring plume of white fire but missed the lunar gleam. Radar and radio tracking showed that its third stage had failed to fire and it fell into the sea.

The Army plan was simpler. The vehicle to be used carried upper stages similar to those that had launched the first American satellite, but, instead of a Redstone, the first stage was a massive Jupiter intermediate-range ballistic missile. The entire vehicle weighed sixty tons (in contrast to the ten tons of the Vanguard rocket), yet the cone that it was to pitch past the moon weighed only 13.4 pounds. There was to be no attempt to circle the moon, which required refined speed control as well as a retro rocket.

On December 6, 1958, the Army made its first attempt. The cone flew out only 66,000 miles, but this shot, named Pioneer III, as well as the deeper probe already made by the Air Force (Pioneer I), sent back information of great scientific importance, as will be seen in the next chapter. On March 3, 1959, after the IGY was over, a second Army attempt was successful. The vehicle achieved enough speed to escape the earth's gravity. Since it was not going fast enough to break free of the sun's gravity, it remained in orbit around the sun. The same was true of the Soviet moon shot launched January 2, 1959.

By the end of the IGY, December 31, 1958, there had been twenty-one announced attempts to launch space vehicles: three by the USSR (all successful) and eighteen by the United States, of which five achieved their announced objectives.[31] The Russian shots were based on a massive rocket developed as an intercontinental ballistic missile. While there may have been unannounced failures, its performance seems to have been quite reliable, as was that of the rockets used in the upper stages. The Russians apparently attempted only those shots almost certain to succeed. A number of the American firings, as stated in advance, were done with minimum expectation of success. Such "long shots" included the first test firing of the full Vanguard vehicle and the Air Force attempts to place a satellite in orbit around the moon.

The most impressive feature of the Soviet space vehicles was their weight. In part to recoup some of the prestige lost to the Russians in this respect, the United States, on December 18, 1958, orbited an Atlas missile with a burned-out weight of 8,750 pounds. It carried 150 pounds of radio relay equipment, but was not part of the IGY program.

During the 1959 follow-up of the IGY, known as the International Geophysical Cooperation, the final four vehicles of Project Vanguard were launched. Of the two that achieved an orbit, one, Vanguard II, was designed to produce crude images of the earth's cloud cover. However, it wobbled so much in flight that no pictures could be reconstructed from its signals. The other, Vanguard III, sent back valuable magnetic data. Of six Explorer vehicles shot into the sky, three went into orbit, all of them far larger than the early vehicles of that series. The flight path of one was made extremely eccentric, so that it could scan the breadth of the radiation belts. Its distance from the earth ranged from 156 to 26,357 miles and each orbit took twelve and a half hours.

Reaching even farther into space, the United States, in 1959-60, fired Pioneer IV past the moon and dispatched Pioneer V to send back data from several million miles out. The Soviet Union's Lunik I flew past the moon; Lunik II hit that body; and Lunik III circled the moon, sending back images of its far side. A number of American satellites with military, meteorological, communications or navigational objectives were sent aloft. At the start of 1961 the United States had placed thirty-one satellites in orbit around the earth (compared to Russia's seven) and had sent two other vehicles beyond the reach of earth's gravity. One Soviet payload had likewise escaped this planet's gravity and another had impacted on the moon. Roughly half of all these vehicles were still in flight, indicating the growing traffic problem in space. Nine of the American vehicles were broadcasting, whereas all the Soviet craft had lapsed into silence.

The following table summarizes the twenty-one known attempts to launch IGY satellites and space probes.

Sources: National Aeronautics and Space Administration, the Smithsonian

Launch date	Name & launcher	Outcome	Remarks (dates refer to fall of scientific satellites)	Weight orbited	Shape & dimensions of scientific satellite
1957					
Oct. 4	Sputnik I (USSR)	Successful	Fell Jan. 4, 1958	About 4 tons (estimated) (scientific satellite 184 lbs.)	Sphere. Diameter 22.8 in.
Nov. 3	Sputnik II (USSR)	Successful	Fell April 14, 1958	About 4 tons (estimated) (payload 1,120 lbs.)	Rocket. Nose length 19 ft. Diameter 4 ft. Over-all dimensions not disclosed
Dec. 6	Vanguard Test Vehicle III (U.S. Navy)	Failed	Thrust lost after 2 sec. Burned on pad	52.35 lbs. (payload 3.25 lbs.)	Sphere. Diameter 6 in.
1958					
Jan. 31	Explorer I (U.S. Army)	Successful	Expected life: 6 yrs.	30.8 lbs. (payload 18.13 lbs.)	Rocket. Length 80 in. Diameter 6 in.
Feb. 5	Vanguard Test Vehicle III Back-up (U.S. Navy)	Failed	1st stage control failed. Swerved after 57 sec. & broke apart	Same as on Dec. 6	Same as on Dec. 6
March 5	Explorer II (U.S. Army)	Failed	Last stage failed to fire	31.5 lbs. (payload 18.83 lbs.)	Same as on Jan. 31

Space Probe Launching Attempts

Institution Astrophysical Observatory, the Soviet magazine *New Times*

Initial maximum altitude	*Initial minimum altitude*	*Inclination of orbit to equator*	*Communications equipment*	*Internal experiments* (excluding internal temperature & pressure)
588 mi.	142 mi.	65.3°	Transmitters on 20.005 & 40.002 mc, 4 whip antennas 4.9 ft. to 9.5 ft. long. Signals died Oct. 27, 1957	None disclosed
1,038 mi.	140 mi.	65.4°	Transmitter frequencies same as on Sputnik I; died Nov. 10, 1957	Cosmic rays, solar ultraviolet and X-radiation, dog experiment
			Transmitters: 1 on 108 mc at 10 mw, 1 on 108.03 mc at 5 mw, powered by 6 solar converters	Micrometeors
1,573 mi.	224 mi.	33.34°	4 22.5-in. antenna whips, plus satellite skin. Transmitters: on 108 mc at 10 mw, died May 23, 1958; on 108.03 mc at 60 mw, died Feb. 28, 1958, after earlier interruption	High energy radiation, micrometeors (2 types)
			Same as on Dec. 6	Same as on Dec. 6
			2 dipole antennas using satellite skin. Transmitters: 108 mc at 10 mw; 108.03 mc at 60 mw	High energy radiation with tape recorder, micrometeors (1 type)

Launch date	Name & launcher	Outcome	Remarks (dates refer to fall of scientific satellites)	Weight orbited	Shape & dimensions of scientific satellite
March 17	Vanguard I (Test Vehicle IV) (U.S. Navy)	Successful	Expected life: 200– 1,000 years	Same as on Dec. 6	Same as on Dec. 6
March 26	Explorer III (U.S. Army)	Successful	Fell June 27, 1958	31 lbs. (payload 18.56 lbs.)	Same as on Jan. 31
April 28	Vanguard Test Vehicle V (U.S. Navy)	Failed	2 electric relays failed to fire 3rd stage	71.5 lbs. (Scientific satellite 21.5 lbs.)	Sphere. Diameter 20 in.
May 15	Sputnik III USSR	Successful	Fell April 6, 1960	7,000 lbs. (estimated) (payload 2,925 lbs.)	Cone. Length 11.75 ft. Width at base: 5.67 ft.
May 27	Vanguard SLV-1 (U.S. Navy)	Failed	Improper 2nd stage cut-off produced high aim. 3rd stage flew 7,500 mi., landed beyond Africa	Same as on April 28	Same as on April 28
June 26	Vanguard SLV-2 (U.S. Navy)	Failed	Flight ended with premature 2nd stage cut-off	Same as on April 28	Same as on April 28

Initial maximum altitude	Initial minimum altitude	Inclination of orbit to equator	Communications equipment	Internal experiments (excluding internal temperature & pressure)
2,453 mi.	409 mi.	34.3°	Antennas: 6 12-in. rods. Transmitters: 108 mc at 10 mw, died April 5, 1958; 108.03 mc at 5 mw, powered by 6 solar converters, will operate indefinitely	None
1,746 mi.	121 mi.	33.5°	Same as Explorer II. Beacon & telemetering on 108 mc stopped May 10, 1958; beacon again transmitted May 15–June 16; 108.03 mc erratic after May 14, died June 5, 1958	Same as Explorer II
			Antennas: 4 rods. Transmitter: 108 mc at 80 mw	Solar X-radiation
1,167 mi.	135 mi.	65.3°	Antennas: folding dipoles & trailing rods. Transmitters: 20.005 mc (& on harmonic-40.01 mc). Chemical & solar batteries. Transmitted until satellite fell.	Atmospheric pressure & composition, positive ion concentration, geomagnetism, solar radiation, cosmic rays, micrometeorites, atmospheric electricity & intensity of earth's electrostatic field
			Same as on April 28	Solar Lyman alpha radiation
			Same as on April 28	Solar X-radiation

Launch date	Name & launcher	Outcome	Remarks (dates refer to fall of scientific satellites)	Weight orbited	Shape & dimensions of scientific satellite
July 26	Explorer IV (U.S. Army)	Successful	Fell Oct. 3, 1959	38.4 lbs. (payload 25.8 lbs.)	Rocket. Length 80.39 in. Diameter 6.25 in.
Aug. 17	No name (U.S. Air Force)	Failed	1st stage exploded after 77 sec.	83.8 lbs. (payload 25 lbs.)	Top-shape. Length 30 in. Diameter 29 in.
Aug. 24	Explorer V (U.S. Army)	Failed	Booster hit upper section, knocking it off course	38.43 lbs. (payload 25.8 lbs.)	Rocket. Length 80 in. Diameter 6 in.
Sept. 26	Vanguard SLV-3 (U.S. Navy)	Failed	2nd stage fuel filter clogged. Final speed reduced. May have made one orbit	Same as on April 28	Same as on April 28
Oct. 11	Pioneer I (U.S. Air Force)	Failed to orbit moon	Excessively steep climb cut speed	84.4 lbs. (payload 39 lbs.)	Same as on Aug. 17
Oct. 23	Beacon (U.S. Army)	Failed	Cluster broke apart	31.5 lbs. (payload 9.26 lbs.)	Rocket. Length 50 in. Diameter 7 in.
Nov. 8	Pioneer II (U.S. Air Force)	Failed to orbit moon	3rd stage did not fire	86.4 lbs. (payload 34.3 lbs.)	Same as on Aug. 17
Dec. 6	Pioneer III (U.S. Army)	Failed to pass moon	Premature burnout in 1st stage	12.95 lbs.	Cone. Length 23 in. Max. width 10 in.

Initial maximum altitude	Initial minimum altitude	Inclination of orbit to equator	Communications equipment	Internal experiments (excluding internal temperature & pressure)
1,380 mi.	163 mi.	50.29°	Antennas same as on Explorer II. Transmitters: 108 mc at 10 mw, died Sept. 9, 1958; 108.03 mc at 24 mw, telemetry illegible Sept. 19, died Oct. 6, 1958	High energy radiation (4 counters)
40,000 to 70,000 ft.	Zero		Antennas: 2 12-in. whips. Transmitters: 108.6 mc at 300 mw; 108.09 mc at 1 watt	High energy radiation, magnetism, micrometeors, moon scanning
			Antennas same as on Explorer II. Transmitters: 108. mc at 10 mw; 108.03 mc at 30 mw	High energy radiation
			Antennas: 4 spring-loaded 30-in. rods. Transmitters: 108 mc at 10 mw; 108.03 mc at 1 watt	Cloud scanning with 2 infra-red photocells
About 70,700 mi.	Zero		Same as on Aug. 17	Same as on Aug. 17
			None	None (Inflatable sphere for external study)
963 mi.	Zero		Same as on Aug. 17 except power on 108.09 mc is 100 mw	Same as on Aug. 17
63,580 mi.	Zero		Antenna: cone itself. Transmitters: 960.05 mc at 180 mw.	High energy radiation (2 counters)

CHAPTER 7
THE BELTS

Sometimes flames are seen in the sky either stationary or full of movement. . . . These fires present the most varied colours: some are vivid red; others resemble a faint and dying flame; some are white; others scintillate; others finally are of an even yellow, and emit neither rays nor projections. Among these phenomena should be ranged those appearances as of the heavens on fire so often reported by historians; sometimes these fires are high enough to shine among the stars; and others so low that they might be taken for the reflection of a distant burning homestead or city. This is what happened under Tiberius, when the cohorts hurried to the succour of the colony of Ostia, believing it to be on fire.[1]

Thus the Roman writer Seneca, in the first century after Christ, described those awesome displays which today are known as the aurora, or northern lights.

Long after other great natural phenomena were understood, these excited superstition and fear. They were the Valkyries, riding across the northern sky, or sunlight reflected by the polar ice. Seemingly authentic scientific reports noted that the most intense auroras made a strange whistling sound that rose and fell in volume. Scandinavians said they had seen the curtains of light descending to the ground against a backdrop of mountains.

Not until rockets first probed above the atmosphere was it possible to unravel part of the mystery by direct observation of what was going on in space near the earth. Yet the chain of clues which ultimately led to the most exciting discovery of the IGY was picked up early in the history of modern science, when the revolution in thinking of the sixteenth and seventeenth centuries introduced systematic inquiry into the nature of our environment.

During the reign of Queen Elizabeth I, her personal physician, William Gilbert, devoted his spare time to the study of magnetism. He shaped a lodestone to resemble the earth—what he called a *terrella*—and found that the distribution of magnetism over its surface closely resembled that on the surface of the earth. Gilbert proposed, therefore, that the earth was in effect a great magnet. The alignment of the magnetism at any point was such as would be produced by a small but very powerful bar magnet buried within the heart of the planet. The effect was not only to align the compass needle roughly north and south, parallel to that magnet; it also produced an increasing downward component of magnetic force as one neared the magnetic poles. Explorers found that the force at the magnetic equator was entirely horizontal, whereas at the magnetic poles it was entirely vertical, causing the compass needle to spin aimlessly.

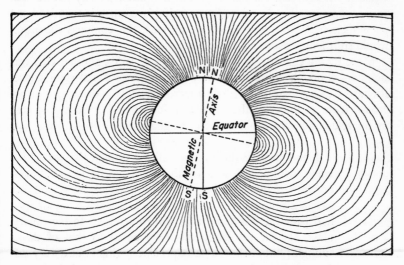

The earth's magnetic field in nearby space. The pattern of force lines resembles that of a hypothetical bar magnet in the core of the earth.

It soon became evident that the compass needle did not point toward the North Pole, but rather in the general direction of another point at some distance from it. This began to emerge when Edmund

Halley voyaged hither and yon across the North and South Atlantic in a little sailing ship called the *Paramour*. Halley, best known today for his use of the mathematics of his friend Newton to predict the return of what is now Halley's Comet, devoted his long voyage to charting the compass error. It was easterly in some regions and westerly in others, falling into a systematic pattern that led to discovery of the magnetic poles.

Halley also noticed that there seemed to be a link between disturbances of the earth's magnetism and appearances of the aurora. In 1741, the year before Halley's death, the Swedish astronomer Anders Celsius and his colleague Olav Peter Hiorter were studying the curtains of light that hung almost nightly over northern Scandinavia. On the night of March 1 Hiorter was using a highly sensitive compass to observe the orientation of the displays. Suddenly he noticed that, when an aurora flashed in the sky, the compass needle moved as much as several degrees to one side or the other. He pointed this out to Celsius, who smiled. He had observed it himself shortly before, but was so amazed that he waited to see if his companion noticed the phenomenon. Within a span of six minutes the compass distortion would shift from east to west or vice versa.

More than a century later, on September 1, 1859, another clue was sighted—although its discoverer was unaware of its significance. Richard C. Carrington, an English astronomer, was drawing sunspot groups from an image of the sun eleven inches in diameter, projected by his telescope onto a plate of coated glass.

> I had secured diagrams of all the groups [he wrote]...
> when within the area of the great north group...two
> patches of intensely bright and white light broke out....
> My first impression was that by some chance a ray of light
> had penetrated a hole in the screen attached to the object-
> glass, for the brilliancy was fully equal to that of direct
> sunlight; but...I was an unprepared witness of a very dif-
> ferent affair. I thereupon noted down the time by the
> chronometer, and, seeing the outburst to be very rapidly on
> the increase, and being somewhat flurried by the surprise, I
> hastily ran to call someone to witness the exhibition with
> me, and on returning within 60 seconds, was mortified to
> find that it was already much changed and enfeebled.[2]

What he had witnessed was a solar flare—an event of awesome magnitude when one considers that, within a few minutes, it envelops many millions of cubic miles in the heat of a nuclear explosion. It seemed, Carrington said, to have taken place high above the general surface of the sun.

At the moment Carrington saw the flare, all three elements of the earth's magnetism, being recorded at Kew Observatory near London, were disturbed; eighteen hours later there broke out one of the most intense magnetic storms recorded up to that time. Auroras spread over much of the world, being seen as far south as Puerto Rico. Only from the hindsight of later years was this flare linked to its effects on earth.[3]

By the mid-nineteenth century there were enough auroral sightings on record so that Hermann Fritz, a young professor at the Confederate Polytechnic Institute in Zurich, could undertake a systematic study of their distribution and frequency. The institute must have been a breeding ground for genius, since it was there, a generation later, that Albert Einstein, a student still in his teens, began formulating the concept of relativity that revolutionized physics. Fritz collected tens of thousands of reports, both on the aurora borealis (northern lights) and on the aurora australis (southern lights) often seen in Australia and New Zealand. In 1881 he published tables of the known occurrences for every year from 1700 to 1874 with a map showing their locations.

It was evident, Fritz said, that the frequency varied in consonance with the waxing and waning of sunspots. What was most puzzling was his distribution map. The displays were most often seen, he found, around a circle with a radius of about 1600 miles, whose center lay neither at the North Pole nor at the Magnetic Pole (wandering mecca of all compass needles, at that time near the Boothia Peninsula of northern Canada). Instead it was centered northwest of Greenland. This apparently marked the axis of the earth's magnetic field in the sky and came to be known as the Geomagnetic Pole. It differed from the Magnetic Pole by about 800 miles, apparently because of magnetic irregularities within the earth.

Fritz reported evidence that auroral displays occur simultaneously at both ends of the earth. He also found that, for some mysterious reason, they were most frequent during the spring and fall equinoxes. They were rarest in midsummer and midwinter. His map of the

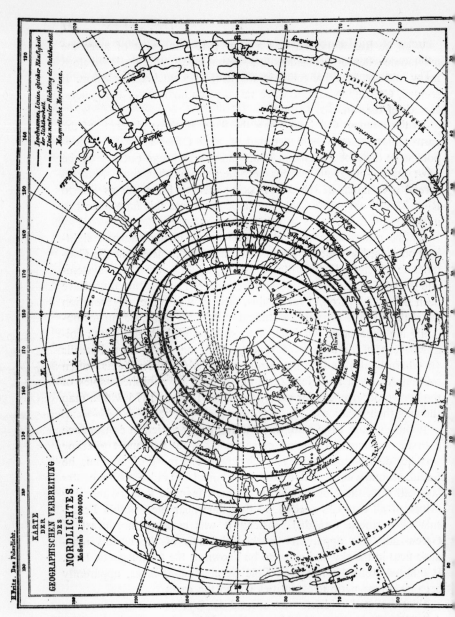

The map published by Fritz in 1881.[4] The numbers following *M* on each circle refer to the average number of displays per year. The light dashed lines are magnetic meridians, converging on the North Magnetic Pole. The North Geographic Pole lies at the center.

circles of equal auroral frequency has been modified only slightly by the more extensive and sophisticated observations of recent years. The occurrences in the maximum region are on roughly two out of every three nights.

The discovery by Fritz that the auroras are concentrated in a circular band centered on the magnetic axis, but a considerable distance from it, confronted geophysicists with a problem which haunted them for half a century. The mapping of numerous displays, over both Greenland and Scandinavia, showed that they tended to form segments of gigantic circles whose center was at the Geomagnetic Pole.

The next clue to the nature of the aurora was picked up during research which helped usher in the science of electronics. In the 1890s Kristian Birkeland in Norway was investigating the rays that emanate from a negative electrode (cathode) when immersed in a gas at very low pressure (what we call today a vacuum tube). He correctly believed these cathode rays to be streams of electrons, and they produced a glow in the tube which reminded him of the aurora.

He built a small sphere which could be magnetized like the earth and, mindful of Gilbert's early experiments, called it a terrella. When electrons were fired at it in a near-vacuum, such as one would expect to find high in the sky, the results were most exciting. In Birkeland's darkened laboratory the terrella was ringed in curtains of light strikingly like the aurora. The nature of the displays varied according to the angle from which he fired the electrons. Sometimes there were luminous rings above the sphere at latitudes 70° North and 70° South—roughly the same areas as the two zones of maximum auroral occurrence on earth. In other situations there was a ring of light girdling his miniature earth at its magnetic equator. The patterns were clearly controlled by the magnetic field. Birkeland suspected, therefore, that the aurora was produced by incoming particles from the sun that were somehow sucked by the earth's magnetism toward the polar regions, where they rained upon the thin gases of the upper atmosphere.

It was already believed that the shape of the earth's magnetic field, in surrounding space, was similar to the pattern assumed by iron filings under the influence of a bar magnet. In the classic schoolroom experiment each sliver of iron lines up along the direction of magnetic force. The resulting pattern is similar to that shown in the figure on page 109.

Birkeland published his terrella results in 1901, observing that the cathode rays seemed to be drawn toward the magnetic poles in gracefully curving trajectories. The experiments fascinated his Norwegian colleague Carl Störmer, who began calculating mathematically why the electrons behaved as they did.

As a starting point Störmer had the work of the French mathematician and astronomer Jules Henri Poincaré, who had calculated the behavior of charged particles (such as electrons) in the magnetic field of a single pole. Poincaré had found that a particle which crossed the field exactly at right angles would go into a circular orbit, the force countering its tendency to fly straight being magnetism rather than gravity.

The chance that the particle would cross the field exactly at right angles was, of course, extremely small. If it crossed at an angle, Poincaré discovered, it would go into a spiral orbit around an imaginary line representing the direction of the field.

In 1907 Störmer published a paper which created no stir at the time but, a half-century later, suddenly became of historic importance.[5] In it he set forth his most recent calculations on the trajectories of charged particles in a two-pole magnetic field, such as that of the earth.

Störmer demonstrated the Poincaré trajectory by drawing a straight line on a transparent sheet which he rolled into a cone. The sides of the cone represented the magnetic convergence toward the pole. Viewed through the transparent sheet, the line had now become a spiral. More remarkable, when the sheet was rolled in a certain way, the spiral reversed direction.

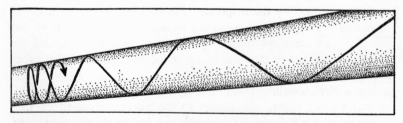

When transparent paper, inscribed with a straight line, is rolled into a segment of a cone, the line becomes a spiral that reverses direction. This illustration was used by Poincaré and Störmer to show the effect of converging magnetism.

This meant that a particle following such a trajectory, instead of continuing down to the magnetic pole (the apex of the cone) would move in tighter and tighter circles until it began to move outward again. Where it reversed direction came to be known as the "mirror point."

In the same paper Störmer showed what could happen to such a particle in the two-pole field of the earth, where a cone of magnetic force, converging on one pole, extends out into space in a great arc which converges, in another cone, toward the opposite pole. When mirrored above one pole, he said, the particle could then spiral over the arc until it was mirrored at the opposite pole. It would then fly back and forth, trapped within the magnetic field.

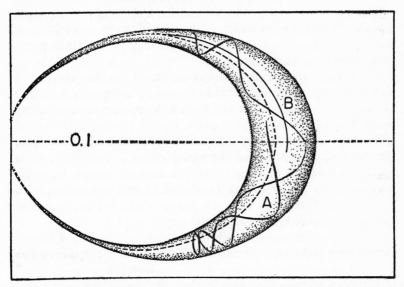

Störmer's historic illustration of how a particle may become trapped within a two-pole magnetic field. The horns of the magnetic crescent converge at a hypothetical bar magnet near the earth's center. (Adapted from Störmer's 1907 drawing)

Störmer himself was not especially excited about this particular idea and his illustration of such entrapment is omitted in his standard work, *The Polar Aurora,* published in 1955. His chief interest was in calculating trajectories that might account for the types and locations of the aurora. The flight of the auroral particles, he thought, was twisted by the earth's magnetism but they were not, as a rule, entrapped.[6]

His contemporaries tended to focus their interest on such of his ideas as the postulated existence of a mighty ring of electric current encircling the earth's equator at a considerable distance in space. Such a current was necessary, he said, to explain why the region of maximum auroral activity was not nearer the magnetic pole. The ring current, Störmer said, pulled the trajectories of incoming particles away from the poles. During a magnetic storm, he added, intensification of this current sucked the aurora even more toward the equator, accounting for its appearance at such times over Puerto Rico, Indonesia, Samoa, and other tropical regions.

The work of Störmer, at his desk at the University of Christiania, was an awesome demonstration of the capabilities of man's intellect, for he was calculating the behavior of particles far too small to see in a region far too remote to visit.

In 1950 another striking feature of the aurora was observed, almost simultaneously, by two scientists in the United States. For a number of years it had been evident that there was something strange about the light produced by such displays. Carl W. Gartlein of Cornell University had been studying the spectrum of auroral light since 1938. He had noticed that, where one would expect a sharp line in the spectrum, produced by excited hydrogen atoms, there was instead a very wide line. "It seemed that it could not be hydrogen," he reported in July, 1950, "because it was too broad . . . I was unable, however, to find anything to fit in this space in the spectrum." [7]

Before the year was out both he and Aden B. Meinel at Yerkes Observatory had found the answer. The width of the hydrogen line was due to the extremely high speed at which protons—the nuclei of hydrogen atoms—were plunging into the atmosphere. The speed was so great that it shortened the wavelength of the light, just as the movement of the approaching train raises the pitch of its whistle. Meinel computed that the protons in a particularly intense aurora on the nights of August 18 and 19 must be arriving at a speed of 2100 miles per second. Gartlein obtained a spectrogram on September 30 which indicated to him a speed of 2000 miles per second.

If the particles had been spewed out by the sun at that speed, they would have made the trip to the earth in a mere thirteen hours. Yet it was well known that the journey took as much as two days. Hence, it was thought, something must be accelerating the particles in the same way that they are kicked to extreme velocities in an atom-smasher.

The more scientists delved into the aurora, the more mysterious it seemed to become.

After World War II, when rockets made possible direct observations in space, scientists in a number of fields lined up for their turn to send up instruments. The Jet Propulsion Laboratory at the California Institute of Technology, with Homer J. Stewart as project director, had developed for the Army a small liquid-fueled research rocket which was christened the WAC-Corporal. In October, 1945, one was fired 43.5 miles into the sky with a twenty-two-pound payload, but rocketry research began in earnest with the firing on the following April 16 of the first captured V-2. It was launched from the Army's White Sands Proving Ground at Las Cruces, New Mexico, with one of Van Allen's Geiger counters on board to measure the intensity of cosmic rays above the atmosphere.

By January, 1952, sixty-eight V-2s, sixty-three Aerobees, and seven Vikings had been fired into the fringes of space. To bring some of the nation's best talent to bear on rocket research, the Upper Atmosphere Rocket Research Panel [8] was formed in January, 1946, with a membership that included such men as Homer E. Newell, Jr., Fred Whipple, William Pickering, Richard Porter, and Van Allen (who became its chairman the following year).

Van Allen's interest in outer space was born in his undergraduate days at Iowa Wesleyan, a small college in his home town of Mount Pleasant. There he had become a disciple of Thomas C. Poulter, a physics professor who was preparing to go south as deputy leader of the Second Byrd Antarctic Expedition. Van Allen wanted to go along, but his parents vetoed the idea on the ground that he was too young. Nevertheless he credits Poulter with having kindled within him a flame of scientific curiosity that burned into his adult years. It was as an undergraduate that he first became interested in cosmic rays, but during World War II he went to work for the Navy on a problem of more immediate importance.

This was to design an antiaircraft fuse that would explode when it passed near an attacking plane. Existing shells were effective only when they made a direct hit—and that was almost never—or when the time fuse within them detonated the shell close to a plane. Because of the precise timing required, such shells were a poor defense against horizontal bombers and were virtually useless against dive bombers. Van Allen worked with the group that developed a miniature radar set that could be carried in the nose of a shell. In flight it sent out radio signals. When it received a strong echo, the shell was exploded.

It was not too long a step from building a pocket-size radar that could be fired out of a gun to designing cosmic ray recorders that could be carried into space by V-2s. As the supply of these massive rockets dwindled, Van Allen, now at The Johns Hopkins University's Applied Physics Laboratory on the outskirts of Washington, induced the government to back the Laboratory's development of a smaller, cheaper rocket that could still lift a 150-pound payload almost as high as the V-2s. Known as the Aerobee, this rocket became the workhorse of American high-altitude research.

Van Allen persuaded the Navy to let him fire Aerobees from shipboard so that, for example, he could take a peek into space on the earth's magnetic equator. During such a firing off Peru, Lieutenant Commander Lee Lewis remarked: "Wouldn't it be easier to lift a rocket on a balloon above most of the atmosphere, and then fire it?"

The idea excited Van Allen, for most of the fuel in a rocket was exhausted driving it up through the resisting atmosphere. One of the little Deacon rockets, fired from the ground, coasted up to a height of ten miles after its burning time of 3.5 seconds; if it could be fired from an elevation of fifteen miles, it would soar to sixty miles. The Deacon was only 6.5 inches in diameter, but it could carry a thirty-pound instrument package. The conventional way to fire it from a point high in the sky would be to shoot it up there with one of the new Nike antiaircraft missiles, but this was costly. However, by now plastic bags of transparent polyethylene were coming into use for wrapping everything from beefsteaks to dry-cleaned suits. They could also be used to make gigantic Skyhook balloons. The use of such a balloon, instead of a Nike rocket, for the first fifteen miles would make each shot a $750 bargain.

The resulting marriage of rocket and balloon was christened the Rockoon. Van Allen, who had returned to his native state to head the physics department at the State University of Iowa, could not try out his new gadget there lest it plummet into an Iowa farmhouse. He therefore asked the Coast Guard to let him ride the icebreaker *Eastwind* during the resupply of arctic stations in the summer of 1952. The *Eastwind* penetrated to within 508 miles of the Pole—farther north, it was said, than any ship had gone under its own power up to that time. As it approached Greenland, Van Allen and his men inflated a great balloon on the icebreaker's windswept helicopter flight deck. It soared to 70,000 feet, but the slim rocket dangling beneath it did not fire.

They tried again, but the same thing happened. Suspecting that the timer might be freezing to a standstill, Van Allen heated orange juice cans and packed them, with insulation, into the firing box that dangled below the rocket. This time it fired.

Van Allen's interest was in cosmic rays, the most energetic of all forms of radiation. Being electrically charged, the rays are affected by the earth's magnetic field, much like auroral particles, with the weaker rays able to approach the earth only in the polar regions. Because these more feeble rays are unable to penetrate the atmosphere, it was necessary to observe them with rockets and the task of the *Eastwind,* to resupply the world's northernmost shore-based weather station at Alert, offered Van Allen a chance to send up a rocket-borne Geiger counter almost directly at the North Geomagnetic Pole. Two successful shots were fired and the next summer two of Van Allen's associates, Melvin B. Gottlieb, assistant professor of physics, and Leslie H. Meredith, a graduate student, rode north on the Navy icebreaker *Staten Island* to make additional flights.

The difficulties they encountered were typical of this early stage of rocketry. The first rockoon rose to 72,000 feet but failed to fire and the automatic cut-down device, installed as a safety measure, apparently froze. The balloon-borne rocket was last observed drifting in the general direction of Bermuda and an unknown fate. The next day three more rockoons failed to fire. It was found that the igniters would not operate in a near-vacuum; they had to be redesigned. As the ship moved northward, the winds increased. It headed downwind for the launchings, but the wind was swifter than the ship and threatened to bang the lethal rocket against the ship's bridge.

To avoid this, the icebreaker was put into a sharp turn as the tall balloon was released; then Gottlieb ran with the rocket in his arms and dumped it over the leeward side. On one occasion, however, the turning ship heeled so abruptly that he fell into the life nets alongside the flight deck. Another time the wind tore the balloon loose prematurely and its towline snaked wildly among the legs of the launching crew before it was snatched into the sky. These balloons can lift close to 300 pounds and, had the line entangled anyone, he would have died a frigid, airless death in the stratosphere. From then on members of the launching crew carried sheath knives, and a 20-millimeter gun was kept at the ready to shoot down the balloon if necessary.

On July 28, when the ship was off the southeast tip of Baffin Island, a successful launching ignited at an elevation of eleven miles and the rocket soared to fifty-six miles. When Gottlieb and Meredith studied the telemetered records, they found an incredibly high radiation count some thirty miles overhead. In a message to Van Allen, then working at Princeton, they asked if there had been any nuclear explosions that might account for the phenomenon. They wanted to take another look, but balloons and rocket engines had been expended. They therefore shifted their apparatus to the *Eastwind,* which was heading homeward from Thule, Greenland, and carried out further shots after new equipment had been picked up at Argentia. The ship returned north to a point off the eastern tip of Labrador so that three shots could be launched in the auroral zone, for it was suspected that there might be a link between that region and the strange high-intensity radiation. Sure enough, the one successful flight, sent up on August 30, detected the same thing, although other shots fired north and south of the zone revealed nothing unusual.

As Van Allen said later, it was obvious that there was "something wild and woolly going on." When, in August, 1954, he, Gottlieb, and Meredith submitted a report on their discovery to the *Physical Review,* they "tentatively discarded" such explanations as radioactive bomb dust. They noted that the radiation had been observed in the region of most frequent auroras, but at a lower level than auroral displays. It also seemed to be constant, in contrast to the ephemeral nature of the northern lights. They proposed, therefore, that their rockets had detected the "high-energy survivors" of a far more intense rain of particles, most of which was filtered out at higher elevations. While a Geiger counter is sensitive to various forms of radiation, the Iowa group finally decided that the frantic pace of the counts was due to X rays produced by high-energy electrons hitting the rocket shell.[9]

In the fall of 1957 Van Allen and his men journeyed to antarctic waters on board the Navy icebreaker *Glacier,* launching a number of rockoons en route. One of these detected the same sort of radiation near the southern auroral zone. The following February one of Van Allen's assistants, Carl McIlwain, fired a series of twenty-seven-foot Nike-Cajun rockets right through auroral displays over Fort Churchill, on the shore of Hudson Bay. These observed directly the high-speed protons (hydrogen nuclei) which had been "seen" from the ground in the spectroscopic work of Gartlein and Meinel. Thus the showering radiation consisted of both electrons and protons, although the electrons seemed to predominate.

In January, 1956, the committee of which Van Allen was chairman (whose name had now been modified to the Rocket and Satellite Research Panel) held a symposium to discuss the most fruitful experiments for the projected IGY satellites. Van Allen proposed a north-south orbit to get a good look at the radiation over the auroral zones. Because of the layout of the Canaveral missile range, a polar orbit was not thought feasible for the early satellites and hence Van Allen was told to go ahead with his alternate proposal, which was a satellite survey of cosmic-ray intensities in the more east-west type of orbit planned for the early shots.

In October, 1957, the author visited Van Allen's laboratories in the basement of a neoclassic limestone building on the campus in Iowa City. George H. Ludwig, a husky graduate student, was putting the finishing touches on a masterpiece of miniature electronics. The circuitry had been mounted on circular palm-size disks, or "decks," which would fit into the cylindrical container for the satellite payload. On each deck was a complex array of electronic gadgetry—pea-size transistors amid even tinier diodes and resistors, linked by a maze of hairlike wiring. The disks were "potted" in plastic foam which, when it hardened, looked like dirty pink soap. This made the circuitry immune to wild vibration, shock, spin, and acceleration. Most impressive to the layman was the tape recorder which was to give the satellite its memory. It was the size of a small alarm clock, designed so that its thirty-six-inch magnetic tape would jump forward once a second for as long as two hours, winding a spring as its wheels revolved. Since each orbit was expected to take about one hundred minutes, two hours left a safe margin. The heart of the package was a Geiger counter, the shape and size of a stubby cigar, whose scaled-down output was to be fed into the tape. The tape's once-a-second jumps would provide a time scale that could be used, later, to calculate where and how high the satellite was when it recorded each batch of counts.

A radio command from the ground was to release the recorder's playback spring and turn on the satellite's more powerful transmitter. The fruit of its most recent trip around the world would then be broadcast in about five seconds, the tape at the same time being wiped clean for the next orbit.

When the Army was told to back up Vanguard with a rush launching, Ludwig's package was hurriedly modified to be the first Army payload, but the tape recorder had to be left out. Fed into a loudspeaker, the radio voice of this satellite, Explorer I, was a discordant chorus of tones, on both its high- and low-powered transmitters. This made it possible to send four instrument readings simultaneously as four modulated audio tones superimposed on a high-frequency carrier wave. Each of the observing instruments was designed so that changes in whatever it was observing produced slight changes in the tone.

Temperature was recorded by "thermistors" whose resistance to the electric current flowing through them varied with heat changes. Two systems were used to record impacts of meteoric dust and fragments. On the outside skin of the rocket there were twelve cards covered with patterns of fine wire. Each breaking of a wire would produce an abrupt change in signal. Inside the vehicle was a supersonic microphone linked by a spring to the rocket shell. This was to report every clink made as a fragment struck any part of the rocket.

The cosmic-ray recorder was similar in principle to the Geiger counters that have become a standard tool in this atomic era, but, instead of ticking every time it was penetrated by a high-energy particle, it put out a small electric impulse. Since the number of counts was expected to be rapid at times, these impulses were fed into a scaler that emitted one pulse for every sixteen it received, much as the distance gauge of an automobile converts wheel revolutions into miles. For every sixteen counts there would be a shift in audio tone, the shifts being back and forth between two frequencies.

After signals from the satellite had been recorded on tape, they had to be run through electronic filters to separate the tones carrying each channel of information. Explorer I's high-powered transmitter was designed to produce signals that could be heard by many stations during the expected two-week life of its batteries. The low-powered transmitter was a gamble on getting data for a longer period. It was to eke out its power supply for two months, sending signals audible only to ultrasensitive equipment.

For the batteries to operate properly, their temperature had to remain between 5° and 185°. This presented a problem, since the satellite spent about a third of its time in the frigid shadow of the earth and the rest in sunlight of unmitigated intensity. The stainless-steel case of Explorer I, if left bare, would have permitted too wide a range of internal temperature. It was calculated that 25 per cent of the rocket cylinder and 30 per cent of its nose should be coated with aluminum oxide. This ceramic was flame-sprayed on in stripes. Signals from the satellite showed that the computations had been excellent; the internal temperature range in the early Explorers was between 32° and 95°.

Channel allocations for the first two successful Explorers were:

Cycles per second	Low-powered transmitter	High-powered transmitter
560	Skin temperature forward	Skin temperature, rear, in Explorer I; silent in Explorer III
730	Nose temp. in Ex. I; Geiger tube temp. in Ex. III	Internal temp. in Ex. I; silent in Ex. III
960	Wire grids for micrometeorite detection	Micrometeorite microphone in Ex. I; silent in Ex. III
1300	Cosmic ray count. 16 counts per freq. change	Cosmic rays. 16 counts per freq. change in Ex. I. Playback of magnetic tape in Ex. III (every 128 counts reported)

The first tapes processed after the launching of Explorer I, on January 31, 1958, were those from stations in the United States. Because the satellite had no "memory," the information it was gathering reached the scientists only when it was within range of a monitoring station. Some 90 per cent of the readings were lost over oceans and remote areas. The remaining 10 per cent, nevertheless, was enough to excite the scientists in Iowa.

The recordings were first run through electronic filters at the Jet Propulsion Laboratory in Pasadena, and the cosmic-ray results were then sent to Van Allen. The first records from United States stations showed cosmic-ray rates which fitted in well with theoretical predictions. But when tapes came from South America, covering the first two weeks of the satellite's life, it was evident that something was amiss.

It was expected that the count would increase with altitude, since the earth acts as a shield against cosmic rays. The farther the satellite was from the earth, the less it would be shielded. During the first two weeks of February the high part of the satellite's orbit was over the Southern Hemisphere, whereas its passes over California were low. The California data showed the expected increase of intensity with altitude, the highest count being about 70 per second in the vicinity of 900 miles elevation. The South American passes were both lofty and moderately low. The lower ones conformed to the California pattern, but when the satellite was up around 1500 miles its Geiger counter reported either a very low count or none at all.

Meanwhile a new instrument package was being prepared, this time with Ludwig's tape recorder on board. It was flown on Explorer II, which fell into the sea, but a duplicate on Explorer III went into orbit on March 26.

Lest some unauthorized person activate the recorder, spilling the data where it might be lost, the frequency of the command signal was kept secret—one of the few such secrets in the IGY. Likewise, to insure orderly gleaning of the results after each of the satellite's 116-minute journeys around the earth, the Naval Research Laboratory in Washington designated only one station at a time to send the command. The stations doing this job were aligned in a north-south "fence" along the east coast of North America and the west coast of South America. For each pass, NRL calculated which of them would be most directly under the satellite. The system did not work flawlessly at first and the data from some orbits were lost. Nevertheless recordings from nine circuits of the earth during the last four days of March reached Iowa City and were hurriedly analyzed. They confirmed the observations of Explorer I. Above 500 or 600 miles the counting rate went up rapidly, then dropped to zero or almost zero.

> One day, as we were puzzling over the first tapes from Explorer III [Van Allen wrote] McIlwain suggested the first plausible explanation for their peculiar readings. He

had just been calibrating his rocket instruments, and called our attention to something that we all knew but had temporarily forgotten: A sufficiently high level of radiation can jam the counter and send the apparent counting rate to zero. We had discovered an enormously high level of radiation, not a lack of it. As Ernest Ray, a member of our group, inaccurately but graphically exclaimed: "Space is radioactive!" [10]

They had a spare instrument package for Explorer I and decided to see what happened when it was exposed, in the laboratory, to a hard X-ray beam. They found, as they had suspected, that at high intensities of radiation the counts came so rapidly that only a few were strong enough to operate the scaler. At very high levels the counts were too rapid to be recorded at all.

A check of counting rates from the satellites showed that, at the highest level before their counters became tongue-tied, the rate was 1000 times greater than what was to be expected.

On May 1, 1958, Van Allen disclosed his discovery to a joint Washington session of the National Academy of Sciences and the American Physical Society. His paper was signed by himself and three of his assistants: Ludwig, Ray, and McIlwain. They explained that the points in space at which they believed observations had been made might be in error by as much as 700 miles along the trajectory, since the Vanguard Computing Center in Washington still had not been able to determine the orbits with any precision. Likewise, they pointed out, the information from Explorer I was limited to that obtained when the satellite was near one of the sixteen stations set up by the Naval Research Laboratory and the Jet Propulsion Laboratory. These were:

California	East Coast USA	South America	Elsewhere
San Diego (NRL)	Blossom Point, Md. (NRL)	Quito, Ecuador (NRL)	Antigua, BWI (NRL)
Earthquake Valley (JPL)	Ft. Stewart, Ga. (NRL)	Lima, Peru (NRL)	Havana, Cuba, (NRL)
Temple City (JPL)	Patrick AFB, Fla. (JPL)	Antofagasta, Chile (NRL)	Woomera, Australia (NRL)
Pasadena (JPL)		Santiago, Chile (NRL)	Singapore (JPL)
			Ibadan, Nigeria (JPL)

They noted that the complete absence of counts on the high passes over South America would indicate fewer cosmic rays up there than on the lower passes. This was inconceivable, since it was obvious that the rays came from far beyond. Hence, they said,

> ... we believe that the extremely low output of the scaler is caused by very intense radiation which "jams" the geiger tube so that it puts out pulses of such small height that they are below the threshold of the counting circuits. Laboratory tests show that this first happens for the present equipment when the radiation reaches ... 35,000 counts per second.[11]

The report that there was such intensive radiation in space created a sensation. It was "hot" enough to present a hazard to space travelers. The Iowa group pointed out that, according to a handbook of the United States Department of Health, Education and Welfare, no person should be exposed to more than .3 roentgens of radiation in one week; yet they calculated that, at the top of the satellite orbit, such a dosage would be received in five hours or less, depending on the nature of the radiation. They suggested that it consisted of either protons or electrons "closely related" to the auroral zone radiation they had detected earlier with rockoons.

There was no mention, in the paper, of entrapment in north-south orbits, as had been proposed by Störmer half a century earlier, but some such mechanism was clearly in the back of Van Allen's mind.[12] At a press conference in conjunction with the meeting, he said the earth's magnetic field seemed to act as an umbrella that kept the radiation particles at least 600 miles above the earth. He envisaged them as being confined within an earth-encircling reservoir only a few hundred or a thousand miles thick. Asked if the discovery could be described as a radiation "belt," he said yes. And so it came to be known as the Van Allen Belt. It probably "drizzled" particles out, particularly over the auroral zones, he said, and was replenished from time to time by the arrival of new gas clouds from the sun. He suggested that fast-moving electrons rained upon the rocket shell "like rain on a tin roof," generating, inside the satellite, X rays whose intensity paralyzed the Geiger tube.

The existence of particles trapped in the outer part of the earth's magnetic field had been postulated by Fred Singer just two years earlier. On April 28, 1956, he had presented a paper before the American Physical Society in Washington, suggesting that the motion of such particles generated Störmer's ring current. Störmer had invented the idea of entrapment, Singer said, but had not considered it important because he thought solar particles slow enough to be caught within the earth's field would be too weak to penetrate it. Singer pointed to the more recent work on entrapment theory by such men as the Swedish astrophysicist Hannes Alfvén and Ernest H. Vestine of the United States, and he suggested that a jet of solar particles would perturb the outer part of the earth's magnetic field. This would open the door enough to admit some particles and allow them to be trapped.

Thus, Singer said, it was possible for a reservoir of trapped particles to be replenished from time to time by solar outbursts. This intensification of the belt could then produce one of the hypothetical phenomena associated with a magnetic storm: an electric current encircling the earth some thousands of miles out in space.

Between solar outbreaks, he asserted, the reservoir could be fed on a lesser scale by particles "splashed" into space when cosmic rays struck the upper air.

A few days later Singer presented a similar paper before the American Geophysical Union.[13] He used one of Birkeland's photographs to show that, at the turn of the century, the Norwegian had, in fact, created a radiation belt around his terrella. The picture showed an auroral-type display on the side of the magnetized sphere being bombarded with electrons, but a faint glow on the opposite side of this miniature earth, Singer said, indicated that some of the electrons had been trapped and had migrated "eastward" to envelop the entire sphere in a doughnut-shaped belt. Singer proposed various rocket and satellite experiments to test his theory.

By the time Van Allen made his exciting announcement of the existence of radiation in space, another manipulator of equations had been at work on entrapment theory. He was Nicholas C. Christofilos who, until recently, had been running an elevator business in Greece. Born in Boston, where his parents ran a restaurant, he had moved to the land of his forefathers at the age of seven and been trained there as an engineer. During an exchange of letters with the Radiation Laboratory of the University of California in Berkeley, he had proposed a "strong-focusing" principle, that, when applied to the magnets in an atom-smasher, would greatly improve its efficiency. Because his mathematics were not sufficiently persuasive, his idea received little attention, but on the day of his arrival in the United States, in 1953, Christofilos saw a copy of the *Physical Review* with a proposal, virtually identical to his own, to be used in designing the powerful new accelerator for the Brookhaven National Laboratory on Long Island. Christofilos pointed out that not only had he proposed this idea some time earlier, but that he had applied for a patent. As a sequel to this episode, Christofilos was hired, first at Brookhaven and then by the University of California's Radiation Laboratory at Livermore. The latter institution was seeking to devise a magnetic "bottle" of trapped particles that could contain gasses hot enough to sustain, in an attenuated, controlled manner, the fusion reaction of the hydrogen bomb. The gas temperatures involved were comparable to those within the sun and hence, it was thought, the only container that could hold such gases would be magnetic. Since this was right up his alley, Christofilos went to work on magnetic bottles, but when the first Sputniks were launched, he began wondering if there might be such "bottles" surrounding the earth. Early in 1958, as a result of his calculations, he proposed a most remarkable experiment, of which the launching of the next American satellite was a part. This was Project Argus, which will be described in the next chapter. When the satellite, christened Explorer IV, was pitched into orbit, Argus was secret. So far as the public was concerned, it was simply a further exploration, under IGY auspices, of the newly discovered radiation.

Explorer IV was the first American satellite to reach near enough to the poles to nudge the auroral zones. It would have been better to fire it due north, into an orbit over both poles, but in case of rocket failure, the vehicle might have plunged into the Carolinas. The best the missilemen at Canaveral could do was a shot northeast over the Atlantic. It carried four radiation detectors, instead of the single Geiger tube on earlier Explorers, and the scientists hoped that, by comparison of readings on the four devices, it would be possible to learn more of the nature and intensity of the radiation. The detectors were shielded to differing degrees to give them varying sensitivity to certain kinds of radiation:

Channel no.	Detector type	Minimum sensitivity (in thousands of electron volts)			Counts reported by each frequency change
		Electrons	Protons	X rays	
1	Geiger counter with lead shielding	5000	40,000	80	32
2	Plastic scintillator	580	10,000	300	8
3	Geiger counter	3000	30,000	40	1024
4	Cesium iodide scintillator	20	400	all	(See note)
5	same counter as channel 2 with different scaler				1024

NOTE: Channels 1, 2, and 3 detected X rays with low efficiency. Channel 4, by gradual frequency changes, reported variations in energy flux.

As soon as the tapes from Explorer IV began arriving in Iowa City, Van Allen's men went to work plotting the results. By October, when I paid them another visit, the rolls of tape recorded from the satellites by the far-flung network of stations filled shelves that reached to the tall ceiling of their archive. It would take years to sift all this material, but they were making spot checks. They played the tape through their electronic filter—they were using their own by now—consisting of a squad of consoles. Nine needles—quivering, pulsing, or wandering—inscribed nine lines on a rapidly moving roll of paper. The pulsing needle marked the passing seconds, as transmitted by station WWV in Washington and recorded simultaneously with the satellite signals. The other needles inscribed the various channels of data: radiation, temperature, and micrometeorites. On the wall was a sign: THIS JOB IS SO SECRET EVEN I DON'T KNOW WHAT I'M DOING.

Carl McIlwain was drafting a series of charts representing space, in cross section, above the chains of observing stations. Changes in the orbit brought Explorer IV over any one spot at a number of elevations, so that, as the tapes came in, it was possible for him to map the radiation intensity in depth.

His most complete chart showed the cross section above North and

South America, where most of the monitoring stations were located. Its lines, representing areas of equal radiation, were similar to those on contour maps showing equal elevation. McIlwain and Ernest Ray, who was Van Allen's deputy, pointed out the more interesting features of the pattern that was emerging. Over the equatorial regions the contours were flat, but in middle latitudes (over Chile and Florida) they turned sharply outward into space. Still farther toward the poles they returned in hornlike configurations aimed at (or slightly on the equatorial side of) the auroral zones where the rockoons had spotted a strange radiation.

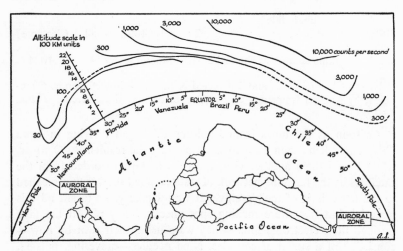

RADIATION BELTS BASED ON EARLY SATELLITE DATA

Contours of equal counting rates (per second) over North and South America as reported by Explorer IV from July 26 to August 26, 1958. The upward curve of the contours over Florida and southern Chile suggested that this might mark the bottom of an inner radiation zone. The "horn" penetrating deeply toward Newfoundland suggested the lower rim of an outer zone. The entire pattern is centered over the geomagnetic equator, which lies south of the geographic equator in this region. Hence the southern "horn" was not detected here, although it was observed over the ocean south of Australia.[14]

These horns were strikingly reminiscent of Störmer's proposal that most incoming solar particles are magnetically channeled into hornlike funnels penetrating the atmosphere over the zone of most frequent auroras. The two men—both still in their twenties—discussed the possible significance of this pattern. They and their colleagues were not yet in agreement. McIlwain felt that the horns were the lower rim of an outer radiation belt, separate from the one detected over the equator; the others were not so sure.

There was an arbitrary ceiling on the information on these charts— the 1380-mile summit of the Explorer IV orbit. Hence guessing at the shape of the radiation belts was a little like trying to draw the plan of a house after seeing only its basement. Since Explorer IV had no memory device, information could be obtained only from the few minutes it was over a tracking station. After data had been recorded from 3600 such passes over sites in North and South America, Europe, Africa, Australia, the West Indies, and Singapore, Van Allen displayed the resulting charts, and his guess as to the shape of the entire region, at a meeting of the American Physical Society in Chicago on November 28, 1958.[15]

In May, Van Allen had arranged to have his radiation counters carried on each of the IGY moon probes and by the time he presented his paper in Chicago he had results from Pioneer I. They were disappointing, due largely to instrument difficulties, but indicated that most of the radiation lay within 10,000 miles of the earth. Beyond, space did not seem to be unexpectedly "hot."

Pioneer III, the final space shot of the IGY, was no more successful than its predecessor in escaping the earth's gravity, but this was a boon to the Iowa group, for its fall back to earth meant a second flight through the radiation region. One of its two Geiger counters was geared to record the highest conceivable intensity. Its scalers provided three outputs: one sent an impulse for every 512 counts; another did so for every 8192 counts; the third transmitted only after receiving 131,072 counts. The counter itself was roughly the size of a cigarette. Its companion, somewhat smaller, was less sensitive and was designed as a check on its big brother.

The outbound and inbound signals from Pioneer III seemed to confirm McIlwain's guess that there were two radiation belts girdling the earth's waist. It appeared that a space traveler setting forth vertically from the geomagnetic equator would pass through two intense regions. The heart of one lay 2400 miles out; the other was 10,000 miles from the earth's surface. At 40,000 miles the radiation fell to what seemed the normal level in interplanetary space.

Van Allen reported to the American Astronautical Society on

December 27 that the intensity within each of the concentric "dough-nuts" reached 25,600 counts per second. This was equivalent to 160,000 particles striking the area of a postage stamp in every second. Since the lowest part of the belts was in the horns, Van Allen proposed that this was where the particles were most likely to strike the air and be knocked out of their entrapment orbits. He likened the belts to a leaky bucket dribbling particles, primarily into the auroral zones, yet periodically replenished by clouds of gas from the sun. The steady leakage, he said, could account for the radiation detected near the auroral zone by his rockoons.

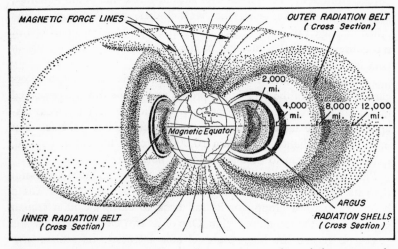

The Van Allen radiation belts, partly cut away to show their structure in cross section. The Argus shells are described in the next chapter.

This could also explain the strange hotness of the upper air in parts of the Arctic, he said. Rocket shots had shown that, at elevations greater than 90 to 140 miles above Fort Churchill, Manitoba, the summer air was at roughly 3100°, compared to only 1500° over the White Sands missile range in New Mexico. Temperature is a measure of the agitation of molecules and atoms. Such high levels of heat in the dense lower atmosphere would melt a rocket, but have little effect in the near-vacuum at such great heights. Van Allen suggested that the heat caused by the impact of incoming particles made the atmosphere expand to levels several hundred miles above those elsewhere. There was also a possibility, he said, that Störmer's postulated ring current flowed through the doughnut-shape region of trapped particles, much as Singer had suggested.

Isadore Harris and Robert Jastrow of the Naval Research Laboratory did theoretical calculations indicating that the influx of electrons would in fact produce extensive heating. Jastrow also suggested an explanation for the frequency of auroras at the spring and fall equinoxes. At those times, he pointed out, the magnetic axis of the earth is at right angles to the direction of the sun, a situation he calculated would favor the "sucking in" of a great number of solar particles.

One of the striking features of the outer radiation belt is that its lower rim does not lie directly over the zone of maximum aurora, but rather several hundred miles toward the equator. Thus, in North America, the auroral zone crosses Hudson Bay, whereas the rim of the outer belt lies across the northern United States. The answer may be that the particles producing day-to-day auroras, as well as those observed by the rockoons, either spiral in directly from the sun or are briefly trapped in the ragged, ever-changing outer fringes of the region where the earth's magnetism is able to hold them. This produces a steady influx into the atmosphere, whereas particles in the heart of the outer belt remain trapped until a magnetic storm upsets the trapping mechanism and they fall, like drops from a wet tree that has been shaken, into the atmosphere beneath the rim, producing the spectacular auroral displays seen at such times in the northern United States.

Van Allen's initial report on May 1, 1958, excited the interest of the Russians. Some scientists believe they might have made the discovery first, had they not been so secretive. The orbit of Sputnik II, before its batteries died, was too low over the USSR to penetrate the radiation zone, but over the Southern Hemisphere it rose higher than 1000 miles. With more advance notice, other IGY nations might have supplied Moscow with recordings of the satellite signal during the high part of its orbit. Neither of the first two Soviet sputniks carried a memory device.

When Sputnik III was launched on May 15, it was equipped with several radiation detectors, including two scintillation counters, which could observe the newly discovered radiation. On July 15 the Moscow newspaper *Izvestia* reported that, thanks to these instruments, "a new phenomenon in science was discovered, a special type of corpuscular radiation which up to now had not been observed in the composition of cosmic rays." Although the press described detection of the belts as a Soviet achievement, the scientists concerned subsequently gave credit to Van Allen.[16] On July 31, Sergei N. Vernov and his colleagues presented to the IGY conference in Moscow several reports on Soviet rocket and satellite results.

Of special interest were the readings obtained with Sputnik III in the vicinity of latitude 60° North, near the auroral zone. The radiation there, they said, was sometimes 50 per cent stronger than else-

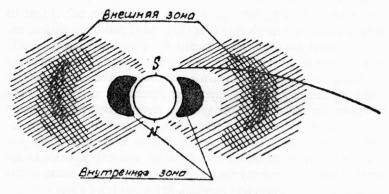

Рисунок 2.

Конфигурация окружающих Землю зон повышенной радиации.
Сплошная линия — траектория движения космической ракеты.

The radiation belts as charted by the Soviet Union. This diagram was published in the Moscow newspaper *Izvestia* on July 15, 1959 (p. 3), to illustrate a summary of results obtained from Lunik I and the Soviet earth satellites. The labels point to the inner and outer zones. The poles are marked with letters of the Roman alphabet. The caption reads: "Configuration of the earth-encircling zones of energetic radiation. The unbroken line is the trajectory of the flight of the cosmic rocket."

where, and they speculated that this was the lower edge of a shell of trapped particles, shaped by the earth's magnetic field. Since the Explorer IV results had not yet been charted, the Russians later claimed credit for discovering the outer belt. They proposed two sources for the trapped particles. One was from the decay of neutrons produced by cosmic-ray impacts upon the upper air. The other was the arrival of gas clouds from the sun. The neutron proposal seemed more satisfactory than earlier concepts of the role of cosmic-ray "splashes." Neutrons, having no electric charge, are not affected by the earth's magnetism, but they live for an average of 1000 seconds, whereupon they split into an electron and a proton (both charged). Thus neutrons, splashed into the sky, could feed electrons and protons into the earth's magnetic field.

The view therefore took hold that the inner belt was the product of cosmic rays, whereas the outer belt was primarily fed by the sun. The driving power of cosmic rays penetrated the magnetic field to its greatest depth, whereas solar particles were too weak to do so. Rocket and satellite observations of the belts during the eighteen months following the IGY showed the inner belt to be a comparatively stable feature and the outer belt to vary radically, consequent to eruptions on the sun. There was some evidence that newly arrived solar particles were accelerated within the belt in the late stages of a magnetic storm.[17] The radiation in the belts did not appear intense enough to preclude space travel, but it could not be ignored. Some protection might be needed, even for a swift trip through that region. More serious was the safety problem on board satellites orbiting in the range from 500 to 40,000 miles. For unprotected passengers, prolonged exposure would probably be fatal and some equipment, such as photographic film, might be ruined.

The question arises whether the dog Laika, the world's first voyager in space, might have died of radiation sickness. This seems unlikely. While her body may have suffered some radiation damage, the comparatively low orbit of Sputnik II probably did not enter a region "hot" enough to produce death so quickly.

For the traveler seeking to avoid the radiation belts, the polar regions seem to offer a cone-shaped escape route free of any hazard.

CHAPTER 8
ARGUS

During the summer of 1958 a number of people concerned with the IGY had perplexing—and sometimes disquieting—experiences. Among these were Edward P. Ney, professor of physics at the University of Minnesota, and Paul J. Kellogg, an assistant professor with whom Ney worked closely in cosmic-ray research. They had what they thought was a dazzling idea. Why not fire a hydrogen bomb in space and see what its effect would be on the Van Allen radiation belt? If it were detonated some 250 miles up in the sky near the southern auroral zone, they calculated, it would produce a sort of crack-the-whip wave in the earth's magnetic field that would travel back and forth, north and south, jarring loose the trapped electrons that constituted the belt's radiation. Artificial auroras would be produced by the falling particles at both the north and south ends of this wave path, they thought, and, at the same time, particles resulting from the bomb blast would be injected into the belt.

Ney and Kellogg were working on a project with the Office of Naval Research and therefore they phoned their friends in ONR, expecting their proposition to be greeted with enthusiasm. Instead they sensed consternation at the other end of the telephone line. They were asked not to discuss their idea with anyone. They drafted a letter to be sent to Herbert F. York, Chief Scientist of the Advanced Research Projects Agency of the Department of Defense, setting forth their proposal in greater detail. When advised of this, their friends in Washington said the letter must be sealed in one envelope to be enclosed in an outer cover, as is customary with confidential government papers.

Ney and Kellogg were puzzled. What they had in mind was a public experiment, not a secret project. In their letter they pointed out that, if such an experiment were carried out soon, the widespread

IGY stations could take part in observing the predicted auroras and the other effects. "It might be amusing," they wrote, "to end the IGY by destroying some of the radiation field first discovered during the IGY."

They were about to send the letter off when they began to have misgivings. From the behavior of the Pentagon, it was obvious that their letter would be stamped "Secret" as soon as received, which was quite contrary to their vision of an open experiment. The letter was never mailed. Instead they decided to submit the idea for publication in the British scientific journal *Nature*.

When the Pentagon heard of this, consternation apparently gave way to full-fledged alarm. An old scientific friend in the government persuaded the two Minnesotans to hold up their manuscript, at least for a while. It was finally published, in modified form, in the issue of *Nature* dated February 7, 1959, a few weeks before Project Argus became known.[1]

Meanwhile a group of New Zealanders at the Apia Observatory in Samoa inadvertently confirmed one of the Ney-Kellogg predictions. Before midnight on July 31, 1958, they saw a flat, horizontal arc of bright violet rays in the western sky. To the north of west, it was 12° above the horizon, sloping gently down until obscured by coconut trees to the south of west. The display lasted fourteen minutes, shrinking, changing in color to red and finally to green.

Several things about the display struck the New Zealanders as strange. It sloped down from the north, although Samoa is south of the equator and the only known previous sighting of an aurora (in 1921) had been far in the south—an aurora australis—associated with an extremely severe magnetic storm. The rapid-run magnetograph in Samoa recorded a sharp and peculiar disturbance at the onset of the 1958 aurora, but magnetic instruments in New Zealand observed nothing of the sort. The storm, if it was that, seemed purely local.

Eleven nights later a somewhat similar display was seen in the western sky. As described by J. G. Keys, the observer-in-charge, "Ten minutes after the initial flash the general effect was that of dawn on an overcast morning."[2]

The New Zealanders quickly learned that the two auroral displays had coincided with hydrogen-bomb explosions high above Johnston Island. The location was some 2100 miles to the north, but the flattened arc of the earth's magnetic field, into which the fireball was thrust, came back to earth over the sea west of Samoa.

The explosions were conducted in secrecy, but were so high and so large that they could not be hidden. In fact the Atomic Energy Commission later called them "by far the most spectacular shots ever fired by the United States." [3] Since a large proportion of the energy was released in a small fraction of a second, the resulting flash did its damage before one could blink. The height gave such range to this effect that, even at a distance of 370 miles, the eyes of experimental rabbits were slightly burned. The first shot, known by the code name "Teak," was set off in the nose of a rocket 252,000 feet above Johnston Island. The second, christened "Orange," was fired 141,000 feet up. Since the height of Teak was almost forty-eight miles, its flash was clearly seen from Hawaii, some 800 miles to the northeast, although the actual explosion was below the horizon even from Haleakala Observatory, 10,000 feet above sea level on the island of Maui.

A series of photographs of the rising fireball was taken from Haleakala; one of them shows a remarkable luminous arc, reaching from the explosion site toward the south. Thus the explosion had produced an aurora at both ends of the magnetic arc in which it occurred: one near Johnston Island and the other near Samoa.

Teak also initiated a magnetic storm in the Central Pacific. It was recorded from the Hawaiian Islands in the north to Samoa and Rarotonga in the south and was attributed to an outward rush of highly ionized gas from the explosion that generated counterclockwise electric currents circling the Johnston Island area. The explosions produced immediate radio blackouts, even on circuits passing no closer than 1800 miles from the site. The blackouts lasted about two hours after each explosion and, after Orange, the effect continued to be observable for many hours.

The New Zealanders were understandably excited about their observations and reported them in the issue of *Nature* for November 15, 1958.[4] The American observers remained silent.

Much farther south another New Zealander was puzzled by the reaction some remarkable observations he had made were producing in the United States. He was Kenneth James Salmon, scientific leader at the joint New Zealand-American IGY station at Cape Hallett, Antarctica. It is customary for the supremely isolated stations in

Antarctica to "shoot the breeze" with one another by radio, and during such an exchange in August, 1958, Salmon heard of the initial Johnston Island blast and the coincidental sighting of an aurora by his countrymen in Samoa.

The magnetic meridian that ran from Johnston Island past Samoa almost bisected Cape Hallett, but the weather at Hallett had been overcast on August 1, the day of the Teak explosion, so there was no chance of an auroral sighting. Nevertheless Salmon had a device whose sky-gazing capabilities were formidable: a Meinel-Oliver Patrol Spectrograph that had been furnished by the Air Force Cambridge Research Center near Boston. During this time of year at Cape Hallett there was a considerable twilight period each day, when the upper atmosphere was in sunlight, yet the ground was dark enough for observations to be made of twilight airglow—a faint luminescence of the upper air induced by sunlight.

> I was very keen [Salmon wrote the author] to finish off the roll of film I had in my spectrograph . . . to see whether anything unusual had been recorded. In fact, I took the film out a few days before it was due to run out! After developing the film and noticing the line [representing a hitherto unobserved form of light] for the first time my first move was to examine all the rest of the film I had recorded for the year to see if any sign of it could be found. *It was not there before Aug. 5th.*

After an exchange of messages with a scientific colleague, Dr. M. Gadsden in New Zealand, he decided that what he was seeing was lithium. Many physicists with no inside knowledge suspected that the fuel of a hydrogen bomb was lithium deuteride. During the twilight period each day he scanned the sky and found that the emission hit its peak on August 18, whereupon it subsided, vanishing on September 15.

Meanwhile Salmon had sent an excited message to Norman J. Oliver, head of the antarctic auroral program at the Air Force Cambridge Research Center. Knowing the ways of the military, he delicately avoided a mention of hydrogen bombs, but noted that the lithium might have followed lines of the earth's magnetic field (in the same manner as the particles that produced the Samoan aurora). No reply. He sent a follow-up message. Still no answer. His third communication displayed a certain gentlemanly annoyance. He could not understand, he said, the lack of interest in his observations.

His messages were far from being ignored, but no one dared tell him what they thought. United States bases in Antarctica were asked to check their spectrographs and, sure enough, all of them except Little America showed lithium lines for that same period. It looked as though the substance might be a by-product of the Teak blast.

Meanwhile Gadsden, at the Awarua radio station near the southern tip of New Zealand, aimed his spectrograph at the twilight sky to the south. On September 5 he saw the same thing and, in the weeks that followed, found that the height and intensity of the emission sank steadily. He submitted a report, on behalf of Salmon and himself, to *Nature*. This was published December 6.[5]

A more disquieting experience, in that it could not be explained by any known occurrence (such as the Johnston Island explosions), was that of the 294 colonists on Tristan de Cunha Island, in the center of the vast, lonely region of the Atlantic that lies between Antarctica, South Africa, and South America. These people eke out a Spartan life raising potatoes on the slopes of a dead volcano. At about 10:30 A.M. on September 9, 1958, G. Francis Harris of the British Colonial Office, administrator of the island group, was out in what they call the "potato patches" when he heard the sound of aircraft approaching:

> Two planes flew along the island coast quite low down, [he reported in a letter to the author] and as soon as we waved to the pilots they turned out to sea. This was thought odd and most unfriendly. The aircraft appeared to be carrier-borne and were suspected of being American, but no one was certain. The islanders had not seen an aeroplane for 15 years, apart from a helicopter, and so they were most surprised.
>
> I asked the wireless operator to see if he could pick up any unusual wireless activity, and for the next three days we heard a lot on the wireless. All was in code, but we were able to advise the Royal Navy in South Africa about unusual activity, and quote to them the call signs of three or four American destroyers. We never were told why they

should have been in our area without telling us, or why they appeared so unfriendly, or why they did not pay us a social call ! ! ! .

Thus scientists, officials, and military men of several nations had peripheral contact with the great secret of Argus, but two of us at *The New York Times* were wrestling with the central problem. About the end of June, 1958, Hanson W. Baldwin, *The Times'* military analyst, put his head into my office and asked if he could talk to me privately for a few minutes. He had learned, he said, that the United States planned to fire several atomic bombs in space. They were to be carried aloft by multistage rockets to be fired from a Navy ship in the South Atlantic, almost equidistant from Antarctica, South Africa, and the southern tip of South America. The bombs would have a yield of about one kiloton—that is, they would be equivalent to 1000 tons of TNT, which was very small for a nuclear explosion—and would be detonated some 300 miles up, well out in space, as compared to the Johnston Island shots, which, although far more powerful, were at an elevation of less than forty-eight miles.

Instead of shaking loose part of the natural radiation surrounding the earth, as proposed the same summer by Ney and Kellogg, the objective was to produce an artificial belt. It was thought that enough of the high-energy electrons resulting from the bomb explosions would become entrapped in the earth's magnetic field to produce a thin, intense shell of radiation around the earth. It seemed possible that such a phenomenon could hamper radio communications and make it impossible to obtain radar echoes from incoming missiles. There might also be other military implications. To observe the effect, Baldwin explained, two satellites were to be launched: one in an orbit passing near both poles, the other in an orbit girdling the equator. The code name of the project was "Argus."

He had obtained this information, he said, in a manner that placed no limit on its use, but he had misgivings about publicizing the operation before it was carried out. I proposed consulting a friend who was so centrally involved in the United States space program that he would be sure to know of the operation. He would also, I felt, give us his candid personal opinion, rather than merely an official line.

My friend was both horrified and amused when I visited his office and laid before him a sheet on which I had typed the salient points about Argus, including the location, height, and yield of the blasts.

"I can't tell you not to print it," he said. "But I can say this: If you do, the operation will never take place." He felt that prior publication would stir up all kinds of diplomatic trouble. Hitherto all American bomb tests had been conducted either in the deserts of the southwestern United States or at the Pacific island testing sites. To fire bombs, suddenly, above an entirely different part of the world would have drastic repercussions, particularly in view of the highly emotional state of the public mind with regard to fallout and the proposed cessation of all bomb tests.

Within little more than an hour I received an urgent phone call from William H. Godel, the security chief in the Pentagon's Advanced Research Projects Agency. He pleaded that we hold the story, at least until he had come up to New York to discuss it with us. Baldwin and I had agreed that the story should not be published prior to the shots and I told Godel that his trip was not necessary. Hanson proposed that, to keep our consciences clear in case of a leak, we tell absolutely no one, and for more than eight months we lived by this rule.

Meanwhile Explorer IV was fired, on July 26, into an orbit as close to the poles as could be managed from Cape Canaveral. On August 24 an attempt was made to launch Explorer V with a payload of four radiation counters, similar to those of Explorer IV, but it failed. By then the far flung ships, planes, rocket-launching and -tracking sites of Project Argus were poised and there was no possibility of postponement.

It was our understanding that Argus would be announced after it had taken place and that we would be told in advance so that we could be the first to publish the news. As the months passed, after the shots were fired, it became more and more apparent that the Pentagon did not want any announcement. The IGY apparatus, including Explorer IV, had been used to observe Argus, and I knew that many of the scientists concerned with the IGY were anxious for the results to be published. They felt that, if secrecy were prolonged, the ultimate disclosure would have so negative an effect that the scientific brilliance of the experiment would be eclipsed. They regarded disclosure as inevitable, for there were thousands of men privy to Argus in varying degrees. The crews of Navy ships that had taken part totaled some four thousand; in addition there were rocket crews in Virginia, Florida, and Puerto Rico and specialists of other types from Spain to California.

The Russians, during scientific discussions at Geneva, had shown that they were aware of the possibilities demonstrated by Argus. When the effects of the Johnston Island shots became known—in particular the propagation of an artificial aurora over a distance of 2100 miles—the significance was not overlooked by Moscow. Two leading physicists in the Soviet Union, pointing to the report of this aurora in *Nature,* proposed that the inner Van Allen belt was formed by high-altitude nuclear explosions fired by the United States.[6] Some of the electrons produced by such explosions, they said, would reach great heights and become trapped in the earth's magnetic field.

The consequences of the explosions over Johnston Island were further revealed in the *Space Handbook* prepared by the Rand Corporation, a government-financed research group in California, for the Select Committee on Astronautics and Space Exploration of the House of Representatives. Distributed on January 9, 1959, it described the disruption of communications on frequencies between 5 and 25 megacycles following the Pacific shots.

The scientific reasoning behind Argus was also made public. Christofilos, the man who had proposed the experiment long before Ney and Kellogg thought of their own idea, presented his calculations on how an electron shield could be placed around the earth at a Chicago meeting of the American Physical Society on November 28, 1958. The only major point he omitted was the use of an atomic bomb to provide the electrons. Instead he proposed orbiting an electron accelerator in a satellite. Electrons shot out by this device, he said, would be relativistic—that is, would have speeds close enough to that of light so that they would spiral in trapped north-south paths like the particles of the Van Allen radiation. It was at this same meeting that Van Allen presented his first Explorer IV results, omitting all of the Argus effects.

The phenomenon that Christofilos proposed to generate had already come to be known, within the secret society of Argus scientists, as the Christofilos Effect.

> My main work for the last five years [Christofilos told the Physical Society] has been the Astron Thermonuclear device, in which a layer of relativistic electrons is employed for confinement and heating of the plasma.[7]

This was the "magnetic bottle" which, it was hoped, would confine and heat a gas sufficiently to sustain a continuous hydrogen fusion reaction—that is, would "tame" the hydrogen bomb. Two magnetic coils were used in the device to reflect, back and forth, electrons trapped in the long cylindrical magnetic field between them.

> Hence it occurred to me, about a year ago, after the launching of the Sputniks [Christofilos continued], to extrapolate [extend] the idea of the electron layer into outer space inasmuch as the earth's field provides a natural mirror effect. Then I investigated the trapping and lifetime of relativistic electrons in the geomagnetic field. When I discovered that relativistic electrons could be trapped and could survive quite a long time in the geomagnetic field, I thought that artificial injection of a measurable density is possible. . . .

Christofilos explained that electrons trapped in the earth's field would not only spiral back and forth between north and south, but would also drift eastward. This is because the strength of the field decreases with elevation. Electrons, being negatively charged, spiral in such a way that at the top of each loop they are going east, whereas at the bottom they are going west. Since the earth's magnetism is weaker at the top, it has less of a hold on the particles and hence the eastbound loops are bigger than the westbound loops. The result is a net drift to eastward. Protons, being of opposite electric charge, drift westward.

"If we continue the injection for an hour or so," Christofilos said, "then a shell of electrons is created around the earth." This envelope, he added, occupies one layer of the earth's magnetic field.[8]

With a succession of equations he showed the assembled physicists how he calculated the probable lifetime of the trapped particles. For electrons of a given energy in that part of the field which curves to meet the earth at 60° magnetic latitude, north and south, he estimated that the life would be thirteen days. The electron shell, he pointed out, would reveal the shape of the earth's magnetic field in space and the observed lifetime of the effect would indicate how much air there is, several hundred miles out, to remove the electrons by collision.

What he did not say was that, three months earlier, three such shells had secretly been wrapped around the earth. The growing body

of published information on the Christofilos effect and related phenomena made Baldwin and myself more and more fearful that a
competitor would print the Argus story before we could do so. On
December 26, 1958, a report on the IGY was made public by Hugh
Odishaw, executive director of the American IGY program, in which
he called attention to the lithium observations in New Zealand and
many parts of Antarctica. "A plain inference," he said, "is that these
new manifestations could be related to nuclear tests carried out during
the same period as the IGY program." He cited the report in *Nature*
on the aurora produced near Samoa and even referred to the Ney-
Kellogg proposal for a bomb explosion in space, although it had not
yet been published.[9]

By displaying how much was already known to the world of science,
Odishaw's article served to strengthen the hand of those scientists
who wished to make Argus public. Accounts of it were displayed
on page one of such newspapers as the Washington *Star*.

On December 27, at a session of the American Astronautical Society, Singer presented a paper, "Artificial Modification of the Earth's
Radiation Belt." He cited the newly published reports which, he said,
concerned a matter hitherto classified secret and said he now felt
free to discuss the subject to a limited extent. Sitting in the audience,
I was fearful that Singer was about to liquidate our news beat, but he
made no reference to Argus. However, at a press conference afterward, we had new cause for alarm. Van Allen, who had just presented his charts showing two radiation belts, was pointedly asked by
Henry T. Simmons of *Newsweek* whether or not Explorer IV had
detected any change in the radiation belt after the Johnston Island
shots. The enhancement, Van Allen replied, was "tremendous."

We had been warned that *Newsweek* had made inquiries regarding
Argus. The next day I wrote a long letter to York, who had just been
promoted to Director of Research and Engineering in the Pentagon.
I knew he had been a key man in Argus and Baldwin had already discussed our problem with him. I summarized all that had come out
about the effects of the Johnston Island explosions, as well as the
publication of Christofilos' calculations. Four months had now passed
since the Argus shots. Their effects had been world-wide at a time
when the whole world was "watching" through the eyes of the IGY
networks. One of the scientists connected with Argus had told me he

strongly suspected the Russians had observed the effect, since Explorer IV passed within range of their Tashkent monitoring station while it was weaving in and out of an Argus electron shell.

I read my letter over the phone to Hanson for his concurrence; then delivered it to York. It concluded by stating, "we no longer believe we can continue to withhold at least a partial treatment of Argus." Because IGY data was open to all, I said that we—or anyone else—could unearth the Argus effect with a certain amount of "concentrated effort."

I then set about trying to prove my point. I phoned the IGY World Warning Agency at Fort Belvoir, Virginia, and asked the forecaster on duty if he had any record of an unusual magnetic storm early in September.

"Just a minute, I'll check," he said. Soon he was back.

"Yes indeed!" he replied. "A rather remarkable event. We issued a special report on it." He mailed it to me and, though brief, it said: "It is difficult to associate this disturbance with any specific solar event." This, however, was only one phase of a four-day magnetic storm, part of which had been attributed to observed solar activity. I wrote York again on January 12, 1959, citing this special report as well as the information in the newly issued *Space Handbook*. Meanwhile, I tried other tacks. I checked the Coast and Geodetic Survey indices of magnetic activity for every three-hour period during the time of the Argus shots (we did not yet know exactly when they took place). I inquired of the IGY Auroral Data Center for visual observations, at Cornell University, if any unusual auroras had been seen. The answer was that the reports for that period had not yet been received. We asked *The New York Times'* London bureau to check with the University of Edinburgh, another of the three World Data Centers. The reply told of widespread displays, but none in the North Atlantic, where they should have been, according to our calculations. The size of the bomb explosions and their location within the earth's magnetic field had, in fact, been calculated with such nicety that most of their effects were evident only to those who knew when and where to look for them.

On January 14 I had a long talk with York and his assistant, William Whitson, in the Pentagon. They had studied my letters and apparently had discussed them with James Killian, the President's science advisor. The Belvoir report, they said, did not refer to an

Argus effect; our discussion was generally inconclusive. They agreed that disclosure of the experiment would not give the Russians any scientific knowledge they did not already have—particularly if we did not reveal the exact size and location of the explosions. That night, in writing to Baldwin an account of our talk, I said: "I am convinced that the only reason we are being discouraged by the Pentagon from publishing a limited report on Argus is to postpone the day of diplomatic reckoning as long as possible." I added that it seemed doubtful anyone in the government would ever say yes. Although we had understood earlier that we would be given first crack at the story, we were now being told that the government could not officially play favorites. The most we could hope for was a tip from a friend that an official announcement was iminent—a rather flimsy arrangement to count on after having kept the secret so long.

I consulted several scientists who, I felt, were of the highest integrity, who were fully briefed on Argus and its military implications (which Hanson and I, of course, were not), and yet who were not so intimately involved that they stood to gain in prestige from its disclosure. They also felt we should publish our story. The chief reason the government opposed it, they said, was to avoid embarrassment. Some of them, however, suggested that I talk the matter over with Killian before we made our decision.

On February 2 he was in New York to give an address. When he finished, I appeared on the dais with a letter in hand, summing up our case for publication and stating again that "we doubt that we can continue to withhold publication of at least a limited account of Argus."

We had been told, I said, that the objections were threefold: fear of unfavorable diplomatic results; fear that partial disclosure would lead to complete disclosure; and reluctance to bring the effect and its military possibilities to the attention of those abroad who previously might not have given them much thought.

Nevertheless, I cited the obligation of the United States to make public, by September, the data obtained from Explorer IV, including its presumed detection of Argus (I had been told in the Pentagon that this would not necessarily be done). Although the satellite was launched, in part, to watch Argus, it was governed by IGY rules. I pointed out that the United States had belabored the Russians for their recalcitrance in publishing satellite data and cited the provision in the by-laws of the IGY, the *CSAGI Guide to IGY World Data Centers,* whose one-year deadline called for delivery of the Explorer IV data by September. "In view of the long battle by the United States to include such a firm commitment in the IGY *Guide,*" I wrote, "it is inconceivable that this country should now back down."

Dr. Killian and I sat briefly in the emptying banquet hall as he read the letter. Rather than refute my arguments, he said that disclosure at that time might scuttle the Geneva talks on a nuclear weapons test suspension. The Russians would be handed the argument that the only untrustworthy participant in the talks was the one that had sneaked off to fire atomic bombs far from its own shores. Dr. Killian repeated that the government could make no pledge to give us advance warning of plans to publish. I said the least the government could do was to allow someone to tip us off informally. His reaction to this seemed to be assent, but we still were left in an uneasy situation.

Later that same month—February, 1959—a ten-day study session was organized by the Department of Defense at the Lawrence Radiation Laboratory in Livermore, California. It was there, late in October, 1957, that Christofilos first proposed the Argus experiment. Now the participating scientists—leaders in many fields—were called together to compare notes on the results. One entire day of the talks is said to have been spent in discussing whether or not the results should be made public. It was known to the group that *The New York Times* was voluntarily withholding the story. At times the arguments were heated. The advocates of secrecy argued that the Argus results had military value and that the United States, having conceived the experiment and carried it out at great expense, should monopolize its fruits as long as possible. Their opponents felt they had been party to an incredible scientific *tour de force* of which their country should be proud. It should be shouted from the housetops, not hidden in shamefaced silence. It was also a question, as stated later by *Science,* journal of the American Association for the Advancement of Science, whether it was proper—especially during the IGY—to carry out an experiment that made itself felt around the world, without telling fellow scientists about it.

At the end of the discussion a vote was taken—remarkable in itself for such a meeting. The outcome, I was told, was seventeen in favor of publication and five opposed. During the second week of March, Hanson Baldwin was informed that plans for a limited announcement had been set in motion with at least some backing in the Pentagon. The Geneva talks were completely bogged down. The disclosure might come within a month or less, he was told. We feared that, once the decision was made in Washington, the machinery might move so fast that we would be left standing in the dust.

On March 16 Hanson decided, with my concurrence, to recommend that *The Times* print the story; two days later we laid the situation before Arthur Hays Sulzberger, the publisher, Orvil E. Dryfoos, the newspaper's president, and Turner Catledge, the managing editor.

"I do not want to do anything that is going to do the country harm," the publisher said, but after hearing our presentation he agreed that we should go ahead. I suggested that, as a courtesy, we notify the White House of our plan. The publisher agreed but said, "If the White House phones and says the story will do serious damage, we are not going to print it."

The hours that followed were frantic, for there were diagrams, maps, and photographs to prepare, in addition to articles on the military, scientific, and secrecy aspects of the operation. I had notified the White House during the afternoon and was told to expect a return call. By evening the juggernaut of our preparations had such momentum that it would be well-nigh impossible to stop it if that call came from Washington. Hanson and I watched the clock tick away the final minutes until the great presses in the basement beneath us began to thunder. They rolled. No call ever came. And the world learned of Argus.

The next morning Donald A. Quarles, Deputy Secretary of Defense, conducted what was probably the most discomfiting press conference of his career. What seems to have distressed him in particular was the fact that the timing of the announcement of so momentous an event was determined by a newspaper and not by the government. He was asked if, by his remarks, he wished to imply that publication of the news at that time was against the national interest.

> I don't think I was saying precisely that [he replied]. I was saying that we were not given [control over] the detailed timing of the thing but I implied to you I think earlier that the National Academy of Science is in the process of formulating plans for the publication of this information

so that I am not alleging that the difference between the few days or few weeks here is a vital national security matter. I will say, however, that it isn't playing the game with the Department of Defense just the way I would like to see it played. I will not make any bones about that point.[10]

Elsewhere, however, particularly in the scientific community and in the press, the disclosure was welcomed. It was generally agreed that Argus had been one of the best-kept secrets in the peacetime history of a democracy, considering how many thousands had been privy to it and in view of its global scope.

Three times the project drew a thin curtain of trapped electrons around almost the entire civilized world. Explorer IV wove in and out of these shells some 250 times. From Virginia, Florida, and Puerto Rico thirteen five-stage rockets were fired to an average elevation of 550 miles to observe the growth, shape, and decay of the radiation. Navy ships at predetermined points in the North and South Atlantic saw artificial auroras appear at the time and place at which they had been predicted. Radio signals across the Atlantic faded; those across the Pacific swelled. An immense looped coil, encircling twenty-six square miles near the Grand Canyon, detected a change in the earth's magnetism within four seconds after one blast.

Six weeks after the disclosure of Argus the National Academy of Sciences held a symposium at which participating scientists reported on their observations. All seats in the Academy's Great Hall were filled; a phalanx of scientists, reporters, and Academy staff members stood in the rear of the hall and lined the walls of its balcony.

Geophysics has been described as the area of science in which the whole earth is the laboratory and nature conducts the experiments. In this case, however, it was man who initiated the events. "For the first time in history," said Richard Porter, chairman of the symposium and head of the Academy's satellite panel, "geophysical phenomena on a world-wide scale were being measured and related to a quantitatively known cause—namely, the injection into the earth's magnetic field of a known quantity of electrons of known energies at a known position and a known time."

He then disclosed the approximate times and locations of the three shots. "A large number of persons," he said, had studied the Argus results during the secrecy period, but now that it was public he expressed the hope that IGY observations by other nations would greatly enrich knowledge of the effects.[11]

The symposium then heard Christofilos tell how he had suggested the experiment in October, 1957. He had calculated that an explosion of megaton range (1000 times larger than that actually used) would produce a shell of such intensity as to "create a radiation hazard in outer space." [12] To avoid this—and to keep the experiment secret— a far smaller yield was recommended. Likewise, an explosion altitude was proposed that, it was thought, would limit the life of the effect to a few days.

The idea had so many implications—scientific, political, and military—that it was referred to President Eisenhower's Science Advisory Committee, headed by Killian. Under the Committee's auspices a special study group was formed comprising both scientific and military men, with Wolfgang K. H. Panofsky, Berlin-born head of Stanford University's High Energy Physics Laboratory, as chairman. The discovery of the Van Allen belts came at that crucial moment, giving strong confirmation to Christofilos' calculations. Therefore, late in April, 1958, preparations for Argus were set in motion. ARPA, in the Department of Defense, was given responsibility for carrying out the experiment and its Chief Scientist, Herbert York, was placed in charge. Frank H. Shelton of the Armed Forces Special Weapons Project (an agency concerned with the development of nuclear weapons) was made the project scientist; William J. Thaler of the Office of Naval Research represented the Navy in the scientific planning. The Air Force assigned to its nuclear warfare research unit in New Mexico, the Special Weapons Center at Kirtland Air Force Base, the task of sending up high-altitude rockets to observe the results. This was given the code name Project Jason. (The mythological Jason, who sailed in quest of the Golden Fleece with the blessing of the goddess Hera, had little or no connection with the mythological Argus, who was Hera's hundred-eyed watchman.) Another Air Force program, seeking to solve one of the most pressing problems of national defense, was told to observe the effects of the explosion over the North Atlantic. This was Project Midas, whose task was to develop an early-warning satellite system that could detect enemy missiles as they left the launching pad. Its interest in Argus was presumably to see if the Christofilos Effect could render the Midas system useless.

The possibility that the Geneva talks might produce a ban on nuclear explosions enforced haste and the first Argus shot was detonated only four months after the decision to go ahead. The Navy task force consisted of nine ships: the aircraft carrier *Tarawa,* the missile-testing ship *Norton Sound* (formerly a seaplane tender), the seaplane tender, *Albemarle,* the destroyers *Warrington* and *Bearss,* the destroyer escorts *Courtney* and *Hammerberg,* and the oilers *Neosho* and *Salamonie.* All of them went to the South Atlantic except the *Albemarle,* their time at sea being so extended that the oilers were needed to refuel the other ships en route. The *Tarawa* served as flagship; the task of its planes, as well as of the destroyers and destroyer escorts, was to see that there was no shipping in the firing area and to make scientific observations.

The vehicle that carried the bombs 300 miles into the sky was a modified version of the Polaris re-entry test vehicle, RTV-3. This was an assembly of solid-fueled rockets used to try out components for the missile the Navy was developing for launching from submerged submarines. It was selected, not only for its climbing power, but also because it could be launched from the deck of the *Norton Sound.* On top of a large first stage were three rockets, mounted as the second stage, plus an additional rocket on the top as final stage with the bomb on board. The entire assembly was about fifty-seven feet tall, a massive vehicle to launch from the deck of a ship rolling in the open ocean, and it was remarkable that all three shots were launched without mishap.

The site selected for the first firing (as announced later) was only forty-eight miles southeast of Tristan de Cunha, a group of volcanic islands deep in the South Atlantic. It was chosen, not only for secrecy and safety, but because of the weakness of the earth's magnetism in that region. The hypothetical magnet in the heart of the earth is displaced several hundred miles in the general direction of Guam. Hence, in the opposite direction, near Rio de Janeiro, the magnetic intensity is less than anywhere else on the surface of the earth (less than .250 oersteds), and near Tristan de Cunha it is still very low (less than .300 oersteds), while in northern Siberia it reaches .630 oersteds. This weakness of the field over the South Atlantic was expected to increase by a large margin the number of particles that would be trapped as the result of an explosion only 300 miles up.

On August 27, 1958, the *Norton Sound* was at its assigned position near Tristan de Cunha. The closest island, Nightingale, was occupied only by multitudes of sea birds, although islanders occasionally went there in their canvas boats to fetch eggs and guano. Some 4800 miles to the north the *Albemarle* lay tossing in the ocean, its large radar trained toward a point in the heavens still 400 miles farther north where, it was thought, an artificial aurora might appear. The ship was placed there, rather than under the expected display, because its radar beam could obtain an echo from an auroral curtain only by hitting it at right angles.

At the airfield on the Azores two pot-bellied Air Force transports (C-97 stratocruisers) were poised, each with radio equipment for sounding the ionosphere as well as other devices. On land, in the Azores, were riometers—receivers that listen to radio noise emitted by the cosmos. They would record any changes in radio transparency of the atmosphere. Similar receivers were switched on in Spain and on the ships. There were all-sky cameras, photometers, magnetometers, and other devices in operation at key points. At Cape Canaveral a launching crew stood by a tall five-stage rocket, set to fly up 500 miles in a path tilted eastward about 20° from the vertical. Similar vehicles stood ready at Ramey Air Force Base in Puerto Rico and at the NASA Pilotless Aircraft Test Station on Wallops Island, off the Virginia coast. At the Cape and on the island of Antigua great parabolic dish antennas sixty feet wide were aimed aloft to track the observing rockets and record their radio accounts of what they detected. At Stanford University, in California, scientists were recording the signal strengths of very low frequency (VLF) radio stations in Japan and Seattle. Others in Spain did the same for signals from a powerful British station. Likewise the Navy ships had their electronic ears cocked in various directions.

At approximately 2:30 A.M., Greenwich Time, when the few residents of Tristan de Cunha were presumably asleep, the *Norton Sound* fired its bomb-bearing rocket 300 miles into space. There was a dazzling flash; then auroral streamers shot out, both upward and downward along the arc of magnetic force.

Less than a minute later, at a point in the sky 5000 miles to the north, the *Albemarle's* radar detected another auroral display. The predictions of Christofilos had been brilliantly confirmed.

The *Norton Sound* moved more than 800 miles farther south for the next two shots. The nominal height of all three, as given at the symposium on April 29, 1959, was 300 miles, with a yield between one and two kilotons. The "approximate" Greenwich Time and position were tabulated as:

Aug. 27, 1958 (2:30 A.M.) Long. 12° West, Lat. 38° South
Aug. 30, 1958 (3:20 A.M.) Long. 8° West, Lat. 50° South
Sept. 6, 1958 (10:10 P.M.) Long. 10° West, Lat. 50° South

Although all three bursts produced brilliant auroras at the southern end of the magnetic arc, the only unmistakable visual display in the North Atlantic followed the final Argus shot (which also produced the thickest and longest-lasting shell). This aurora began near the horizon as a blue-green spear of light that climbed behind a cloud, then reappeared above it. So brilliant was the display that, when hidden, it outlined the fringes of the cloud as does a full moon. At this point the radar on the *Albemarle* picked it up at a range of 500 miles. A scientist, standing near the ship's stern, said the first light appeared about half a minute after the explosion had occurred a fifth of the way around the world. He was sure of this, since he had just set his watch by radio time signal from Washington.[13] Although the display seemed, from the ship, to start near the horizon, this was an illusion that resulted from the curvature of the earth. It probably lay between 150 and 350 miles aloft.[14] Its red crown suggested that protons or heavy ions from the atomic explosion may have flown along the magnetic arc, in addition to the expected electrons.

The first Argus explosion was fired at such a point in space that the electron shell it produced was superimposed upon the inner Van Allen belt of natural radiation. Nevertheless it was clearly detected by Explorer IV. After the *Norton Sound* had moved south, the next two shots injected their shells in the comparatively clear area between the two natural belts and hence they remained visible for a longer period of their decay.

However on September 4, five days after the second shot, the first two shells faded away sharply. There was a severe magnetic storm that day, and it was assumed that this upset the trapping mechanism or increased atmospheric density near the northern and southern extremities of the shells, causing the particles to collide frequently and fall from orbit. The third shell, created two days later, could still be observed by Explorer IV on occasional favorable passes when its flow of data ended about September 21.

When Pioneer III was fired at the moon on December 6 it detected a "probable" residuum of the shell, but none was observed by Pioneer IV on March 3, 1959. Thus the third shell seems to have survived at least fourteen weeks.

Explorer IV wove in and out of the shells many hundreds of times during its transmission lifetime, but only some 160 passes were detected. On other penetrations the satellite was either out of radio range or else it poked through the shells where they were too weak to be detectable. The tally of observed intersections was as follows:

Burst	No. in Northern Hemisphere	No. in Southern Hemisphere	Observation period
ARGUS I	28	9	Aug. 27–Sept. 6
ARGUS II	27	12	Aug. 30–Sept. 6
ARGUS III	61	27	Sept. 6–21

The shells remained remarkably constant in position and did not thicken with age, although they naturally weakened in intensity. Van Allen and his men also found that, the higher Explorer IV was when it pierced a shell, the greater the number of trapped electrons it encountered. This meant that a large part of the particles had been injected into the magnetic field at altitudes much greater than those of the bomb explosions. This was because the electrons were not produced directly by the burst. Rather they resulted from the radioactive decay of fission fragments hurled upward by the blast and themselves spiraling around the magnetic force line. Such particles, usually within a few minutes, emitted an electron which itself became trapped.[15]

Plotting of the shell showed that the shape of the earth's magnetic field in space was quite close to predictions. The auroral display in the area some 200 miles west of the Azores was estimated to be within less than sixty-five miles of its predicted site.[16]

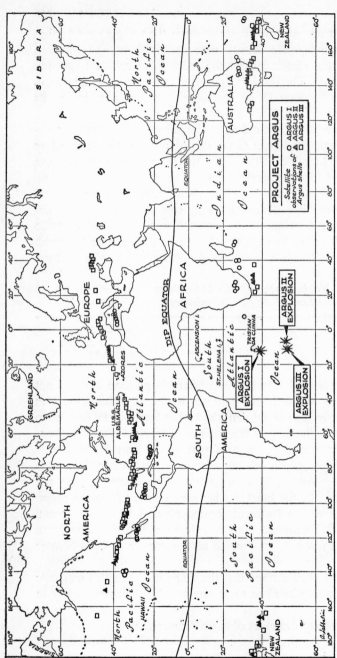

PROJECT ARGUS

Satellite
observations of ○ ARGUS I
Argus shells △ ARGUS II
□ ARGUS III

ARGUS I
EXPLOSION

ARGUS II
EXPLOSION

ARGUS III
EXPLOSION

The three electron shells with which Project Argus enveloped the world extended out about 4000 miles around the magnetic "dip equator." However, shaped by the earth's magnetic field, they curved in close to the earth along lines north and south of that equator, as shown by the satellite observations recorded on this map. The data obtained over the Soviet Union was recorded from Explorer IV by sta-

tions in West Germany. There were large gaps in satellite observations in the Southern Hemisphere. Although the *Albermarle* lay almost directly under the area where Explorer IV observed the shells, the aurora seen from the ship was several hundred miles farther north, where the sloping shells descended to the atmosphere.

The shells were believed to extend out about 4000 miles from the earth's surface, although they could be observed by Explorer IV and the Jason rockets only at much lower altitudes. It was calculated that, to account for the observed decay rate, the traces of atmosphere at 1000 kilometers (621 miles) elevation must be ten times as dense as previously believed.

Before and during the lifetimes of the first two shells, Jason rockets were pitched into the sky from three points, all aimed to fall into the area between Bermuda and Florida. One of them, however, flew from Wallops Island over Norfolk, Virginia, and down the coast of the Carolinas, plunging into the sea fifty miles southeast of the mouth of the Savannah River.

The rocket combination in Project Jason used the Army's Honest John, a twenty-mile missile, as the first stage. Nike boosters served as the second and third stages, a Recruit as the fourth stage, and a T-55 carrying a fifty-pound payload as fifth stage. Its instruments consisted of eight Geiger tubes, shielded and aimed in various ways to obtain information on the energy and direction of the radiation. They were protected during ascent through the atmosphere by a cone that was jettisoned some 400,000 feet up. A commutator sampled the output of each tube five times a second, the duration of each sampling being 1/75th of a second.

The opening shot of the Jason program was fired from Cape Canaveral on August 15, twelve days before the first Argus explosion. Its task was to map the natural radiation in advance, so that whatever was added by Argus would be readily identifiable. To their amazement, the Jason scientists found that there was already a barely detectable shell of artificially injected electrons around the earth.

This was presumably produced either by the Orange explosion, less than three days earlier, or by Teak, which had taken place fifteen days before but had been almost twice as high. Its elevation of almost forty-eight miles was still far too low for efficient injection, but, being a hydrogen bomb of devastating force, it could have sent particles flying upward to decay and inject electrons at much greater altitude. Two subsequent Jason shots, fired from Florida on August 27 and September 2, also apparently detected trapped radiation from the Pacific shots.[17]

The first Jason rocket launched after the initial Argus blast was sent up from Canaveral an hour and three minutes after the explosion and soared to 582 miles, higher than any other rocket of the project. All nineteen vehicles of the program had been fired before the final Argus burst, thirteen of them successfully.

The shell produced by the first explosion was expected to lie farther south than the planned impact area and only three rockets were aimed at it, one of which failed. Another, from Puerto Rico, apparently pierced the shell. The second Argus radiation shell, however, hung above the Carolina-Georgia coast and hence was an easy target for the rockets fired from Wallops Island.

The first successful Wallops shot was launched twenty-eight minutes after Argus II, the second bomb exploded over the South Atlantic. After thirteen minutes of flight, the rocket's Geiger counters reported to the ground that it had pierced the shell over a point west of Savannah and south of Cape Hatteras. The missilemen at Cape Canaveral sought to aim their shots in that direction, but aircraft in the heavily traveled East Coast airlanes made this impossible. Hence, although all five of the Wallops Island firings hit the target, those from the south were unable to do so. Ramey Air Force Base, in Puerto Rico, got off only two shots in six tries, due to rocket and telemetry troubles.

The rockets from Wallops observed the shell over a period of some eighty-eight hours. It seemed fixed in space, as though on an invisible scaffold, its thickness a constant twelve miles.[18] If it moved at all, the distance was no greater than five miles. During that period the trapped electrons—the stuff of which the shell was made—spiraled back and forth between North and South more than a million times and, migrating eastward, made more than a hundred trips around the world.

The Air Force physicists who studied the Jason results suggested that the trapped electrons were gradually drained out of the shell by an intense slump in the strength of the earth's magnetism over Capetown. This, they said, would sufficiently lower the mirror points (where the electrons reverse course and head north again) so that the electrons would tend to hit particles of air and drop out of orbit.

The aircraft observations, based at the Azores, were badly hampered by weather, although they were not completely fruitless. In one case an ionospheric sounder, mounted in one of the aircraft, recorded the passing of an ionized cloud (known as "sporadic-*E*") which was apparently an Argus by-product, although the plane never left the ground.

The idea proposed by Ney and Kellogg that an atomic burst in space might produce a crack-the-whip effect in the earth's magnetic field and shake loose some of the trapped radiation appears to have been substantiated. Two minutes after Argus II, Explorer IV—then southeast of Bermuda and a few hundred miles west of the explosion meridian—detected a small but definite radiation effect. The eastward-migrating shell of electrons could not have encircled the earth that fast; for this reason and from detailed study of the properties of this radiation one of Van Allen's associates, Carl McIlwain, has attributed this effect to the dumping of naturally present, trapped protons from higher up.[19]

The possibility of wave motions in the earth's magnetic field had also been thought of by the Argus scientists. Since they were expected primarily to follow the lines of magnetic force from the South to the North Atlantic, a number of special recorders were set up in the Azores, including a wire coil encircling an area the size of a football field. These instruments recorded evidence of such waves after all but the first explosion, when the effect may have been lost in fluctuations resulting from a natural magnetic disturbance. What was remarkable, however, was that these waves apparently shot out in all directions. Instead of merely following the high arches of the earth's magnetic field, they also seem to have been channeled within layers at the highest levels of the atmosphere, so that they traveled along direct routes parallel to the earth's surface. During the previous months the Army's Signal Research and Development Laboratory had completed two sets of immense loops designed to observe magnetic waves on frequencies as low as one cycle per second. One, in the Kaibab National Forest south of the Grand Canyon in Arizona, enclosed twenty-six square miles. It consisted of two-conductor telephone wire laid on the ground and connected to form a two-turn loop. This gave the device an effective area of fifty-two square miles.

In the Wharton Tract of Burlington County, New Jersey, two similar loops were laid out with effective areas of twelve and twenty-three square miles. Both regions were remote from power lines or other sources of interference. From the beginning of August until completion of the Argus experiment all three were operated continuously except when animals or vehicles broke the wires.

Within four seconds after the third explosion the resulting pulse was recorded in Arizona and a second pulse followed at twenty seconds. Assuming the waves traveled via an upper-air route, the initial wave covered the distance at about 3700 miles per second. Comparable results were obtained in New Jersey, and a check of magnetic records in Iceland, Sweden, Maine, Africa, and Antarctica confirmed the world-wide nature of the effect. It was calculated that the initial wave followed a path 1000 miles above the earth and that the route of the second was 1500 miles aloft.[20]

While American researchers made public the travel times of these impulses, they were not allowed to specify the starting time (that is, the precise moment of the blast) or the moment of arrival at each station. It was for the Russians to disclose this "secret" information. Valeria A. Troitskaya, secretary of the Soviet IGY committee and a well-known authority on rapid fluctuations of the earth's magnetism, found that all of the Argus shots and the explosion of the second Johnston Island hydrogen bomb had been recorded by some or all of a dozen Soviet stations. The latter were scattered across the full width of the USSR and were also at such remote sites as Spitsbergen and Oazis in Antarctica. Carefully avoiding political comment, she described Argus, in her 1960 report, as a remarkable experiment. However, she reported that the approximate times given by the United States were well off the mark.

Thus the needle on the earth current recorder at Alushta on the Black Sea jiggled at 10 hours, 12 minutes, and 34 seconds, GMT, on September 6, indicating, she said, that the explosion had taken place a fraction of a second earlier, whereas the official time for that explosion was 10:10 P.M. Mme. Troitskaya reported that the travel times for the initial pulses appeared to equal those of light waves, or were almost that fast—contrary to accepted theory for wave motions in a magnetic field. The pulse from this, the final Argus shot, was received at nine Soviet stations, from Sakhalin to Spitsbergen, within a recorded span of three seconds. Allowing for instrument errors, she estimated that the actual receipt was simultaneous to within a fraction of a second.

Further analysis of the Argus results, she said, "will undoubtedly shed light on the mechanism exciting a number of natural types of electromagnetic disturbances." The Johnston Island shot, fired below the ionosphere, resulted in a single "splash" effect, observed at Oazis, at Petropavlovsk on the Pacific Ocean, at Alma Ata in Central Asia, and at Borok north of Moscow. The times all fell within two seconds.

The Argus shots each produced a series of rhythmic pulses that, in some cases, lasted twenty minutes. The patterns varied from one shot to the next, apparently because a magnetic storm altered the ionosphere. In all cases the observations were made with recorders that detected tiny electric currents induced in the crust of the earth by

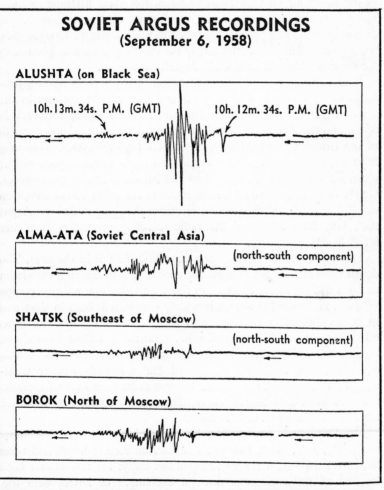

Earth current observations of the final Argus explosion. The four stations recorded the effect within less than a second of each other, the estimated error in each case being a half second or less. (V. A. Troitskaya. Adapted by *The New York Times*)

corresponding currents and magnetic activity in the sky. She did not suggest that the explosions were recognized as such before they became public knowledge.[21]

Of concern to such American projects as the missile-monitoring satellite was the extent to which Argus affected the radio transparency of the upper air on various frequencies. Receivers listening to radio noise from the cosmos in Spain, the Azores, on the *Albemarle,* and on a ship in the firing area were tuned to 30, 60, and 120 megacycles. They observed no effect after any of the shots—presumably good news for those working on an antimissile defense system.

It was known that variations of signal intensity from distant, low-frequency broadcasts were a good indicator of disturbances in the ionosphere. After the second and third Argus shots, receivers in Spain and the Azores recorded an abrupt drop in the signal strength of the British station GBZ, operating on 19.6 kilocycles. This may have been due to absorption of the signals in lower regions of the upper air that had been ionized by the heavier particles from Argus. On the other hand, a slight improvement in reception was observed on circuits across the Pacific, where electrons dropping out of the Argus shell may have improved the radio-reflecting properties of higher levels in the ionosphere.

The explosions apparently produced little fallout in the area. The debris from nuclear blasts in nearby space must, eventually, fall victim to the earth's gravity, apart from those particles that achieve escape velocity. However the fallout is widely distributed, both in time and in geography. Peter A. Day, who succeeded G. Francis Harris as administrator on Tristan de Cunha, reported a fallout increase of roughly three times between early summer and October, 1958, but, according to analysts of the United States Atomic Energy Commission, this was not significant. There was an even sharper increase recorded in July at Buenos Aires, although no bombs had exploded anywhere in that part of the world.

Mr. Day—and, presumably, his fellow islanders—did not know until July, 1960, that, two years earlier, an atomic bomb had been fired over a position roughly sixty miles away. He and Harris both learned of the explosions through exchanges of letters with the author. Although Day's reply was dated July 26, 1960, he explained that the mail would not leave the island until late October, "owing to our extreme isolation."

In a lecture early in 1960 at Ohio State University, Van Allen said that Argus could perhaps be described as "one of the greatest experiments in pure science ever conducted." He spoke out strongly against its secrecy, which he termed "a masterpiece of administrative stupidity," for when the project finally became known, it appeared to be "a sinister sort of military experiment," instead of the great scientific achievement that it was.[22]

One of its most brilliant successes was the precision with which the participants predicted the global effects that followed the explosions. These included:

1. The shape and location of each shell in space, based on the position of the bomb burst.

2. The length of time it would take for a shell to form (roughly one hour).

3. The shell thickness (which remained unchanged, for each shell, throughout virtually the entire period of observation).[23]

4. The longevity of the effect.

5. The energy spectrum and intensities of particles in the shell.

6. The direction from which the spiraling particles would strike the rocketborne Geiger counters.

7. Hydromagnetic waves, traveling thousands of miles in a few seconds.

8. The location and extent of the auroral displays. (Too heavy an injection of particles would have produced a shell of such density that the auroral displays would have spread around the world, spanning the entire Soviet Union).

The confirmation of these predictions was an intellectual triumph, but the real wonder of Argus was the grandeur of an experiment that enveloped almost the entire planet and was carried out successfully after only four months of preparations, making use of satellite techniques that, less than a year before, had been beyond human experience. Even without its dramatic manifestations, Argus seemed assured of an important place in the history of science.

CHAPTER 9
ELECTRIC WINDS

At most points on the earth, north as shown by the compass is not quite the same at noon as it is at midnight. Such twenty-four-hour variations in the direction and intensity of the earth's magnetism are slight, but the cycles are strikingly uniform from day to day. Furthermore, the pattern varies from place to place. The variations are more marked in daytime, in summer, and at sunspot maximum than at night, in winter, or at sunspot minimum.

A first step toward a satisfactory explanation was made by Gauss, who suggested early in the nineteenth century that there might be changing electric currents in the sky. But what could produce such currents? In 1882 the Scotsman, Balfour Stewart, in an article on terrestrial magnetism for the *Encyclopaedia Britannica,* proposed that there is a great dynamo in the sky. It is remarkable that a concept so far in advance of its time should first have appeared in a non-scientific publication. Stewart postulated the existence of an ionosphere and introduced the dynamo theory, which has since been refined and, in large measure, confirmed.

The engine which drives this "dynamo" is the tidal movement of the upper atmosphere. On the surface of the earth we can easily observe the rise and fall of the sea; by studying daily changes in air pressure over many years it can be shown that the ocean of air also has its tides. The higher layers of the atmosphere move up and down a mile or more. Since the air particles are ionized at that height, their movement back and forth across the lines of magnetic force acts as a dynamo, generating great horizontally flowing sheet currents of electricity.

Whereas the moon's gravity is the primary factor in producing ocean tides on earth, the sun is chiefly responsible for tidal movements of the air. This is because the sun's rays have the added effect of heating the atmosphere, causing it to swell. Hence the great current patterns remain oriented toward the sun, traveling around the world with the westward march of noontime. The effect is to produce a daily cycle of magnetic variation at any one point on the earth.

In 1932 it was noticed, from records kept at the observatory of the Carnegie Institution of Washington at Huancayo, Peru, that the daily magnetic variations are extremely marked. A check of observations in Togoland and Uganda showed somewhat similar results. In each case the station was on or near the magnetic equator. It was therefore proposed that the circulating systems of electricity in the Northern and Southern hemispheres are of opposite symmetry, coming together at the equator to form a strong flow from west to east at about 11 A.M. local time. The puzzling thing was that the intensity was double what would be expected from this pattern. The current was christened by Chapman the Equatorial Electrojet.

During the IGY some 190 magnetic observatories, scattered over the entire globe, kept continuous records that should make it possible to map the current patterns in detail. The development of rockets also offered an opportunity for on-the-spot verification of these electric winds in the sky.

The first such attempt was made before the IGY, in March, 1949, when the USS *Norton Sound* launched three Aerobees in the Pacific Ocean some 1000 miles west of Huancayo. This was more than nine years before that ship played its central role in Argus. One of the rockets carried radiation detectors provided by Van Allen. The other two each carried, in addition, a magnetometer, prepared by Fred Singer and two Navy scientists to enable them to detect the Electrojet. The first shot missed it, but the ship moved sixty miles to the southeast for the next try, on March 22, and an abrupt change in magnetism was recorded at a height of fifty-eight miles. When the rocket rounded the summit of its flight path some sixty-five miles up, it seemed to be close to the top of the jet. Singer and his associates felt they had proved the existence of the Electrojet and had thus confirmed the dynamo theory. Nevertheless, because of various observational difficulties, they reported that the information obtained was "insufficient for detailed conclusions." [1]

The device carried by the Aerobees was a flux-gate magnetometer of limited sensitivity, but, by the beginning of the IGY, nuclear physics had provided a far more sensitive instrument for measuring weak magnetic fields: the proton precession magnetometer.[2] Van Allen's men in Iowa went to work to design a rugged, miniature version of this device to be flown in rockoons so that current patterns in the sky could be explored. From August 5 through November 10, 1957, they fired (or tried to fire) fifty-four rockoons from positions ranging from near Thule, in northern Greenland, to the fringes of the pack ice off

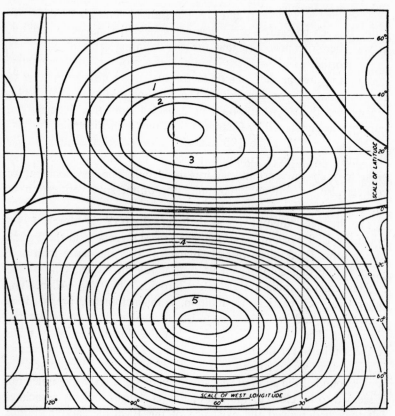

Electric currents in the sky postulated in 1935, showing the pattern when the sun is on the geographic equator over northern Brazil (almost at the center of the map). Europe and Africa are on the right edge of the map; the west coast of the United States is on the upper left margin. The pattern was based on observations in 1923 of diurnal magnetic changes at Agincourt, near Toronto (*1*), Cheltenham, near Washington, D.C. (*2*), Vieques, Puerto Rico (*3*), Huancayo, Peru (*4*), and Pilar, Argentina (*5*). (Drawn by A. G. McNish, who points out that the pattern now appears to be far more compressed toward the equator.)

Antarctica. Of these shots, twenty-three carried the new magnetometers. If a sheet current were pierced, a sharp change in magnetic readings was expected to tell the tale. The other thirty shots were instrumented for measuring radiation—either cosmic rays, or the radiation already detected by rockoons near the auroral zones, or both.

The first phase of the program was carried out between Virginia and northern Greenland aboard the USS *Plymouth Rock,* an ungainly looking craft known as a Landing Ship Dock, which could inflate a large balloon on its helicopter flight deck and release it to hoist a slender research rocket into the sky. During August, 1957, the second month of the IGY, it sent up eighteen of these rockoons. Four did not fire; the telemetering system in three others failed or died prematurely; and the instruments froze or malfunctioned in another three shots, leaving seven flights that produced good-to-excellent data (plus one that, at last report, was still being processed). In the infant art of rocketry this was about par for the course.

One of these shots, launched between Greenland and Baffin Island during a magnetic storm on August 6, pierced a sheet current flowing across the polar cap, as had been predicted by theorists. It was observed between fifty-six and sixty-two miles overhead, moving in what was thought to be a southwest direction at 11 amperes per square kilometer.[3]

Hardly a month after the return of the *Plymouth Rock* a new batch of rockoons (using modified Loki II rockets) went to sea from Boston on the icebreaker *Glacier,* bound for Antarctica. Altogether, thirty-six shots were attempted. Seven did not fire; two ran amok; six were lost track of due to equipment failures; and one was hurled into the sea at launching by a sudden squall. It was on this voyage that the Iowa group detected a region of intense radiation near the Antarctic comparable to that observed off southern Greenland. The regions proved later to be the lower rims of the outer Van Allen belt.

The operation also sought to confirm the existence of the Equatorial Electrojet. In planning the IGY, emphasis had been placed on problem areas such as the poles, earth-sun relations—and the Electrojet. It was to be attacked on several fronts. A closely spaced chain of observatories was set up along the west coast of South America, spanning the path of the Electrojet.[4] In the mid-Pacific another chain was set up on three of the most remote fragments of land in the world: Fanning, Palmyra, and Jarvis islands. They, too, lay in a north-south line across the assumed location of the Electrojet and, farther west, similar observations were made on Koror Island. Finally the *Glacier* was diverted from its journey toward the Antarctic so that a series of rockoons could be fired in the vicinity of Jarvis and its two neighboring islands. This would make it possible to fit results from high in the sky into the daily pattern of magnetic variations observed at the islands.

The establishment and maintenance of these stations was no easy task. Jarvis is a far cry from the classic picture of a South Sea island. It is a treeless hump of sand and coral two miles long and fifteen feet high, whose only contribution to past generations had been sea-bird guano, periodically collected there as fertilizer.

The Scripps Institution of Oceanography at La Jolla, California, which was given the task of setting up the stations, found a remark-able man to do the job: Martin Vitousek, a young mathematician for whom the call of the South Seas was stronger than that of the campus. He had a doctorate in philosophy from Stanford University and had taught at the University of Hawaii, but in the words of Roger Revelle, the head of Scripps, "He decided he would rather be a South Sea Island trader than a university professor."

About six years before the IGY, while still in his twenties, Vitousek bought a seventy-foot schooner and sailed between the coconut islands, picking up copra as well as carrying moving-picture crews and other passengers. Revelle put him in charge of establishing and running the three stations and he not only saw that the job was done, but threw in a few research projects of his own.

When the *Glacier* reached the area in October, 1957, Vitousek told the ship by radio that observations ashore placed the Electrojet nearer Jarvis than to the other two stations. The icebreaker thereupon made ten attempts to shoot through the current. The shots, fired between October 14 and 20, 1957, were spaced along a north-south line of more than 650 miles to be sure to straddle the target. The northern-most and southernmost of the six successful shots observed nothing unusual. The magnetic intensity decreased as the rocket soared, and increased as it fell, in a smooth manner.

On October 17, a balloon-borne rocket was sent aloft from the icebreaker's helicopter flight deck into a region thought to be well north of the Electrojet, but when radioed data from the rocket was examined, it was found that there was an abrupt change in magnetic readings at a height of sixty-five miles, indicating penetration of a current sheet, or electric wind. Two and a half miles higher the rocket emerged from the current and continued on to seventy-eight miles without detecting anything further. The striking thing was that the changes in magnetism produced by the current were in the direction opposite those expected from the postulated west-to-east flow. Apparently a counterjet had been discovered, so thin and weak in relation to the Electrojet itself that it had not been detected from the ground. The same observations were made by the rocket on its return plunge into the sea.

Shortly after noon the next day a rockoon was aimed at the bull's-eye. The ship was thirty miles northwest of Jarvis Island and the launching was timed to coincide with the expected midday maximum in the current. An hour and thirteen minutes after the crew let the balloon go, a barometric pressure switch fired the dangling rocket and, at a height of sixty miles, it entered the main current. At sixty-eight miles the readings had returned almost to normal, but at seventy-two miles a new sheet of electricity was penetrated and when the rocket reached its summit of seventy-six miles it still had not completely pierced this upper current. Another flight southwest of Jarvis rose to eighty miles and pierced both layers, apparently reaching, or approaching, the top of the upper current. The latter was slightly higher than in the previous shot, and the intensities of both currents were much greater.[5]

When Laurence J. Cahill, Jr., one of Van Allen's associates, published the results in 1959 he pointed out that many questions remained to be answered. How many electric ribbons were, in fact, wrapped around the earth, one above the other? Two had been detected, but it seemed quite possible that there were others, higher up (perhaps alternating in direction and thus canceling each other out in terms of their effect on magnetic instruments below). Why was there more than one? Cahill suggested that one might lie at the height of maximum conductivity and that the other might be due to clouds of ionization, known as "sporadic-E" because they appear in the E layer of the atmosphere. Finally, why was the intensity of the current double what was expected from theoretical computations? Cahill and others suspected that it might be because of extreme conductivity of the atmosphere where the magnetic field lies precisely transverse to the direction of the current.

Two peculiar phenomena were thought to exist high over the equator. One was sporadic-*E* (at a height of about seventy miles) and the other was "spread-*F*" (above 125 miles), both apparently consisting of ionized clouds dense enough to reflect radio waves. Their periodic appearances were obviously part of the complex machinery of earth-sun relationships.

It was suspected that such clouds accounted for the strange propagation of very high frequency (VHF) radio signals across equatorial regions. Normally transmissions above about 30 megacycles per second are not reflected by the ionosphere. They go out into space and are lost. The same rule applies to signals traveling the other way —from a satellite to the earth—and it was for this reason that the Russians picked 20 and 40 megacycles for the early Sputniks; the higher frequency would come through reliably, whereas the lower one would serve as a sensitive indicator of conditions in the ionosphere. Likewise, a number of VHF bands had been allocated to radio amateurs with the expectation that their chatter would not be reflected back to earth.

However, in August, 1947, amateurs in Mexico City and Buenos Aires, 5500 miles apart, found to their delight that on some evenings they could communicate with each other on 50 megacycles. They reported their discovery and, during the next four years, the amateur operator's journal, *QST,* told of other such instances. Then there was a lapse in these unusual propagations until they began to reappear in 1955. There seemed little question that the effect was dependent upon sunspot activity. It was observed along many routes: The desperate messages of policemen on revolt-torn Cyprus (on 70 to 72 megacycles) were clearly heard in Rhodesia in southern Africa. Television Channel 4 in Caracas, Venezuela, traveled the length of South America to Argentina. Radio "hams" in Australia or New Guinea heard their counterparts in Japan, and vice versa. The striking thing about these propagation paths was that in all cases their midpoints lay roughly on the magnetic equator. Furthermore such transmissions almost invariably were at their best when the hour, at the point where the path crossed the equator, was between 9 and 10 P.M. Likewise the effect seemed strongest at the equinoxes.

Radio amateurs have a long tradition of public service, be it the relaying of emergency messages or the improvement of radio technology. They volunteered to help in the IGY by observing this "transequatorial scatter" in a systematic fashion (and at their own expense), submitting their reports to the American Radio Relay League in West Hartford, Connecticut, which punched the information onto cards for machine analysis. Hundreds of amateurs took part, many of them standing watch much of the night. Some transmitted continuous beacon signals so that their distant colleagues could observe the hourly changes in signal strength.[6]

American professionals made a similar study between the Philippines and Okinawa and an elaborate program was carried out in South America, centered on five closely spaced stations in Ecuador and Peru.[7] To see what was responsible for the effect, vertical radio soundings were made continuously at these points and it was found that at Huancayo, almost directly on the magnetic equator, clouds of sporadic-E were overhead more than 65 per cent of the time; yet at Chiclayo, less than 500 miles to the north, the figure was about 5 per cent. From the sounders it appeared that the clouds were about thirteen miles thick; IGY rocket shots through E-layer clouds over North America showed them to be only a mile thick. The equatorial clouds may therefore be of a fundamentally different nature. They persisted throughout daylight on most days, but sometimes in the early afternoon would vanish suddenly for periods ranging from a few minutes to several hours. These disappearances seemed to keep step with the phases of the moon.[8]

The E-layer clouds were presumably too low to provide mirrors that could account for the long-range transmissions across the equator, although they were found to make possible shorter reflection paths. Furthermore, they were a daylight phenomenon, whereas the long hops were made at night. The latter, it was felt, must be due to the newly discovered phenomenon known as spread-F, thought to consist of cigar-shaped blobs of ionization elongated along magnetic force lines in the lofty F layer of the ionosphere. Only at the magnetic equator are these force lines parallel to the earth's surface and hence such clouds would serve as particularly efficient mirrors in that region.

To search for them, a more widespread network of sending and receiving stations was necessary. The United States National Bureau of Standards undertook to fill gaps where local radio facilities were inadequate—for example at Trujillo, an oasis in the coastal desert of Peru. Four electronic trailers were fitted out and, after some of them had been tested in the Middle West and had been floated down the

Mississippi by barge to New Orleans, they were shipped and hauled to their destinations.

The network of stations, all working in the neighborhood of 50 megacycles, was as follows:

Senders	Receivers	Expected reflecting layer
Arequipa, Peru	Trujillo, Peru	E
Antofagasta, Chile	Guayaquil, Ecuador	F
	Huancayo, Peru	E
	Clorinda, Argentina	E
	São Paulo, Brazil	F
Huancayo, Peru	Guayaquil, Ecuador	E

The circuits from Chile to Brazil and Argentina were designed to compare east-west propagation with that on the north-south routes. A study of the results showed that, when the vertical sounder at Huancayo detected sporadic-*E* overhead, the signals on all six circuits usually were good, suggesting that the low clouds (sporadic-*E*) and the high ones (spread-*F*) were all part of the same mechanism. The Electrojet was also clearly involved, for when it was most intense (as reflected in the horizontal strength of the magnetic field at Huancayo), communications between Arequipa and Trujillo were at their best. Huancayo lies midway between those points. Another finding of the study was that magnetic storms wiped out the beneficial effects of these equatorial clouds and electric winds.

Thus, thanks to a multitude of observations, carried out by hundreds of amateurs and professionals—rockets fired into the sky, magnetic readings on desolate islands, ionospheric soundings from the spine of the Andes, and radio observations in a score of nations—the perplexing phenomena encircling the equator came to be better known, although a complete understanding of their unity must await further observation, speculation, and study.

CHAPTER 10
FLARE PATROL

The sun is the source of our warmth, energy, and light. The power in the gasoline that moves our cars or in the coal that generates our electricity came originally from the sun. Its gravity holds the earth in orbit and its nuclear ferment makes life possible on our planet. Its atmosphere is a region of wild processes that seem to generate temperatures far higher than those of the sun's own core. Great bubbles of light, dwarfing the earth in size, burst in this superheated region, sending out radiation that creates violent disturbances in the earth's atmosphere.

When the sun is viewed through a filtered telescope or through a coronograph, it is an awesome sight. Glowing material races outward at speeds of 1000 miles a second, then arches back. Flames materialize 100,000 miles above the sun, raining down upon it like waterfalls of fire. Although we are the slaves of this fiery genie, we have been unable to explain the many things we see there; we are a long way from understanding this rather average star, whose daily reappearance is to us a symbol of youth, joy, and the rebirth of life. During the IGY the first concerted effort was made to observe the sun continuously, at observatories around the world, keeping records of its various changing and eruptive features as well as recording the earthly phenomena apparently dependent upon them.

Galileo's sunspot drawings, made with his new telescope in 1612, inaugurated a watch on the sun that has traced a succession of sunspot cycles with an average duration of about eleven years. At the maximum the sun is extensively flecked with spots; during the minimum period hardly any are to be seen. This eleven-year pattern has become a scapegoat for many terrestrial problems. It has been related to the breeding rates of Canadian rabbits and Atlantic salmon, the frequency of meningitis, the quality of vintages, and the occurrence of boom-and-bust economic cycles. While scientists have ridiculed such suggestions, some of them believe there may be other effects. It has been reported that at sunspot maximum temperatures are lower in rainy areas of the tropics. IGY mapping of weather at 30,000 feet produced what some regard as evidence of a direct link between solar eruptions and storm paths. An apparent eleven-year cycle in the width of Arizona tree rings has been attributed to the sensitivity of trees, as antennas, to radio emissions from the sun. A scientist who analyzed yarn breakages in New England cotton mills found a link he attributed to sun-induced electrical phenomena. Some scientists in Europe have reported that the precipitation rate of bismuth oxychloride from a suspension varies with the solar cycle. While such relationships are controversial, magnetic and auroral records leave no doubt that a broad range of geophysical effects is directly controlled by the level of sunspot activity.

In 1908 George Ellery Hale of the Mount Wilson Observatory in California noticed that lines in the spectrum of light emitted by sunspots were split in a way that could be caused only by very strong magnetic fields. The analysis of light from other parts of the sun showed that it has an over-all field, like that of the earth, which is far weaker than the magnetism characteristic of sunspots. When the moon hides the sun's blinding light in a total eclipse, a luminous halo known as the *corona* can be seen. Its pattern varies, but at sunspot minimum it is reminiscent of the classic picture of the earth's magnetic field: tufts fan out into space from the two magnetic poles and, in between, there is a suggestion of arching lines such as those in which the Van Allen belt is entrapped.

Perhaps the strangest discovery has been that, every eleven years, the sun does a magnetic handspring. Its north pole (magnetically) becomes its south pole and vice versa. Some believe that, in the distant past, similar changes of polarity have occurred on the earth, but why they should take place is not known.

The sun is presumably heated by a thermonuclear process somewhat similar to that in the hydrogen bomb. The core of the sun is thought to consist of hydrogen gas compressed to ten times the density of steel and heated to 27 million degrees. At such temperatures the atoms are completely ionized—that is, their nuclei have been stripped of electrons. In the solar furnace four of these hydrogen nuclei (protons) are thought to combine to form one helium nucleus, leaving a surplus of matter that is released as a burst of energy. An estimated 564 million tons of hydrogen are fed into this furnace every second, producing 560 million tons of helium. The remaining 4 million tons are largely converted into energy spanning the full spectrum from X rays only about one angstrom in wavelength (a hundred-millionth of a centimeter) to very low frequency radio waves more than a mile long. At these extremes the radiation varies from hour to hour, but the output of light and heat, nearer the center of the spectrum, is very steady. Hence weather is primarily (if not entirely) due to events within the atmosphere—not beyond it.

This output of solar radiation is known as the *solar constant* and various attempts have been made to see how constant it really is. The trouble is that changes in the transparency of the atmosphere are so great that they mask any variations in solar output. Shortly before the IGY an ingenious method was devised at the Lowell Observatory near Flagstaff, Arizona. This consisted of measuring, simultaneously, the brightness of sunlit planets and neighboring stars. The stars provided the standard of comparison. Any variation in transparency of the atmosphere would affect the light both from the planet (in effect, sunlight) and from the star, canceling out this source of error. From 1953 to 1958 a record of comparative brightness was kept on two of the outer planets, Uranus and Neptune, and sixteen nearby stars. The observing was done in blue light, on the ground that this portion of the spectrum was particularly sensitive to heat changes at the source. During that five-year period the sun was found to have become roughly 2 per cent brighter. In the heavens are many pulsating (variable) stars whose light intensities change radically in cyclic periods that range from a few hours to many months. Some now regard our sun as a variable star and look to these changes as an explanation for the ice ages. The difficulty, in this respect, is that the successive ice ages of the last million years seem to have been the exception, rather than the rule, in the great span of the earth's history.

One of the most puzzling features of the sun is the high temperature of its outer atmosphere, or corona, in relation to the temperature of the solar surface that we see. The visible disk of the sun is at about 10,000° (compared to the 1200° of a blast furnace), but the corona temperature is believed to be 2 million degrees. This seems to defy some of our most fundamental laws of physics. The temperature of the corona should be less than that of the sun's visible surface, which is under greater pressure. As one solar physicist puts it, "We can prove it can't be so; but there it is."

The visible surface of the sun is a changing map with many types of phenomena making up its topography. The best known are the spots, for anyone with a pair of binoculars can see them—without being blinded—by aiming an eyepiece so that the solar image is thrown onto a shaded piece of paper. Their "blackness" is due to their low temperature in relation to the area surrounding them, but they, too, are emitters of light. Because of their appearance, they were once regarded as the vortices of solar cyclones. They look like holes into which cooler material is subsiding, in contrast to the upwelling of the bright areas near them, but their nature is still uncertain.

Surrounding the spots are glowing "storm" areas (*plages*) and brilliant gas clouds (*faculae*). All that we see on the sun is on a gargantuan scale and a sunspot may be 10,000 miles wide. Viewed in light from narrow bands of the spectrum, features can be seen that are crowded out by the brilliance of unfiltered sunlight. In the light of calcium it looks like a great, mottled orange. In the red light of hydrogen it is a glowing ball with bright patches, black spots, and dark filaments that snake across part of its surface. When the sun rotates so that these filaments are seen on the rim, they stand up like mighty fences, or fountains of fire tens of thousands of miles high (quiescent prominences).

Such prominences on the rim could not normally be seen until, in 1930, the Frenchman Bernard Ferdinand Lyot set up a new instrument at an observatory 9300 feet above sea level on the Pic du Midi in the Pyrenees. Known as a coronagraph, it consisted of a telescope in which the blinding disk of the sun was artificially eclipsed. This enabled Lyot to take moving pictures of what was going on above the sun's rim. The results were breathtaking. Brilliant "surges" shot out at almost incredible speed, vanishing into space. Other geysers of fire curved back into the sun, seemingly along magnetic lines of force.

Even more important, from our point of view, are the flares. These are solar events of cataclysmic suddenness and magnitude. Within a period ranging from less than a minute to ten minutes or more they spread over an area of 100 million to 1 billion square miles and to a height of about 50,000 miles. They then take from twenty minutes to more than two hours to fade away. Their chief brilliance is in certain portions of the spectrum, such as the red light of hydrogen, known as *hydrogen-alpha,* in which they are ten times as bright as the rest of the sun. Hence they are only rarely seen with ordinary telescopes, a notable exception being the original sighting by Carrington cited in Chapter 7. Flares occur most frequently in the neighborhood of a sunspot cluster.

Other solar features are longer-lasting. Sunspots may endure for an entire rotation of the sun. Being gaseous, the sun does not rotate in the manner of a solid body. Spots near its equator make the trip around more rapidly than those in higher latitudes, the average rotation time, as seen from the earth, being roughly twenty-seven days. It has long been observed that some magnetic disturbances on earth occur in a twenty-seven-day cycle. Apparently there are semipermanent locations on the sun that squirt out particles, like water from a lawn sprinkler, in a manner that sweeps the earth once every trip around.

With the approach of the minimum in the eleven-year cycle the spots appear in lower and lower latitudes, whereupon, as a prelude to recovery, they suddenly begin to show up in high latitudes again—a symmetry of behavior as mysterious as it is magnificent.

Interest has focused on the flares because they usually are followed by dramatic changes on the earth. One group of effects occurs at the instant the flare is seen, a result of radiation that moves at the speed of light. Something, at such moments, "sunburns" the lower ionosphere in the D region, producing dense ionization. The invariable result is a radio blackout, throughout the sunlit hemisphere of the earth, on the high frequencies used for air-to-ground, ship-to-shore, and long-range international communications. At the same time, a "crochet" appears on magnetic records in the daylight part of the world, due apparently to a sudden intensification of sheet currents, caused by the added ionization and a resulting increase in atmospheric conductivity.

These blackouts last from a few minutes to an hour and completely halt most radio circuits. One of the IGY objectives was to find out what caused them. Probably the favorite explanation for this sudden sunburning, prior to the IGY, was a form of ultraviolet radiation that lies on the same side of the light spectrum as that which scalds the unwary beach-lover. Known as *Lyman-alpha,* it is a characteristic emission of hydrogen. It does not penetrate to the earth's surface, but appears to be responsible for a large portion of normal upper-air ionization. Early rocket experiments had hinted that—unlike most sunlight, which was steady—Lyman-alpha radiation might vary radically. Some also suspected that X rays generated in flares were responsible for some of the ionization.

While major flares produce flash effects as soon as their light reaches the earth, they are not always followed by magnetic storms and related phenomena, such as auroral displays and earth currents. Likewise the lag, before the storm, varies between twelve and thirty-six hours. Thus, in addition to emitting radiation that travels at the speed of light, reaching the earth in eight minutes, at least some flares squirt out particles that take a day or two to make the trip. The variations in travel time and the failure of the particles, on many occasions, to reach the earth at all, suggests that they fan out in a manner that sometimes misses the earth and sometimes reaches it by a curved path.

IGY observation of the sun was subdivided and various observatories were given the task of collecting world-wide data on specific parts of the solar picture. Thus, for example, the Swiss Federal Observatory in Zurich intensified its traditional work of cataloguing the numbers of sunspots, using photographs sent in by twenty-one observatories; the Fraunhofer Institute in Freiburg, Germany, collected information for daily maps of the chromosphere—the layer of the sun's atmosphere immediately below the corona and seemingly the birthplace of flares; information on plages was assembled by the observatory at Arcetri, Galileo's old home near Florence; records on surges were compiled by the High Altitude Observatory at the University of Colorado, and those on flare photometry at the Crimean Astrophysical Observatory in the Soviet Union.

Because flares are the key to so many effects on earth, forty-four stations watched for them during the IGY, in most cases photographing the sun automatically every thirty seconds in the red light characteristic of hydrogen. The flare-watchers were spread around the world so that the sun would never set on the network, and they were distributed in latitude in the hope that, if one was clouded over, another would have a clear view. Thus they ranged from Japan to India, from Sweden to Australia; six were in the United States and Hawaii; ten spanned the great width of the Soviet Union. More than 6700 flares of Class 1 or above were reported to World Data Center C, at the Meudon Observatory in France.[1]

Photography did not give an instantaneous warning of a flare, since the film had to be developed, but another method did: the monitoring of radio emissions from the sun. While a good deal of solar radiation, at radio frequencies, is absorbed in the atmosphere of the earth—and to some extent of the sun—certain wavelengths come through with special strength. Perhaps the strongest is at 200 megacycles. This emission seems to originate in the upper chromosphere and has been traced to the cascades of fire sometimes seen in that region. When a flare erupts in the chromosphere, there is a great burst of radiation on this frequency. In the winter of 1942 British radar operators, watching for a renewal of the aerial attacks on London, were perplexed by a strange sort of jamming that they at first blamed on the Germans. The true source was soon found to be eruptions on the sun. Some thirty IGY stations monitored the sun on 200 megacycles with small, dish-shaped antennas that followed it in its daily course across the sky. One of them, at Alert in the Canadian Arctic, was able to keep a continuous watch during the summer period of perpetual daylight.

One of the more remarkable projects of the IGY was the Rocket Flare Patrol, carried out on San Nicolas Island within the United States Navy's Point Mugu missile range on the California coast. The objective was to launch rockets during the brief flash of a solar flare to see what it was that sunburned the atmosphere and caused radio blackouts. The problem was to get a rocket into the sky fast enough to catch the fleeting phenomenon. In the summer of 1956, before the IGY, an attempt was made to do this by hanging a Deacon rocket from a balloon on top of the atmosphere and waiting for a flare. From the USS *Colonial,* stationed off the west coast of Central America, a rockoon was sent aloft every morning, equipped so that it could be fired by remote radio control from the ship. The trouble was that flares were infrequent and the wind, in a few hours, carried the rockoon beyond operating range. Despite these difficulties and the usual rocketry troubles, one shot out of ten tries was partially successful. It reached the upper atmosphere ten minutes after the flare began and found evidence of abnormal X rays. No increase in Lyman-alpha was observed. The flare, however, was so small that it produced no radio blackout and, at the time of the observation, had almost faded from sight (as seen in the red light of hydrogen). Hence the results were regarded as inconclusive.

The IGY Rocket Flare Patrol, organized like a fire department, made constructive use of a by-product of the trend toward "pushbutton" warfare. This was the Nike antiaircraft rocket, designed to be kept on the alert for prolonged periods. Its booster served as the first stage and a Deacon was used as the second stage. The resulting combination, known as a Dan, could be launched within one minute and could be kept in readiness for days, awaiting a big flare. Fourteen were allocated to the program and all but one were fired during the summer of 1957. Three observatories agreed to send immediate notification of a flare to the launching site, eighty miles to seaward off Los Angeles. They were the Mount Wilson Observatory in California, the Sacramento Peak Observatory at a point appropriately named Sunspot, New Mexico, and the High Altitude Observatory in Colorado. Furthermore the men on San Nicolas Island kept radio receivers tuned to stations in various directions to obtain the earliest possible warning of a flare effect. When there was a sudden fading of radio reception, they hurried to the rocket stand and usually, within a few minutes, messages from the mountaintop observatories would report a flare.

During most of that summer the launching crew of half a dozen men spent eleven hours a day, seven days a week, on the pad. Each morning, as the sun came up, they armed the rocket igniters and then stood by. At sundown they disconnected the igniters as a safety measure, and headed for their camp.

Ten times during those months they pressed the launch button after receiving notification of a flare, holding their fire only long enough to make sure that a major eruption was in progress. The other three shots were fired when the sun was quiet to provide a basis for comparison. All told, five shots failed to reach the ionosphere and battery failure on another one prevented receipt of its observations, leaving seven that sent useful data. As the program drew to a close, a dazzling Class 3+ flare—the fiercest variety—erupted and the rocket crew jumped to its posts. The Nike booster pushed the Deacon upper stage high into the sky, but the latter failed to ignite and tumbled into the sea. The big chance might have been lost, but fortunately a second rocket assembly was being mounted and was fired less than twelve minutes later. This time all went well and it sent back the most exciting information of all the shots.

What it disclosed was a dramatic intensification and "hardening" of X rays from the sun. Hardening means an increase in rays of short wavelength. In this flare X rays with waves as short as two angstroms were detected. These hard rays are more penetrating and the rocket encountered them at 39.5 miles—a lower elevation than during any of the flares previously observed in the program. None of the shots detected an increase in Lyman-alpha, although Herbert Friedman of the Naval Research Laboratory, who was in charge of the project, conceded that there might be a burst of this form of ultraviolet radiation at the start of a flare, since the rockets were not on the scene at that time. Nevertheless he placed the blame for flare-induced blackouts squarely on X rays.

He and his colleagues also estimated that, to produce the short-wave rays that they had detected, temperatures of perhaps 18 million degrees were necessary in the corona over a flare. Further rocket shots in the summer following the IGY led the NRL group to revise this figure upward to 180 million—seven times hotter than the estimated temperature at the core of the sun.

In announcing the detection of X rays indicating such temperatures, the National Academy of Sciences pointed out that Sputnik III had been instrumented for X ray detection, but had not seen any such radiation, even during a series of strong flares. "The reason the Russian scientists did not observe these emissions," the Academy said, "was that the sensitivity of their equipment was not great enough. . . ." [2] Although highly penetrating, the rays were extremely scarce at the shorter wavelengths, and this was where the carefully designed X-ray counters carried by the rockets paid off. On each of the four flights that sent data during a flare, strong emissions were observed.

It has been proposed that electrons near the sun may be accelerated by rapid changes of magnetic field strength until their speed is a substantial fraction of the speed of light. They may then become trapped in Van Allen-type belts above sunspots until, when a flare erupts, the magnetic fields are squeezed in a manner that pinches the flying electrons and produces extremely high temperatures. If, in fact, the "hard" X rays are produced by a pinch effect, this means that nature has achieved what scientists have been striving for since the first hydrogen bomb was exploded. This is the production of temperatures high enough to tame the hydrogen bomb, through a controlled thermonuclear reaction, giving man, on earth, the virtually unlimited power now generated on the sun. [3]

CHAPTER 11
ECLIPSE

When a new instrument of research or vehicle of exploration is developed, new discoveries come in rapid succession for those fortunate enough to be the first to use them. Herbert Friedman and his fellow scientists at the Naval Research Laboratory had used rockets to see what happens at the time of a solar flare. Now a new opportunity presented itself. On October 12, 1958, the moon was due to pass between the earth and the sun, casting a narrow shadow that would sweep across the South Pacific from north of the Solomon Islands to a point inland from Santiago, Chile. The eclipse, being total, would do what no man-made instrument can achieve—completely obscure the light and other radiation from the sun's disk. Lyot's coronagraph, which artificially eclipses the sun, cuts off only part of the light. The rest is scattered by the atmosphere, making it impossible to see the faint, plumelike outer corona.

The moon performs the same function as the coronagraph except that, being out in space, it cuts off the light before it is scattered. A total eclipse also does something else no man-made instrument is capable of: like a mighty curtain drawn slowly across the face of the sun, it provides an opportunity to record what happens as various parts of the sun and its atmosphere—including large sunspots—are obscured. With rockets it might be possible to find out where the X rays and Lyman-alpha rays are generated.

The eclipse offered opportunities for many other studies, including observation of the rarely seen light of the corona. The result was what is said to have been the largest and most elaborate eclipse expedition in history. Satisfactory observations could not be made from South America, since the sun would be setting when eclipsed there. The only other bits of land along the shadow path were a few pinpoint islands. The United States picked Pukapuka atoll (also known as the Danger Islands), a necklace of three islets threaded on a coral reef that encloses a three-mile-wide lagoon. It is administered by New Zealand. Farther west a British-New Zealand expedition set up its instruments on the island of Atofu, while Japanese scientists landed to the east on Suwarrow Island.

The USS *Point Defiance,* a sister ship of the Landing Ship Dock, *Plymouth Rock,* that had served as a rockoon launcher off Greenland, unloaded five teams of scientists at the atoll many weeks before the eclipse. Being able, by partial submergence, to launch ungainly landing barges, as well as rockets and helicopters, the ship could send instruments into the sky and ferry them ashore over coral reefs. As in many wartime amphibious operations, frogmen blasted a channel through the reef so that a small detachment of Marines could drive the barges into the quiet waters of the lagoon.

The selected observation site was on Motu Kavata, one of the two uninhabited islands of the atoll. There were three Polynesian villages on Pukapuka, largest of the islands. One of these farmed the coconut trees on Motu Kavata (copra being the chief export of the atoll), another village farmed the trees on Pukapuka, and the third tended those on the other unoccupied island, Motu Koe.

Although the launching area was forty miles northeast of Pukapuka, the rockets were picked up and mounted in the quiet waters of Pago Pago harbor in Samoa, some 400 miles to the southwest. There, in the jungle-draped crater of an extinct volcano that has been breached by the sea, the ship could be kept steady for such a delicate and risky operation. The rocket combination, which had never before been fired from shipboard, consisted of a Nike booster, which lifted the vehicle one mile in its three-second burning time, and an Asp rocket that then coasted upward, on its own, to 40,000 feet before igniting. In six seconds of firing it lifted its seventy-five-pound payload to 150 miles.

Two test firings were carried out before the eclipse, one of which was a success, sending back information on radiation from the uneclipsed sun that could be used as a basis for comparison.

For the eclipse observation, six rockets were mounted on the forward end of the flight deck. They were tilted slightly to fire out over the stern and, to cancel the effect of the ship's roll, were wired so that, once the firing switch was closed, they would not ignite until the ship came to an even keel. The chief problem was to fire them so that they would be in the moon's shadow at the top of their trajectory.

This was somewhat like trying to shoot through the top of a thunderhead. The shadow was an elongated cone moving rapidly east. The ship, its stern bristling with rockets like a hedgehog's tail, placed itself ahead of the oncoming shadow, turned its stern toward the target, and prepared to open fire.

On the day of the eclipse there were a number of sunspots close to the eastern edge of the solar disk. It was therefore decided to fire the first rocket ten minutes before totality so that the speckled eastern crescent of the sun would still be exposed. Since each flight lasted about eight minutes, this first shot would observe the sun during the final minutes before its fulminating eastern edge was covered, furnishing data that could be compared with the results of the next two firings that were to see the sun totally eclipsed.

A tropical downpour swept over the ship as the critical moment neared, but it halted soon enough for the firing crew to send the first rocket roaring up through the turbulent cloud cover. The rocket was soon out of sight, and the sun itself was invisible, but clouds were no impediment, as telemetering antennas, mounted on the ship's three-inch guns, were aimed at that part of the heavens from which the rocket was sending its information. The incoming signals were wired to a van on the well deck, where they were fed into oscillographs and tape recorders. Ten minutes after the initial shot, two rockets were sent up less than a minute apart, aimed to pierce the cone of darkness some 120 miles above the sea to the west, remain within it to their summit at 150 miles, then emerge from the shadow during their plunge to the ocean. The fourth rocket was launched ten minutes after the two shots aimed at the shadow. By this time the eclipse had reached the ship's position and those on board caught a brief glimpse of it through the clouds. The first four vehicles proved highly reliable, reaching heights estimated at 139, 148, 152, and 150 miles. The fifth and sixth shots were to follow at ten-minute intervals, but when the switch was closed to turn on the instrumentation of the fifth rocket, thirty seconds before firing time, nothing happened. With time running out, the crew tried to fire the sixth rocket, but the same thing happened.

The firing crew rushed out from sheltered observation points to see what was wrong. They found that the blast of the earlier shots had loosened the connections. One rocket was readied within eight minutes and was fired immediately. The last was held for the next day and, by a stroke of luck, was aloft when a flare occurred.

Recorded radio signals from the two rockets that pierced the cone of darkness showed that, within a few seconds after they entered the shadow, the Lyman-alpha radiation had dropped to almost zero (.05 per cent). On the other hand, roughly 10 per cent of the X rays detectable in broad sunlight could be observed throughout totality.[1] Furthermore, the rockets that watched the sun as its rim vanished and as it reappeared reported a strong X-ray emission from the edges, indicating that the sun is ringed by a halo of intense X rays.

The implications were that Lyman-alpha emanates from the sun itself, whereas X rays are produced, at least in part, higher in the solar atmosphere.

One of the most surprising results was that, in the cone of darkness high over the Pacific, electronic eyes carried by the rockets were blinded by what, to them, was a brilliant light. One of these devices, known as a photocell, peered out the side of each rocket, reporting light intensity so that it would be possible to determine the spin rate and aim at any moment of the flight. The photocells designed to observe within the moon's shadow were made sensitive to visible light equal to half that of a full moon, but they were heavily overexposed whenever they looked upward. This could have been due to airglow (discussed in Chapter 14), but airglow would be expected below a rocket at that elevation—not above it.

Meanwhile, the scientists ashore on Motu Kavata had made painstaking and elaborate preparations for the eclipse. Instruments had been mounted on concrete pedestals to avoid vibration and had been tested, checked, and rechecked to avert any mishap during the few precious moments of totality. Some of the spectroscopic observations made use of movie-style film.

As the time approached, a group of brown-skinned, wide-eyed Polynesian boys stood and watched the final preparations. The scientists watched the sky, which looked anything but promising. Perhaps the ominous weather preoccupied them, for when they came to thread fresh film into their instruments, they found test film was still on the take-up reels. It might have been a serious problem, but help was at hand. The barefoot boys were given one end of the worthless film and told to run. With shouts of glee they raced across the island, spirals of film flying after them. In almost no time at all the reels were cleared and threaded with the fresh film.

But the boys might as well have saved their breath. The scientists stood forlornly and watched the clouds above them. Here and there shafts of sunlight broke through and struck the distant sea. At the critical time the sky blackened, but no hole appeared in the sun's direction. After journeying halfway around the world and setting up their optical instruments with all possible care, they had to go home empty-handed.

The other two expeditions were more fortunate. On Atofu the British and New Zealanders had clear skies and on Suwarrow the clouds parted at the last moment for the Japanese.

Not all the American experiments ashore were frustrated. Those which used radio signals to study changes in the ionosphere were not affected by clouds. These observations were carried out by a team from the High Altitude and Sacramento Peak observatories that used devices especially developed for indirect detection of flares. One of these consisted of a radio receiver listening to cosmic noise —the emissions generated in various parts of our own galaxy and in other galaxies. It was tuned to 18.5 megacycles, so close to the critical frequency of the upper atmosphere that the loudness of cosmic noise is highly sensitive to changes in upper-air ionization. A sudden drop in signal strength normally means that a flare has sunburned the upper atmosphere. The chief interest, in this experiment, was to see what would happen when sunlight was suddenly closed off from the ionosphere. It was thought there would be a sharp drop in ionization of the E layer and hence a sudden jump in the intensity of cosmic noise, but this did not prove to be the case. It may, therefore, be that the E layer is produced primarily by X rays (which were not entirely cut off during the eclipse) rather than by ultraviolet, as many had supposed.[2]

This was not the only solar eclipse of the IGY. There were two others. On October 23, 1957, there was a total eclipse that touched a small part of Antarctica, where the British, at Halley Bay, attempted some observations, but extensive studies were out of the question. The other was an annular eclipse—one in which the moon's elliptical orbit does not bring it near enough the earth to obscure the solar disk completely. At the maximum of such an eclipse the moon is ringed by a thin rim of sunlight so that observation of the outer corona is impossible. Nevertheless, on April 19, 1958, the movement of the moon across the sun's face offered another chance to see what happened as active sunspot groups were obscured, one by one. All three of the IGY eclipses were, in fact, regarded as of sufficient importance to have the date of each designated a Regular World Day for intensive observations.

The April 19 eclipse could be seen from China, Hawaii, and Alaska and an expedition consisting of thirty-one Chinese and twenty-two Soviet specialists was organized to observe it from Hainan Island, off southeast China. They set up seven radio telescopes, observing on a number of frequencies, in the hope that the curtainlike action of the moon would make it possible to pluck, from the chaos of solar radio noise, those emissions coming from the chromosphere above sunspots.

The expedition reported that, as the moon covered various parts of the solar disk, there were sharp drops in radio signals on 9375, 9091, 6667, and 5882 megacycles, but none on the higher frequencies of 37,500 and 150,000 megacycles. It had been expected that the noise sources would prove to be diffuse areas over each spot cluster, but instead the emissions came from distinct points in the "sky" over these areas. Two of the sources were to one side of the sun and, it was thought, might be above active sunspot clusters on the far side.

There was also a particularly strong emission from the edge of the sun on 6667 megacycles, calling to mind the strong X rays seen in the same area by American rockets a few months later. Perhaps both are generated in the solar atmosphere and are therefore "brightest" when looking along the side of the sun through a maximum volume of atmosphere.

Another result of the Hainan observations was to show that the peculiar nature of the magnetism in sunspots extends into the sky above them. Analysis of light from sunspots had shown that they tend to form in pairs, one positive and one negative. Most remarkable of all, the pairs have an order of march dependent upon the sunspot cycle. During one cycle the eastern spot in the northern hemisphere of the sun will be "north," magnetically, and the western spot will be "south," whereas the order in the southern hemisphere is the other way around; but when the sun does its magnetic flip-flop, about every eleven years, the entire pattern is reversed. In 1957 Harold and Horace Babcock, in California, detected a polarity shift in the sun's south pole, but its north pole did not change until the next year, so that for a time the sun had two positive poles. On Hainan the polarity of radio signals from above the spots was analyzed and it was found that the magnetic characteristics of each spot extended high above it.

The Chinese members of the expedition concentrated on optical observations, but were somewhat hampered when clouds swept across the sun close to the moment of maximum. A three-day seminar was held afterward in Peking to review the observations and these discussions—as well as the eclipse itself—seem to have been decisive in persuading the Academia Sinica to embark on a program of radio astronomy.[3]

CHAPTER 12
THE GREAT CLOUD

At exactly 8:26 P.M. New York time, February 11, 1958, the earth sailed into a gigantic cloud of electrified solar gas. If the human organs of balance and orientation depended upon magnetism rather than gravity, every man in the world would have been dizzy, yet a large portion of this planet's population sat or slept comfortably at home, unaware of what was going on. In fact, the public would have been completely unaware of it had the resulting magnetic storm not been one of the most severe on record. Sheets of light enveloped the night side of the earth, moving from the poles almost to the equator. The Toronto area of Canada was suddenly darkened as circuit-breakers cut off electric power. Lights flickered in farmhouses from Minnesota to Montana. Radio communications between Europe and North America were completely severed. The pilot of a large Air Force plane, headed across desolate ice fields and stormy seas toward Antarctica, found himself isolated; he could communicate with no one, either to report distress or safety. An estimated 100 airliners in flight across the Atlantic were in somewhat the same predicament. Mighty electric currents flowed under the oceans, and radiation near the earth, as recorded in the low part of its orbit by Explorer I, tripled in intensity.

The recording of this event on a global scale was one of the major achievements of the IGY. As with the thorough examination of a patient—making use of electrocardiograms, a half-dozen laboratory tests, and direct observation—the mass of assembled information may make it possible to diagnose more accurately the exact nature of a magnetic storm.

It had all begun at 4:08 P.M. EST two days earlier, when the sun was over the Pacific Ocean between the Americas and Hawaii. At that moment the Honolulu Observatory sighted a flare close to the central meridian of the sun. Honolulu reported to the World Warning Agency in Virginia that the flare was Class 2—a big one, although not in the most spectacular Class 3 category. At about the same time a scientist at the Sacramento Peak Observatory in New Mexico was watching the sun in a narrow band of the light spectrum, his attention focused on a cluster of sunspots and other symptoms of activity just below and to the left of the center. The group covered three billion square miles and was rated one of the ten largest on record since systematic sunspot observations had begun eighty years earlier. The region was obviously fuming for seven small flares already had been seen there that day.

Suddenly a new flare appeared. This time it kept on growing. Bright filaments lighted up nearby. Hurriedly the observer notified the High Altitude Observatory in Colorado, whose director, Walter Orr Roberts, was in charge of American sun-watching during the IGY. "Looks as if it'll go Class Two or Two-plus, and it's still rising," he cried over the special radio circuit linking the two observatories.

Meanwhile, in a remote valley of the Davis Mountains in West Texas, screened by 1500-foot mountain walls from man-made radio interference, a parabolic antenna twenty-eight feet in diameter was following the sun in its march across the sky. It had been doing so faithfully every day since it went into operation, seventeen months earlier, under Air Force auspices, as the Radio Astronomy Station of the Harvard College Observatory. Instead of watching the sun on a single radio frequency, it did so with three receivers, each sweeping across a portion of the radio spectrum three times a second. As a result, the antenna was monitoring the sun's radio emissions on all frequencies from 100 to 580 megacycles. This technique, devised by J. P. Wild in Australia, painted pictures of solar eruptions in terms of time and radio wavelength. The radio outbreaks thus recorded fell into four distinctive categories, the most impressive of which was the "continuum outburst"—a roar of radio emission on almost the full span of recorded frequencies, usually lasting an hour or two.

Three minutes before the February 9 flare this observatory began detecting sporadic bursts of radio noise. Thirty-two minutes after the flare an intense continuum outburst began that lasted, unbroken, for sixty-six minutes. Alan Maxwell, the observatory director, classed it "magnitude major plus." At the High Altitude Observatory, in Colorado, the sky was overcast, but its antennas could hear the radio storm and the same was true in Ottawa, Canada.

At the World Warning Agency in Virginia a decision had to be made whether to call a Special World Interval (SWI). Because of the ominous appearance of the sun a few hours before the flare, the World Warning Agency had sent a code message to all sixty-six nations taking part in the IGY: *ALBEG,* meaning "Alert begins." It was the nineteenth such alert of the IGY. But was there a solar cloud actually on the way toward the earth?

Solar science was not sufficiently precise, at that time, to give an answer. The flare had not been of the largest type. In fact, since the start of the IGY, there had been forty flares of the larger Class 3 variety, but only seven SWIs had been called.[1] Each SWI was a strain on scientific budgets and they had to be rationed with care. The World Warning Agency therefore decided not to call an SWI. In fact, two and a half hours before the magnetic onslaught, forecasters associated with the center predicted that transatlantic radio transmission was to be fair to good during the next six hours.

A preliminary analysis of the events that followed the February 9 flare has been carried out by John R. Winckler and his associates at the University of Minnesota. The storm was summarized by the author in *The New York Times* and, in greater detail, by John Brooks in the *New Yorker* magazine. A procession of scientific papers has dealt with its specific manifestations. The sequence that has emerged was as follows (in New York time):

Between 7:30 and 8 P.M., February 10, there was a slight indication of an increase in cosmic-ray intensity as recorded at Climax, atop the Rocky Mountains in Colorado; on Mount Washington, in New Hampshire; and at Deep River, Canada. This may have been due to the "splashing" of cosmic rays off the approaching cloud.

Between 8:15 and 8:25 P.M. a sudden though small (1 per cent) decrease in cosmic ray intensity was recorded at the same points.[2]

At 8:26 P.M. the storm actually began with a slight jiggle of recording needles on magnetic instruments in many lands. This is known as a "sudden commencement" and is remarkable for its world-wide simultaneity. The precise observations of the IGY showed, however, that the jiggles were not actually simultaneous. They tended to take place first near the poles. In this case the first observations were in Alaska and Antarctica, and some thirty seconds later were recorded at stations nearer the equator. In all cases the jumps were in the horizontal intensity of the earth's magnetism.[3]

At 8:59 P.M. the intensity increased so rapidly that the rapid-run magnetograph at the Fredericksburg Observatory in Virginia could not keep up with it. At the Geophysical Institute in Alaska the needle of a similar instrument swept right off the page. Presumably this was the moment when the gas cloud first met the earth's magnetic field. At the same time electric currents began flowing through the earth.

During the next minute radio contact on all circuits used by the American Telephone and Telegraph Company between Europe and the United States, as well as those of its competitors, faded into oblivion. Clearly the ionosphere over the Atlantic was in a state of turmoil and would not reflect the signals. As a backstop against such emergencies the radio companies use equatorial stations to establish triangular circuits that by-pass the storm area. Thus RCA Communications hurriedly routed its London and Paris traffic via Tangier in North Africa.

At 9 P.M. a remarkable blood-red aurora began to spread over the skies of Canada and the northern United States, so brilliant that it could be seen through cloud cover. At the same time stations throughout the world recorded a 4 per cent to 6 per cent drop in cosmic-ray intensity. Such decreases, a mysterious concomittant of about 20 per cent of magnetic storms, are known as Forbush decreases, for the man who discovered them, Scott E. Forbush of the Carnegie Institution of Washington. They appear to be due to the immersion of the earth in a cloud of solar gas whose magnetism diverts the rays, but the effect persists, to a slowly diminishing degree, long after the cloud has passed. In this case recovery was not yet half completed four days after the storm. Furthermore, despite the storm's record-breaking intensity, the decrease was not as great as that accompanying many run-of-the-mill magnetic disturbances. Thus, whatever it was that made this storm severe apparently did not control the cosmic-ray decrease.

At 9:01 P.M. traffic over Western Union's transatlantic submarine cables began to be seriously interrupted by earth currents. The gigantic sheets of electricity generated in the sky by the arrival of the cloud had their counterparts within the earth. The electric potential between Europe and North America rose rapidly.

At 9:02 P.M. the Bell System's North Atlantic telephone cable between Oban, Scotland, and Clarenville, Newfoundland, showed a potential of 2650 volts, with such polarity as to drive the current from

The CSAGI Bureau—the IGY's international board of directors. Left to right: Beloussov of the USSR, Berkner of the U.S.A., Nicolet of Belgium, Coulomb of France, and Chapman of Britain.

A landing barge, lower left, discharges onto the beach at Cape Hallett during resupply of that joint New Zealand–American IGY station in Antarctica by the U.S. Coast Guard icebreaker Eastwind. *The icebergs forward of the ship are aground.*

Upper left: *The payload of Sputnik II protruding from what appears to be the nose cone of the rocket that placed it in orbit. The canister at the top contains solar radiation scanners. The sphere below it is, in effect, a duplicate of Sputnik I. Beneath that, with what appears to be a porthole, is the tank that carried the dog.*

Upper right: *Laika, the first space traveler, in the tank in which she rode into orbit aboard Sputnik II. This picture, originally published in* Pravda, *was subsequently retouched.*

Below: *What is believed to be a twin of Sputnik III, held in reserve in case a second launching attempt was necessary, on display in Moscow.*

The first photograph of the six-inch sphere of Vanguard I taken by the Baker-Nunn camera at Organ Pass, New Mexico, on January 10, 1959. The shutter was held open for 19.3 seconds as the camera swept the sky to reduce the motion of the satellite. This captured enough light for an exposure, but caused stars to appear as horizontal streaks. The heavy line is 12 Triangulae. Breaks in the diagonal line formed by Vanguard I are probably due to its rotation. The cameras, one of which is shown below, observed this sphere at ranges up to 2,500 miles—equivalent to photographing a .30-caliber bullet at 200 miles.

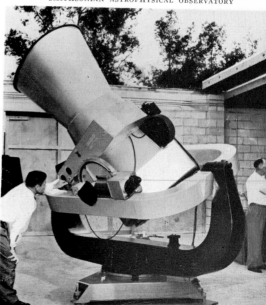

Vanguard I, smallest, yet one of the most productive, of IGY satellites, stands exposed atop its launching rocket shortly before its enclosure in the nose cone and its firing from Cape Canaveral on March 17, 1958. The spikes protruding from the little sphere are antennas.

Launching the first United States satellite, Explorer I, on the night of January 31, 1958. The tub of rockets at the top, including the needle-like final stage, is spinning at some 400 r.p.m. Ice, coating the frigid tank of liquid oxygen, is slipping away as the great rocket rises from the pad.

The largest antenna available for tracking IGY satellites was this radio telescope at Jodrell Bank in England. Its "dish" is 250 feet wide.

An Aerobee rocket is fired at Fort Churchill, Canada, packed with 19 grenades that were successively shot out its nose as a test of upper-air wind and temperature. The launching frame is tilted to correct for crosswinds and the servicing area is enclosed as protection against the Arctic winter.

In the midday dusk of the total eclipse in 1958 a rocket soars from the U.S.S. Point Defiance to make the first observation of such an event outside the earth's atmosphere.

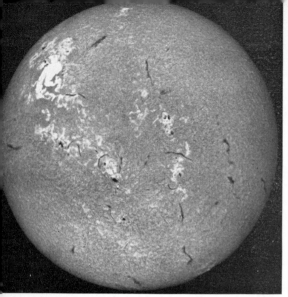

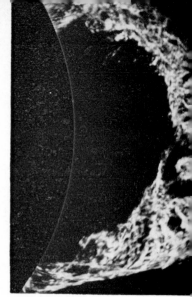

LOCKHEED SOLAR OBSERVATORY

HARVARD COLLEGE OBSERVATORY, CLIMAX, COLORADO

Upper right: *Probably the most dramatic solar event ever photographed: a gigantic prominence arching out from the sun's rim as seen with a coronagraph.*

Upper left: *The sun, photographed in the red light emitted by hydrogen, showing a Class 3+ flare (white area) in eruption on May 10, 1959. The light areas are plages; dark lines are filaments; specks are sunspots.*

Lower left: *A midwinter watch on the sun is kept by the observatory atop the Pic du Midi in the French Pyrenees. It was from this dome that Lyot first observed the dynamic events on the rim of the sun with his coronagraph.*

U.S. NAVY

Above: *Launching a rockoon from the* Glacier *in the Antarctic pack. The rocket hangs, needle-like, just above the men on the flight deck.*

Lower right: *Window on the heavens at the South Pole. Snow that has drifted flush with the roofs of the station reaches unbroken to the horizon. Within the plastic dome is the all-sky camera used to photograph the aurora.*

Lower left: *Aboard the icebreaker* Glacier *James A. Van Allen checks out electronics on one of his rockoons before it is fired into the Antarctic sky. These shots, launched in 1957, detected the southern rim of the radiation belts.*

OFFICIAL U.S. NAVY PHOTO   ARLO LANDOLT, NATIONAL ACADEMY OF SCIENCES

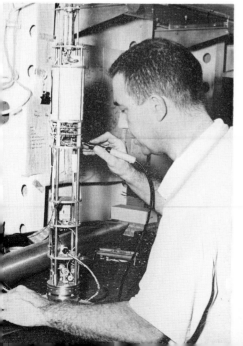

The zodiacal light, photographed from Chacaltaya by D. E. Blackwell and M. F. Ingham. It is probably sunlit dust near the earth's orbit. Above the snowy Andes, west of the observatory, star tracks formed during the ten-minute exposure are almost vertical, showing the nearness to the Equator.

Curtains of auroral light hang over College, Alaska, site of the Geophysical Institute which is one of the World Data Centers for auroral observations.

west to east. The result was that American voices, heard in Europe, were weak or squawking.

At 9:09 P.M. the current under the Atlantic reached a new peak, but in the opposite direction. The storm also produced about 250 volts in the cable linking Alaska with the state of Washington, a line about one-third the length of the transatlantic cables. The California-Hawaii cable was not noticeably affected. Thus the current system seems to have been centered over northeastern North America, although disrupting land-line communications as far east as Holland and Sweden. In North America the currents were playing havoc with power systems, imparting to them sudden overloads that tripped the circuit-breakers installed as a safety measure. Bolts of lightning often have the same effect, but only for an instant. When circuit-breakers tripped at transformer stations in the Toronto area, the community was suddenly thrown into darkness, except for the red auroral glow overhead. F. W. Lachicotte, operations officer of the Missouri River Basin Project power system, serving western Minnesota, the Dakotas, and eastern Montana, said the storm's effect on his electric net was "startling." As described by Brooks in his *New Yorker* account, "the men operating the system, practically none of whom had had any previous encounters with a magnetic storm, were amazed at what was going on backstage; some unseen hand seemed to have taken charge of their equipment, causing violent fluctuations of voltage, which brought the automatic regulators clicking into operation to compensate." [4]

At 9:45 P.M. American Telephone and Telegraph lost radio contact with its stations in South America.

At 10 P.M. RCA found it could no longer relay to Europe via Tangier, but tried to keep one jump ahead of the spreading storm by shifting farther south, to Paramaribo on the coast of Surinam, north of Brazil.

At about 11 P.M. the relay via Paramaribo died and for the next hour and a half all circuits between Europe and North America were at a standstill, including such vital links as those which announced the departures and safe arrivals of passenger aircraft. Planes could communicate with each other and with the ground so long as they were within line-of-sight range of each other, but without a smooth ionosphere they could not send or receive messages around the curvature of the earth. Airliners on the long haul across the Atlantic attempted to keep track of one another by air-to-air relaying of messages.

At 1:20 A.M. February 11 a brilliant aurora appeared in the southern sky over Fargo, North Dakota. Its progress was recorded by an all-sky camera, installed there as a link in the transcontinental chain of a dozen such cameras designed to cover the entire sky over North America. The image of the sky was caught in a convex mirror, reflected up into a flat mirror and back through a hole in the convex mirror to a camera that photographed it at one-minute intervals throughout the night. Fortunately the weather in Fargo was clear.

Two minutes after its first appearance, the aurora recorded by this camera had reached the zenith. At this moment the bottom dropped out of the earth's magnetism, as recorded at Fredericksburg. This slump in the horizontal component of the magnetic field is typical of such storms and is known as a magnetic "bay." Also, at this instant, a balloon over Minnesota detected a series of rapid-fire X-ray bursts. The balloon had been launched ninety-seven minutes earlier by two men from the University of Minnesota at a small airport near Minneapolis. They labored in subzero winds so furious that the filmy plastic bag was almost torn to ribbons before it could be prepared. The balloon, although about a hundred feet in diameter when fully inflated, was only filled to about 1 per cent of its ground-level capacity so that it would not burst when its helium expanded in the thin air near the top of the atmosphere. As one man released the impatient bag, the other sprinted downwind with the precious payload of instruments in his arms, lest it be dragged across the field. A moment later the soaring balloon snatched it from his grasp and it sailed serenely aloft, vanishing through clouds toward the hidden, aurora-lighted sky above. In addition to the X-ray bursts, the ion chamber dangling under the balloon found that, compared to recent balloon flights (the latest only two days earlier), there had been a 21 per cent drop in cosmic rays in the high atmosphere. World-wide ground-level counters showed a 4 to 6 per cent decrease, affecting rays of even very high energies, but radio signals from the parcel under the balloon showed that the effect was far more marked on lower energy rays that could not penetrate to the ground.

At 1:24 A.M., as shown by film from the camera in Fargo, the entire sky over the Dakotas was aflame. Despite clouds over Wisconsin, the clock on the all-sky camera at Yerkes Observatory in Williams

Bay was so brightly illuminated that it was badly overexposed in the automatic photographs. An unusual feature of these northern lights was that they moved up from the south. During this climax of auroral and magnetic activity there was a marked muffling of cosmic noise, as recorded at Boulder, Colorado.

At 1:45 A.M. the aurora reached its maximum brilliance over Sunspot, New Mexico. In February, 1955, sensitive light recorders had been installed there to map celestial distribution of the faint light known as airglow. On seven clear nights during the next three years, light considered to be characteristic of aurora—rather than airglow—was detected, but that of February 11, 1958, was by far the most intense. Somewhat similar equipment recorded faint auroral light at Tonantzintla, near Mexico City, where the time of maximum intensity coincided with that of the display over New Mexico, a thousand miles to the north.[5]

At 2 A.M. H. K. Pyles, junior third officer on the S.S. *President Taylor,* was standing watch as the ship steamed along the west coast of Mexico in roughly the same latitude as Mexico City. It was midnight local time, and he recorded in the log the remarkable fact that the northern horizon was aglow with a red light bright enough to be reflected in the heaving sea. The aurora was also seen in Cuba, in the same latitude on the eastern side of the continent. Apparently the heavy blanket of light was advancing southward.

At 2:30 A.M. the X-ray bursts monitored by the Minnesota balloon came to an end.

At 3:50 A.M. there was a second magnetic slump in Virginia and new X-ray bursts were observed by the balloon. Likewise, as during the previous magnetic bay, particularly intense auroral displays appeared at the zenith over Minnesota and Wisconsin and the loudness of cosmic noise plunged in Colorado. Two antennas north of Boulder, Colorado, were recording the 18-megacycle emissions from that point in the northern sky known as Cygnus A. For a time this radio noise faded out completely.[6]

At about 5 A.M. the aurora reached its southernmost extent. Carl Gartlein, in charge of the IGY World Data Center for visual auroral observations at Cornell, was one of those who had to be satisfied that night with seeing a diffuse redness in the clouds overhead, but when he pieced together reports by hundreds of observers organized for just such an event, he found that the aurora, at its maximum, lay over

North America like a blanket 600 kilometers thick, 400 kilometers wide (in a north-south direction), and 9600 kilometers long (east and west), with its base 200 kilometers aloft. (A kilometer is approximately 1.6 miles.) The displays seem to have been concentrated over North America, although some were seen as far away as Manchuria and the Eysk Marine Hydrometeorological Station on the Sea of Azov, south of Moscow.[7]

By 8:30 P.M., twenty-four hours after its start, the storm was virtually over.

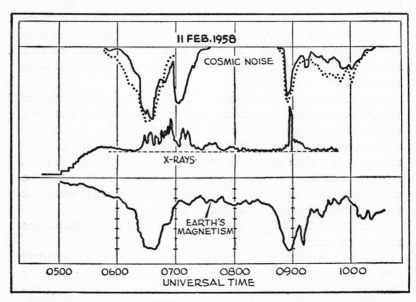

Simultaneous effects as the cloud enveloped the earth. The upper line represents the intensity of radio noise from the cosmos, as recorded at Boulder, Colorado. The center line shows bursts of X rays detected by a balloon over Minnesota. It rests upon a dashed line representing the high-altitude cosmic ray background. The bottom line delineates the horizontal intensity of the earth's magnetism at Fredericksburg, Virginia. (National Academy of Sciences. Adapted by *The New York Times*)

After pulling together all readily available information on the storm, Winckler (who was one of the chief IGY investigators of cosmic rays) and his associates at the University of Minnesota tried to reconstruct what had happened. They estimated that, to produce the observed effects, the cloud of solar gas must have been 46 million miles long and at least 23 million miles wide. Thus, when its nose arrived at the earth, its tail reached halfway to the sun. This length was derived from its speed and the twenty-four-hour time the cloud apparently took to pass. Assuming that it was ejected during the observed two-hour duration of the February 9 flare, its front traveled earthward at 870 miles per second and its tail at 435 miles per second. The minimum width was calculated on the assumption that the gas shot straight up from the flare and then fanned out sufficiently to embrace the earth.

The leading edge of the great stream of solar gas must have been sharply defined, in view of the abruptness of the start of the magnetic storm on earth. More difficult to explain was the apparent existence of additional fronts within the cloud, responsible for the two great magnetic bays and their related events. The Minnesota scientists found it a hopeless task, however, to try to trace these structures to specific episodes of the flare, despite the detailed record of its radio outbursts.

Presumably the two bays, or slumps in the earth's magnetism, were due to sudden ionization of the E layer of the upper atmosphere, producing strong sheet currents. The muffling of cosmic noise was attributed to heavy ionization of the D layer. These effects, as well as the auroral displays, were all thought to have been caused by showers of electrons, which had perhaps been accelerated when the cloud came under the influence of the earth's magnetic field. What was strange, however, was that, if electrons (or the X rays they generated) penetrated as deep as the D layer—only forty miles up—why was there no visible aurora below 125 miles? As the Minnesota scientists put it, "one is left with a contradiction which at present is not resolved." [8]

CHAPTER 13
NATURE'S ATOM—SMASHERS

The thrilling and awesome experience that has been the quest for the source of cosmic rays began at the turn of this century. Henri Becquerel had discovered radioactivity in 1896 and many scientists were conducting experiments on the effect of radiation on gases. It was found that the more intense the radiation, the greater the electrical conductivity of the gas, due to its ionization. Conversely, it was calculated that, if the gas could be isolated from all radiation, it should become completely nonconducting. But every experiment designed to test this hypothesis was unsuccessful. No matter how carefully the gas was shielded, there was always a little conductivity left.

This meant that there was some strange sort of radiation still ionizing the gas. Some thought there must be a little radioactive material in everything, even in the walls of the container holding the gas. Others felt the radiation came from somewhere within the earth, but neither of these ideas stood up when subjected to experiment. One way to test the idea of terrestrial origin was to take the ionization chambers out of the laboratory and carry them up in balloons. If the degree of ionization decreased with altitude, the implication would be that the source was the earth. During the years immediately preceding World War I a number of scientists tried this out, notably Victor N. Hess of Austria, who himself piloted six flights in 1912 that reached as high as 17,800 feet. He found that, above 2000 feet, instead of decreasing, the radiation intensity rose extremely fast. At the ceiling of these early balloons it was many times greater than at sea level. This could lead to only one conclusion, he said: the effect observed in laboratories on the earth was the thin residuum of a far more intense radiation coming from outer space and filtered by the atmosphere. Since it could pierce several feet of lead, it was assumed this radiation must be a powerful relative of the gamma rays—the most penetrating form of electromagnetic waves known at that time. Hence the phenomenon came to be known as cosmic rays.

In the 1920s there were still many who doubted that the rays could come from outer space. Their experiments showed that a large portion of the "cosmic" radiation observed at sea level was far too weak to have penetrated through twenty miles of air. Eventually it was shown that this was secondary radiation produced as the primary cosmic rays struck air particles.

In 1928 the invention of the Geiger-Müller counter opened the way for some of the most startling discoveries of the century. In that year preliminary studies were made of relative cosmic-ray intensities at different locations and, in the early 1930s, it was established that the intensity increases steadily as one moves away from the magnetic equator. Thus the rain of rays on a square yard at the equator is 2000 per second; at New York City it is roughly 10,000.

The implication was almost incredible. If the "rays" were affected by the earth's magnetism, they could not be electromagnetic waves (like light); they must be charged particles of matter, moving at such speeds that they could go through six feet of lead.

But if they were bits of matter, what were they? Where did they come from? And how did they acquire such great energies? The eager efforts of physicists throughout the world to find answers to these questions introduced an entirely new field of science: particle physics. It was found that, when cosmic-ray "bullets" hit the nucleus of an atom inside a cloud chamber, all sorts of fragments were produced, including that bizarre family of particles termed "anti-matter." To shatter atomic nuclei in a controlled manner and explore this challenging area of physics, giant accelerators were built, although they could not hope to match the more powerful cosmic rays. Atom-smashers currently planned or in operation are designed, at most, to produce particles with energies less than 100 BEV (billion electron volts), whereas cosmic rays of 5 billion BEV have been detected. It has been calculated that a proton-synchrotron accelerator as big around as the earth, with a magnetic field of 20,000 gauss, would still kick protons up to only 4 million BEV. The energy released by the fission of a uranium atom in an atomic bomb is far less than 1 BEV.

Hence, for the most powerful atom-smashers, man must still look to the heavens, although cosmic rays of the most extreme energies are comparatively rare. By 1961 about thirty different nuclear particles had been identified among the debris produced by cosmic-ray impacts. Apparently they are not all bits and pieces of the nucleus. Instead, they are, in part, created by the conversion of energy into matter—reversing the process of a nuclear explosion. Cosmic-ray physicists have marched hand in hand with those who sought, with man-made accelerators, to learn more of the force that holds the nucleus together—a force compared to which magnetism is a weakling and gravity even feebler.

The building of accelerators strains the budget of even the richest nation, but a far less expensive device—the lowly balloon—came into its own after World War II as a tool of cosmic-ray research. Until that time, high-altitude balloons had been made of rubberized fabric. They carried the instruments steadily upward, the gas within them expanding as the air became thinner until finally the bag burst. The new plastics, such as polyethylene, provided a substance far thinner than paper, yet very strong. Balloons made of this light material could carry loads far higher than before and, equally important, they could easily be rigged to hover at a preselected elevation, providing a platform for observation on top of almost the entire atmosphere for periods of a day or longer. In contrast to the complex ballasting systems used to keep some balloons at a steady height, these were fitted with an open sleeve at the bottom which allowed the helium to escape whenever the balloon rose so high that the gas expanded beyond the bag's capacity. The balloon was injected with a small bubble of gas at ground level which filled it at the summit of its flight, the height being determined by such factors as the size of the bag and its load.

The first such "Skyhook" balloon was launched on September 25, 1947, carrying a sixty-three-pound load to about 100,000 feet. It began a period of intensive balloon exploration of cosmic rays, particularly in the United States, where the work was largely subsidized by the Office of Naval Research.

For some of the experiments it was necessary to recover the instruments, and this was achieved with a surprising degree of success. The load was suspended from a deflated parachute which, in turn, hung from the balloon by a cord that passed through a metal firing squib. This was exploded by a timer set to cut the cord before the balloon drifted too far afield. In the frigid upper air the fully inflated balloon became quite brittle. As soon as the load broke loose and parachuted down, the balloon shattered and fell. Air-traffic authorities were notified before each launching, but the loads were designed to be harmless if a plane hit them. The packages were usually limited to six pounds with each flight carrying no more than two, strung ten feet apart on a line dangling below the balloon.

From 1954 to 1960 the University of Minnesota—to name only one participant in the American program—launched some 175 of these bags. Each load bore a tag offering a small reward to the finder, and, when the hunting season opened, there was a rash of finds in the lonely forest lands of northern Michigan, Wisconsin, Minnesota, and neighboring Canada. About 95 per cent of the loads were returned.

At ground level only about one in 100,000 cosmic-ray particles is in its original form, the rest all being by-products of collisions with the atmosphere. One way to get closer to the original rays was to observe from mountaintops, and during the IGY this was done at many points. The highest such observatory was at Chacaltaya, Bolivia, 17,100 feet above sea level. A special "telescope" was built for this site in the cosmic-ray laboratory of Imperial College of Science and Technology, in London, under a grant from UNESCO. Its trays of Geiger counters were arranged so that they could distinguish, in general terms, the direction from which each particle arrived.

Physicists nevertheless wanted to place their instruments much higher—at 100,000 feet or more, where 80 to 90 per cent of the incoming rays are unaltered. The development of emulsions that could be flown by balloon at that height made it possible to learn the composition of the rays. Were they just hydrogen nuclei (protons) or did they represent a sample of some part of the universe?

This was a question of such fundamental importance that emulsions were sent up on some of the earliest Skyhook flights in 1948.[1] An emulsion performs somewhat the same function as a cloud chamber. When an invisible particle shoots through it, a visible wake of ionized material remains. Although the effect in a cloud chamber is transient, in an emulsion it is permanent. However, as with the emulsion of a photographic film, it must be developed. When one of the first 1948 emulsions was processed, it showed the fat track of a heavy particle whose path, unlike those observed at ground level, did not die in the midst of the retarding emulsion. It went right through—indicative of tremendous energy.

The rays were found to include the nuclei of all the lighter elements, as well as the heavier ones up to iron. The proportions were similar, broadly speaking, to those in stars (as shown by their light), with hydrogen accounting for about 86 per cent, helium 13 per cent, and the heavier elements the remaining 1 per cent. The rays, however, have far more lithium, beryllium, and boron than appears to exist in the stars and it is thought possible that these elements are the fruits of some sort of transmutation that takes place during the flight of the rays through space.

Although researchers have occasionally reported finding regions of the sky which were particularly "bright" in cosmic rays, it has generally been felt that they strike at the earth equally from all directions. They seem to come more from the west than the east, but this is thought to be due purely to the fact that most, if not all, of the rays are positively charged, causing them to be bent in the same direction by the earth's magnetism.

The estimates of maximum cosmic-ray energies have been based on observations of "showers" produced when a single particle hits the air with such immense force that it sends to earth, not a handful, but an army of electrons knocked off a great many air atoms. The detection of these showers is a major undertaking, since a great many radiation counters have to be laid out over a wide area and wired so that they record only those impacts which hit all or most of them at once. At the time of the IGY there were several of these in operation. One, in the Soviet Union, made use of 5000 counters. Another, more than 500 yards in diameter, set up by the Massachusetts Institute of Technology, recorded 2.6 billion incoming particles almost simultaneously. It is thought that the parent particle must have had an energy of about 5 billion BEV. Some believe the entire galaxy of which the sun is a part is not large enough to accelerate a particle to such a level. Our galaxy is a spiral of star clouds shaped like a discus with a spherical bulge in the middle. Its visible portion is the Milky Way, but its center and far side are obscured by dust clouds. If the accelerator that boosts bits of matter almost to the unachievable limit (the velocity of light) is larger than the galaxy it must either encircle it—or lie somewhere far beyond.

Modern physics rests on the assumption that all electromagnetic radiation, from X rays to radio waves, travels at approximately the speed of light. As matter approaches this speed, however, its mass (and therefore its energy) grows with increasing rapidity. If it could reach the speed of light, its mass and energy would be infinite, but this it cannot quite do.

The cosmic-ray program of the IGY was given a memorable send-off by an event that occurred more than sixteen months before the official start of the Year. Shortly before 9 P.M. February 22, 1956 (4 A.M. February 23 Greenwich Time), an observer named David Dogden emerged from the darkroom at the Climax site of the High Altitude Observatory, astride a Rocky Mountain pass in Colorado. He had been developing the day's run of sun photographs. Suddenly he became aware of a frantic clicking down the hall. He called Richard Hansen, a fellow observer, and they hurried into the room housing a small atomic pile used to monitor cosmic-ray neutrons.

The rate at which it was clicking was so rapid that they felt the machine must be out of order. They put in a phone call to the home of John A. Simpson, professor of physics at the Enrico Fermi Institute for Nuclear Studies at the University of Chicago. The monitor at Climax was being operated there on his behalf. Simpson had hurried off to the laboratory, they were told. It seemed there was something "wrong" with the cosmic-ray recorder there too.

"Wow!" cried Hansen to his colleague. "That means it's the real thing."

Because of the approaching IGY, universities and institutes around the world had set up new cosmic-ray devices, and the burst of radiation was widely observed. It took place when the sun was overhead in Japan, where a solar flare of the largest type was observed. The burst of rays that followed was recorded by some fifty stations, their counting rates rising rapidly to as much as fifty times normal. But what struck Simpson, when he analyzed the records, was that the event was recorded in Europe and Asia some ten minutes before the rays reached Canada and the United States. Since the rays were traveling at close to the speed of light, those recorded on the night side of the world, he thought, must have first traveled far beyond the earth and then echoed off some sort of spherical wall enclosing the inner solar system. Likewise, the rays continued to arrive long after the main event was over, as though they were ricocheting within this hypothetical shell.

It was proposed that the shell was a region of disordered magnetic fields at the farthest reach of solar gas clouds, where they mingle with the thin material and magnetism of our galaxy.

Another strange aspect of the event was that the source of the rays appeared to be a portion of the heavens that, while centered on the sun, was considerably larger, implying that the particles had been accelerated near the sun, rather than within it.

This great flare, by its violence, led the way to a discovery that cast a long shadow across the plans for manned space travel. For many years communications in and across the Arctic had been beset by sudden blackouts that were limited to the polar regions. The growing strategic importance of the North, with its chains of early-warning radar stations, meant that these blackouts were of more than academic interest. Although they were usually brief, after the great 1956 flare polar communications were paralyzed for three days. It occurred to some of those who studied this event that the lesser blackouts might be due to cosmic rays thrown out by the sun with insufficient energy to reach ground-level monitors. Relatively weak cosmic rays, such as those the sun might be expected to produce, would be likely to penetrate the earth's magnetic field only near the poles, although the exceptional 1956 flare shot out rays so strong that, like a tank plunging through barbed-wire, they were able to cut across the magnetic force lines and reach the earth even at the equator.

Among those who sought to look farther into the problem of polar blackouts was C. Gordon Little, an Englishman whose fascination with magnetic storms and the aurora had drawn him—like Sydney Chapman—to the Geophysical Institute in Alaska. Thanks largely to his initiative, a network of riometers was installed in the Arctic. (The riometer, as noted earlier, is a radio receiver that records fluctuations in the strength of cosmic noise.) Those used in this project differed from the riometer employed during the October, 1958, eclipse in that they listened on a higher frequency—27.6 megacycles. Three were installed in Alaska: at the Geophysical Institute in College, at Point Barrow, and at Fort Yukon; a fourth was placed at Thule, Greenland. During the IGY they disclosed that, within a few hours after a considerable number of flares, the Arctic was capped with a dense layer of ionization. Eighteen such events were recorded, including one that followed the flare of February 10, 1958, by a little less than ten hours.[2] It was suspected that this ionization in the polar atmosphere was produced by showers of protons thrown out by the flare at a speed many times greater than that of the gas cloud ejected at the same time. The cloud itself was thought to consist of both protons and electrons.

The idea that polar blackouts were caused by protons with cosmic-ray energies was confirmed by an IGY balloon flight on August 22, 1958.[3] The bag was released from Fort Churchill, Canada, during a blackout, and its payload, prepared by Kinsey A. Anderson of the State University of Iowa, detected protons on the spot. During the next year Harold Leinbach at the Geophysical Institute in Alaska phoned Minneapolis when there was a severe blackout, and the University of Minnesota launched a succession of balloons to maintain a steady watch atop the atmosphere. It was found that the proton showers extend as far south as the northern United States and that their intensity is sometimes a thousand times the normal cosmic-ray level. The shielding properties of the atmosphere are equal to those of a lead wall more than three feet thick and hence the protons do not reach the ground, but because of their penetrating qualities and unpredictable appearances, they came to be regarded as the chief hazard to space travel.

Although these proton showers seemed to originate with solar flares, some of the most severe ones were not followed by magnetic storms or auroral displays. Thus a flare can result in a burst of protons, a magnetic storm, both, or neither.[4]

The 1956 flare raised other questions.

If, during the brief history of cosmic ray observations, a fifty-fold increase had been recorded, was it not possible that on rare occasions there were cosmic-ray bursts of far greater intensity—enough to cause radiation damage on earth? Furthermore, if the rays are many times more intense high in the stratosphere, what might this mean for jet pilots who spend many hours a week at such elevations? The quest for an answer to this question was one of the objectives in seeking to determine the weight and energy of incoming particles by means of balloon-borne emulsions.[5]

A major portion of the IGY effort in cosmic rays was aimed at the strange cycles that affect their intensity. The blizzard of particles that rains upon the earth's atmosphere, seemingly from all directions, is controlled by several cyclic variations that should provide clues to conditions existing in the sun, in interplanetary space, and in the vast reaches of the universe beyond.

The eleven-year cycle

Before the IGY began there was strong evidence that the intensity of cosmic rays reaching the earth varies in step with the eleven-year sunspot cycle. The nature of this variation was brought to light, in large measure, by a series of balloon flights begun in 1936 by H. Victor Neher of the California Institute of Technology, who continued them through the IGY. During 1958 alone he and his men flew eighty balloons, sixteen of which were released in latitudes between southern Texas and Thule, Greenland. Similar flights from Bismarck, North Dakota, were timed to coincide with each of these and, during another series of twenty-four flights, released from the icebreaker USS *Atka* between Seattle and Antarctica, coincident flights were made by Neher from Invercargill, at the southern tip of New Zealand. The fruit of these efforts was a demonstration that the more sunspots there are, the fewer are the low-energy cosmic rays. Thus a sunspot maximum coincides with a cosmic-ray minimum. Neher found that, at Thule, during the solar maximum of the IGY, the intensity of rays striking the atmosphere was one-quarter what it had been three years earlier. Thule is so near the Geomagnetic Pole that rays of even the lowest energies can come in, whereas farther south the earth's magnetism cuts off the weaker ones.

Although the shift in cosmic-ray intensity was most clearly seen from balloons near the top of the atmosphere, the instrument known as a neutron monitor, being particularly sensitive to low-energy rays, was able to observe it from the ground.[6] The one at Climax recorded a 25-per cent drop as the solar cycle drew to its maximum in 1957–58. Similar declines were recorded by the monitor in Chicago, by one atop Mount Washington, and by another in Ottawa.

The cutting off of 75 per cent of the lowest-energy rays (as observed over Greenland) implied that something had changed throughout the inner part of the solar system, if not beyond. The next step was to find out what it was. There still is no agreement on this point. In fact a difference of opinion arose as to the very nature of the drop. A group in Canada interpreted it as a steady decline, once the effects of magnetic storms had been smoothed out. John A. Lockwood of the University of New Hampshire found, from his work with the monitor on Mount Washington, that the decline came in a series of dramatic plunges, each pushing the intensity to a lower level from which it never fully recovered. It was as though there were a great valve shutting off the low-energy rays in a series of abrupt turns. One of the possible explanations, he said, was that solar clouds, after producing magnetic storms, passed on out through the solar system, continuing to expand and thin out for several months, but remaining dense enough to deflect cosmic rays. As sunspot maximum approaches, according to this theory, the clouds are generated in sufficiently close succession to have a cumulative effect.

The twenty-seven-day cycle

By correcting cosmic-ray records for the day-to-day effects of weather, it was possible, before the IGY, to identify a twenty-seven-day cycle, although it was barely observable. From July to October, 1957, Martin A. Pomerantz and his colleagues at the Bartol Research Foundation in Swarthmore, Pennsylvania, conducted a series of balloon flights that showed this cycle to be far more marked on top of the atmosphere during sunspot maximum. There is a similar cycle in magnetic activity, and, since twenty-seven days is roughly the rotation period of the sun (as seen from the moving earth) both are thought to be due to some region on the sun.

The same cycle was observed by the Russians. Cosmic-ray balloons were launched one or more times daily from several stations, including those near Yakutsk in Siberia, Moscow, and Murmansk in the European Arctic. In October, 1958, Sergei N. Vernov, a Stalin-prize winner who was in charge of the project, and several colleagues reported that, based on data from 212 days, they had found a cycle of roughly 28.6 days.[7]

Forbush decreases

In 1935 the Carnegie Institution of Washington began a constant watch on cosmic rays that has become the longest unbroken record of this phenomenon to be published. Furthermore it enabled the head of the program, Scott E. Forbush, to identify the sudden decreases in cosmic rays that sometimes accompany magnetic storms. IGY balloon observations of these Forbush decreases showed that the intensity drops as much as 30 per cent on top of the atmosphere.

It was widely believed that virtually all the rays come from beyond the solar system and that the decreases are caused by the same magnetic clouds that produce magnetic storms on earth. However it was also thought possible that the steady flow of cosmic rays comes—at least in part—from the sun and that Forbush decreases might result from a reduction in this output.

An experiment was carried out to throw light on this question. As has been noted, about 86 per cent of the rays are hydrogen nuclei and 13 per cent helium nuclei. If the decrease was caused by magnetism, it would affect the ratio of hydrogen and helium in a predictable manner. If it was due to some other mechanism within the sun, this would show up as a different alteration of the ratio. To see which was the case, seven balloons were flown over Canada by the group at the University of Chicago, the bags remaining at their peak altitudes for as long as twenty hours. On August 30, 1957, a Forbush decrease took place while a balloon was up, and ran virtually its full course before the flight ended. A quiet-day flight two weeks earlier provided a basis for comparison, and it was found that the changes in hydrogen and helium intensity pointed to magnetism as being responsible.

An unexpected discovery was a gradual rise in the influx of helium nuclei during each morning. Since this was the time when the sun was rising in the sky, it was suspected that these additional particles were of solar origin.[8]

Another study of Forbush decreases kept a bomber crew of the Strategic Air Command, based at Lake Charles, Louisiana, on constant alert. It was linked by special phone to the office of John Simpson in Chicago. If his neutron monitor showed that a decrease had begun, he sounded the alarm and the airmen scrambled for their six-jet B-47. Climbing steeply to 30,000 feet or more, they flew a fixed line between Lake Charles and a point north of Sioux Lookout, Ontario. A cosmic-ray counter in the nose of the plane observed rays of lower and lower energy, as it moved toward the magnetic pole, until it reached a point —the "knee"—where this effect leveled off. From there on north no change was recorded because something in space cut off the rays of lower energy. At sunspot maximum this knee moved south to the vicinity of Chicago. Simpson believed that, if it moved even farther south during a Forbush decrease, it would show that such decreases were likewise produced far out in space, rather than by a more local phenomenon, such as a ring current around the earth. After the plane had flown some thirty-five round trips, Simpson felt the results pointed to the distant source, a conclusion that received further support in 1960 when a Forbush decrease was observed simultaneously on the earth and aboard Pioneer V, some 3 million miles away.[9]

It may be a decade or more before cosmic-ray data acquired during the IGY has borne its most important fruits. Still unresolved, after the

Year was over, was the challenging question of the rays' origin. Two basic theories were vying for scientific favor. According to one, the rays are generated at specific points in the cosmos—probably as a result of supernovae. These are fearsome star explosions, generating light that is sometimes brighter than that of the entire galaxy of which the sun is a part. The other theory is that the rays are particles thrown out by many, if not all, stars (including the sun) and then gradually accelerated by the magnetic fields of moving gas clouds. This speed-up may take millions of years, as the particles shoot about the galaxy in random fashion.

Bernard J. Peters, at the University Institute for Theoretical Physics in Copenhagen, terms it "practically certain" that at least some cosmic rays result from supernovae.[10] These explosions leave in their wake rapidly expanding, swirling clouds of hot, magnetized gas, an example being the Crab Nebula, attributed to a supernova that awed the inhabitants of earth in A.D. 1054. Actually the event occurred four thousand years earlier, but it took that length of time for its light to reach the earth.

The light presently arriving from the nebula has puzzled astronomers because of the strange fuzziness of its spectrum. This same spot in the heavens is one of the strongest emitters of radio noise. Peters believes both the noise and the light are produced by the same phenomenon: *synchrotron radiation*. In the laboratory a similar light is produced in a synchrotron accelerator by electrons whirling at close to the speed of light, and the same effect generates radio signals. Electrons spiraling in the earth's magnetic field should produce radio noise and, during Project Argus, attempts were made to listen for it in the Van Allen belts although, as suspected, it was too weak to be heard.

Many experiments have been carried out to see if cosmic rays come from well-defined points in the heavens (such as recent supernovae). Those of lower energy are so bent, in their flight, by magnetic fields in space that they reach the earth from all directions. Furthermore, it is thought, they are magnetically trapped within the galaxy. On the other hand, those with energies of about 100 million BEV or more are so slightly affected by galactic magnetism that they can escape, and therefore the few that reach the earth must have traveled a fairly direct path. Attempts have been made by Bruno Rossi at the Massachusetts Institute of Technology and others to find out if such extremely energetic particles come, preferentially, from certain parts of the sky. Rossi estimates that less than one in 10 billion cosmic-ray particles is of sufficiently high energy for this study. Hence the only way that has been found to observe them is through the showers of secondary particles they produce when they hit the atmosphere. In 1959 he reported that the showers so far analyzed seemed to come evenly from all directions. "However the present results," he added, "can only whet our curiosity; they do not enable us to draw any definite conclusion." [11]

The theory of gradual acceleration was proposed by Enrico Fermi. As noted earlier, our galaxy is thought to be insufficiently large to boost particles to the speeds observed in the most energetic rays. However, some believe the galaxy may be enveloped in a complex of immense Van Allen radiation belts big enough to do the job. Here seemingly remote fields of inquiry come together, namely cosmic rays and radio astronomy. A charting of radio-noise sources has shown many of them to lie in a spherical region surrounding the galaxy and within a radius of about 50,000 light years (a light year being the distance that light travels in one year at 186,000 miles a second). No stars can be seen at these points and hence it is assumed the emissions are produced by trapped particles, moving at close to the speed of light in a halo of turbulent, magnetized gas surrounding the galaxy. Similar emissions have been detected in spherical regions surrounding other galaxies, such as the Great Spiral Nebula in Andromeda, which is the only galaxy other than our own that is faintly visible to the naked eye.

The proposal has even been made that, on infrequent occasions, the solar system sails through the gas cloud produced by a supernova, increasing the cosmic-ray intensity ten to a hundred times for a period of perhaps 2000 or 3000 years. Since genetic mutations increase with a rise in radiation exposure, the number of new species of plant and animal would be very large. The present energy contribution of cosmic rays is roughly equal to that of starlight, but nevertheless they are sufficiently omnipresent to have an influence. Some thirty or forty of them flash through the body of every person on earth every second. Occasionally they are bound to strike the miniscule genes that pass hereditary characteristics on to future generations, bringing about radical changes. The density of the rays at high altitudes appears enough to change the hair color of black mice living there. They are said to develop scattered white hairs, due to cosmic-ray damage to the hair cells.

It has been estimated that the earth may enter a supernova gas cloud every 200 to 300 million years, and a glance at the history of evolution shows that, at such intervals, there have been periods of rapid change, as when reptiles became dominant over insects or mammals gained the ascendancy over reptiles. These developments have been attributed largely to climate changes, but the cosmic-ray theory is a challenging one.

Cosmic-ray physics emerged from the IGY as, in a sense, the broadest-ranging of all man's intellectual endeavors. It deals with the most immense concepts (entire galaxies and the space between them) and the tiniest (the fragments of the atomic nucleus and the force that holds them together). It concerns itself with the broadest panorama of time, in the millions of years possibly required to accelerate some of the particles, and with particle lifetimes measured in billionths of a second or less.

CHAPTER 14
NIGHT LIGHTS

For some animals, as long as they are out in the open, it may never get dark. To them, if they can see sufficiently well into the red end of the spectrum, all but the brightest stars are invisible, the night being illuminated to a perpetual twilight by the airglow. Our eyes are poor sensors of red. Had it been otherwise, the history of astronomy would have been different indeed.

Other forms of light appear in the night sky, the best known being the aurora. In low latitudes one can see zodiacal light, which may be brighter than the Milky Way, and a dim relative called gegenschein. Likewise, at times, strange luminous streaks appear aloft, known as noctilucent clouds. All became targets of IGY exploration.

The aurora

Auroral observations probably involved more amateur enthusiasts than any other IGY effort. They provided a picture of the displays more extensive than any previously possible. It is easy enough for one man to look up and see an aurora, but to combine the sightings into a global pattern was the unique contribution of the IGY. The Auroral Data Center at Cornell received about 18,000 hourly reports a month from some 430 American sky-watchers, including 30 airline pilots and an assortment of seafarers, amateur astronomers, science teachers, and the like. In addition, 130 stations of the United States Weather Bureau made observations every hour. The report cards came in almost equal numbers from the volunteers and from the weather men. More than 1200 were sent in on the great aurora of February 10–11, 1958, making it "the world's most widely observed display up to that time." [1]

One of the mid-century developments that offered hope for digesting the mountains of data assembled in the IGY was the advent of business machines and computers. Nowhere were these tools more essential than in the aurora program. In preparation for the IGY, "mark-sense" cards were designed on which information could be entered by darkening certain squares with a pencil. These cards could be processed entirely by machine, the first step being automatic "reading" of the pencil marks and punching of the information in standard business machine fashion. On another type of card, used particularly by volunteer observers, the display was sketched and then, upon receipt at the center, the information was transcribed to punch cards by a machine operator. The cards could then be run through machines by the tens of thousands to obtain answers to questions that auroral physicists had been asking for years.

Lest the volunteers feel that their reports were vanishing, like stones thrown into the sea, Carl Gartlein, head of the Data Center, and his associate, Gale Sprague, circulated a monthly news letter, giving individuals a glimpse of the big picture they had helped piece together. For example, he told them of his effort to determine from the IGY data if auroral displays tend to move westward. This would not be surprising, he noted, since the phenomenon is linked to the westward-moving sun. Likewise he sought to find out, through machine analysis, whether the average motion changed at midnight (when the sun passed beneath the observer and began its return toward the eastern horizon).

> The results surprised us [he wrote] . . .
>
> 1) The predominant average motion of auroras is toward the east, in the direction opposite to that of the sun and stars.
>
> 2) Although the average motion of an aurora depends on the time, there is no reversal at midnight.[2]

Another fundamental problem concerning the aurora was the extent to which displays at opposite ends of the world coincided. Auroral records from Ellsworth Station, the United States Antarctic outpost on the Weddell Sea, were compared with those of the North American stations and it was found that the frequency of displays over Ellsworth was about the same as that over the St. Lawrence River. Hourly reports for times when the sky was adequately clear at both ends of the world showed that in more than 99 per cent of the cases auroras occurred simultaneously. In fact, there was only one exception during the period studied (June through September, 1957): At

6 A.M. Greenwich Time, July 3, an aurora appeared over the United States, but the sky was clear and dark over Ellsworth.

It was also found that auroral motion in the Antarctic tends to be easterly and that the form of the displays does not always coincide north and south; that is, the display over the United States may be what is known as a pulsating arc, whereas the southern lights might be "flames."

There had never been such extensive auroral observations near the poles, and the results were somewhat perplexing. The Russians concluded, from the data that they collected, that there were two zones of particularly frequent auroras. One—the most intense—they said, lies, as had long been supposed, on a circle of about 1700 miles' radius, centered on the geomagnetic pole. The second, they found, lies on a circle of roughly 1100 miles' radius.

The existence of such an inner, lesser auroral zone had been proposed by both A. P. Nikolsky of the Soviet Union and Hannes Alfvén of Sweden in 1954–55, based on their studies of the earth's magnetism and calculations of particle trajectories. During the winter before the IGY, the Russians at North Pole 5, an ice-floe station adrift in the Arctic Ocean about 240 miles from the North Pole and 1022 miles from the Geomagnetic Pole, saw a large number of auroras directly overhead, almost none to the north and few to the south.[3]

Gartlein, working primarily with the American observations north and south, envisaged an auroral zone that expanded each night, reaching its greatest circumference at local midnight. During the long period of total darkness at the South Pole, the record of hourly observations showed that, when the sun, below the horizon, was opposite the magnetic pole, auroras were virtually never seen in the sun's direction. Twelve hours later, when the sun lay in the same direction as the magnetic pole, auroras again shunned the quadrant of the heavens toward the sun.

Reports from the antarctic stations made it possible to chart, tentatively, the region of maximum occurrence and it was found that the circle was centered between the Magnetic Pole and the Geomagnetic Pole rather than at the latter, as had been assumed on the basis of charts of the northern auroral zone dating back to the days of Fritz, more than seventy-five years earlier.

Near the center of the circle the behavior of the aurora became strangely erratic. For example Ralph Glasgal, who did the first year's auroral observations at Wilkes Station, found that, whereas in lower latitudes the auroral arcs lined up neatly along lines of magnetic latitude, here, close to the pole, they were aligned one way one night and at right angles to it the next. At Wilkes the Magnetic Pole is due

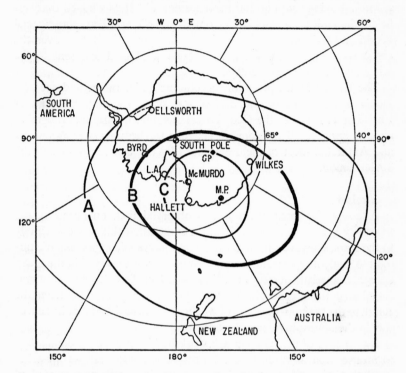

Aurora Australis. Line *A* represents the outermost edge of the biggest auroras seen from the South Pole and other stations during the IGY. Line *B* is the outer edge of the region where the greatest number of auroras are seen. Line *C* bounds a zone inside which "irregular" auroras occur. *LA* identifies Little America Station, *MP* the magnetic pole, *GP* the geomagnetic pole. (National Academy of Sciences)

east and the Geomagnetic Pole due south, so it was almost as though the two poles engaged in a nightly tussle to see which would control the aurora.

Gartlein's wife, Helen, used data assembled from far and wide to chart auroral displays at hourly (and sometimes fifteen-minute) intervals throughout their duration. The maps showed the shape of each display, its intensity, colors, and movement. Sometimes the picture that emerged from the assembled data was awesome. At one point, as reported by Gartlein, "there was a wall of light as long as the U.S. is wide, over 100 miles tall, with its bottom 60 miles from the ground, moving south at 700 miles an hour." [4] It was hoped that sufficient data could be assembled from Regular World Days and Special World Intervals to make possible the mapping of displays over the entire globe. Charts, when done, were microfilmed and sent to the other two World Data Centers.

The United States program for photographic, radar, and spectroscopic observations of the aurora was organized separately under Christian T. Elvey at the Geophysical Institute in Alaska. Altogether about a hundred all-sky cameras scanned the heavens over the Arctic and Antarctic, most of them emplaced by the United States and the Soviet Union.

Airglow

Although for many years it was observed that, on occasion, the night sky is strangely bright, it was assumed that this was due simply to the stars. However, in making long photographic exposures of starlight to study its spectrum, a strong emission was observed in the green light characteristic of oxygen. This aroused suspicion and when it was found that the green light became systematically stronger from the zenith to the horizon—instead of weaker—it was evident that its source was in the atmosphere, not beyond.

By the start of the IGY enough work had been done on the airglow to arouse even more curiosity. Its brightest component was just beyond the range of the human eye, in the infra-red, and seemed to come from a layer of hydroxyl about forty-four miles up. Hydroxyl is water vapor in which ultraviolet sunlight has detached one hydrogen atom from each molecule (making it OH instead of H_2O). American rocket shots had located other glowing layers. One, at about fifty-three miles, emitted the yellow light of sodium. Another, some sixty-two miles up, displayed the green glow of oxygen. When one rocket reached its crest at ninety-six miles, a red glow, also characteristic of oxygen, was still above it.

The explanation seemed simple enough at first. During the day, radiation from the sun ionized atoms and split up molecules at these levels of the atmosphere. Then, at night, they recombined, emitting light in the process. But more careful observation disclosed some strange things. The glow was not uniform, as had been supposed. Its intensity varied from one part of the sky to another, forming clouds of dim light hundreds of miles wide that raced across the heavens at astonishing speed (some 225 miles an hour). Were these wave movements that stimulated the recombination process? Were they clouds of sporadic-*E*, such as those associated with the Electrojet? Did beams of incoming radiation sweep across the heavens like so many searchlights?

The chief organizer of the American airglow program was Franklin E. Roach at the Boulder, Colorado, laboratories of the National Bureau of Standards. He operated an airglow-monitoring station on Fritz Peak, which rises from the foothills of the Rockies behind Boulder. There, as at other points, a photometer swept the sky in successive circles parallel to the horizon and at various elevations above it. The device covered the heavens in four minutes, then shifted to sweep again on a different wavelength. The entire sequence began over again every fifteen minutes. The intensities were continually recorded on a strip chart and then transferred to punch cards so that, as with the aurora, the voluminous data could be processed by machine, a digital computer correcting for such effects as the apparent increase of intensity toward the horizon.

As darkness fell on the evening of September 29, 1957, L. R. Megill, operating the equipment among the crags atop Fritz Peak, noticed that there was something peculiar about a special photometer that was sweeping the sky from the northern to the southern horizon. Every time it neared the zenith, the intensity trace ran off the scale. The instrument was set to record light on 6300 angstroms, one of the red lines of oxygen. The moon was still up, but after it had set at 10 P.M. local time, the pen still ran off the moving roll of paper. He decided that something unusual must be going on and turned down the sensitivity enough to keep the trace on scale. The light intensity proved to be fifty times normal.

Meanwhile, at the Haute Provence Observatory in southern France, Daniel Barbier had been operating a battery of photometers, one of them using eight different filters. He detected what he considered to be a faint, red auroral arc spanning France a little north of the station.

Because of the time difference between the two stations, his arc vanished with the dawn light just as extinction of the last evening twilight made the glow detectable over the Rocky Mountains.

Four such arcs were seen by Barbier during a period of about one year and he reported that, at Tamanrasset in southern Algeria, an oasis and French military post on the trans-Saharan auto track, the glow intensity changed tenfold within periods of two or three hours.

A faint aurora was visible on the northern horizon at both the French and American observatories during the September 29 phenomenon, but Roach found that it was separated from the red glow by about 560 miles. When he had the French and American data, it occurred to Roach that the light over France and Colorado might have been a single arc, 350 miles wide, extending around a considerable portion of the earth. He suggested a possible link with the inner Van Allen radiation belt, whose trapped particles hung in the sky high above the area in question.[5] The aurora on the northern horizon lay, perhaps significantly, under the outer radiation belt.

Another photometer, looking straight up, went into operation at the United States Air Force Base at Thule in October, 1958, and during the next two months got in only sixteen nights of observation—a rather sad commentary on the weather of northern Greenland. Scanning for the green light of oxygen (5577 angstroms), it recorded both auroras and airglow, but, when the intensities were plotted graphically, it was found that the aurora merged smoothly into the airglow. Apparently, so far as this part of the spectrum was concerned, the only distinction between the two grew out of the weakness of the human eye. The evidence, said Roach and his associates, "strongly suggests that a common physical mechanism should be sought [to account] for both." [6]

When the IGY was over, however, neither Roach nor the other specialists were able to explain the various forms of airglow to their mutual satisfaction. Most of the layers seemed to store up the energy of sunlight and then radiate it at night at wavelengths characteristic of the emitting atoms. This seemed to be true of the water vapor (hydroxyl) and of the sodium. The seasonal change in the sodium light, however, was still a mystery, for it is bright in winter and perhaps completely absent in summer. Nor was it known where the sodium comes from, for it is not an ordinary component of the atmosphere. Some said winds carry salt from sea spray aloft, where sunlight breaks it down into sodium and chlorine. Others suggested meteors or clouds of solar gas as the source.

The chief excitement concerned the peculiarities of the oxygen emissions. Not only did the green glow seem part and parcel of the green aurora, but its intensity, in the middle latitudes, seemed to be subtly correlated with the level of magnetic activity. The red light of oxygen, emitted far higher (above 125 miles), and forming what seemed to be earth-girdling arcs, was even more clearly associated with magnetic storms.

Still unaccounted for were the airglow motions. The green oxygen light came from just above a region of minimum temperature, where Roach speculated there might be jet streams. Other possibilities were convection currents or some form of turbulence. He cited the newly detected sheet currents and the patchiness of electron density known as sporadic-E, all of which might play a role.

"From the present study," he and his men reported, "*one* mechanism cannot be pointed to as the only possibility. This is perhaps not a very happy situation, but it may be that Nature is using two different mechanisms to generate the observed emissions." [7]

Zodiacal light

One of the phenomena that stirred superstitious awe among the ancient Egyptians was a pyramid of light that appeared in the east during the final hours before dawn in autumn and in the west after spring sunsets. This is zodiacal light. Because it can be seen clearly only between the tropics of Cancer and Capricorn, where the zodiac, at suitable times, is perpendicular to the horizon, it was unknown to European astronomers until the seventeenth century. The zodiac is the highway across the heavens along which the sun and planets appear to travel. To observe the light to best advantage, several expeditions went south during the IGY.

Interest in the phenomenon was more than casual, for it seemed to hold a clue to the nature of the path between the sun and the earth. It had long been thought that the light was produced by a great, lens-shaped cloud of dust circling the sun in roughly the same plane as the planets. It was calculated that the particles needed to be no closer than five miles to one another to account for the observed light, whose spectrum indicated that it was reflected sunlight.

In 1953, however, more refined observations disclosed that about a quarter of the light was polarized. This seemed to mean that a substantial part of it was reflected by free electrons forming part of the lens-shaped cloud, but it was difficult to explain why electrons would stay there. It was therefore suggested that interplanetary space might be far less of a vacuum than had been supposed, with as many as 600 or 800 electrons per cubic centimeter (that is, per half thimbleful) at the earth's distance from the sun. They would be visible, in the zodiac, because of their tendency to reflect light at right angles. The idea that there might be so many electrons in space raised many problems with regard to earth-sun relationships.

Two IGY expeditions undertook the study of zodiacal light as their chief goal, in the hope of resolving some of these problems. One, from the Soviet Union, chose a site in the Egyptian part of the Libyan Desert, about twenty miles south of Aswan and almost directly on the Tropic of Cancer. The question of who was to aid the Egyptians in building their high dam across the Nile was still a plaything of great-power politics and the road that was to lead to the dam ended abruptly in the desert. This was an ideal site for observations—remote from light-giving communities, yet accessible. The dry desert air would be particularly stable, optically, and the Egyptian authorities were likely to be cooperative, especially since the Soviet Academy of Sciences assigned responsibility for the expedition to a regional academy in the country's largest Moslem area, the Kazakh Soviet Socialist Republic. It was organized by the Astrophysics Institute in Alma Ata and Vassily G. Fesenkov was placed in charge of the five scientists who made the journey, one of them a woman, Mme. Pyaskovskaya-Fesenkova. Two Egyptian scientists, including another woman, joined the group after its arrival. They reached the site by truck with more than a ton of supplies: food, tents, awnings of sun-reflecting white, "topographic umbrellas," camp furniture, and their scientific instruments.

Fesenkov, who had proposed the expedition to the Academy in Moscow, apparently suspected that the polarization observed in the zodiacal light was due either to properties of the dust (as opposed to electrons) or to some effect produced by the earth's atmosphere. He therefore assigned one group, including the two women, to observe light from the daytime sky. For them, he reported, working conditions in the dry heat were particularly severe. The whole group suffered from lack of sleep, due to a heavy observing schedule. Within commuting distance, at the existing Aswan Dam, the Egyptian government provided a rest house complete with a cook, two servants, and a military guard, all of whom lived in army tents set up on the edge of the property. A guard was also maintained at the observing site.

"The protection assigned to us was actually necessary," Fesenkov said, "especially at the observation area; without it, the members of the expedition themselves would have had to continuously post a watch. At one time, our guards had to fire on 100 attacking jackals, which surrounded us." [8]

Daylight from the almost moistureless desert sky was found to be strongly polarized, presumably by atmospheric dust and air molecules. The data were sent to the Laboratory of Machine Mathematics at the Kazakh Academy of Sciences for computer analysis, to see if this could account for polarization of the zodiacal light. Fesenkov decided that it did—entirely—and he therefore concluded that zodiacal light was virtually all produced by dust. Instead of 600 to 800 electrons per cubic centimeter of space, he concluded, there could be no more than 20 or 30.

In addition, the Russians on the desert had observed the other celestial glow, known as gegenschein (opposite-shine). This is a faint spot of light, almost circular, that appears in the heavens directly opposite the sun. Thus, at 3 A.M., when the sun was halfway up from the nadir to the eastern horizon, the gegenschein was midway between the zenith and the western horizon. As sunrise neared in the east, the gegenschein sank in the west, vanishing at the first hint of daylight. It seemed to be related to zodiacal light and, in fact, at times the Russians could see a faint band arching across the entire zodiac. Presumably this was the less efficiently illuminated part of the dust cloud.

Two members of the Russian party, including Fesenkov, journeyed to China, soon after their return home, to have another look at the zodiacal light and to make a more thorough study of the gegenschein. They joined the Sino-Soviet expedition that went to Hainan for the April, 1958, eclipse. Here they were much nearer the equator than they had been at Aswan. To escape the light of scattered Chinese villages they set up their instruments several miles from the eclipse party, taking observations of the gegenschein spectrum, of variations in its brightness and of its parallax.[9]

As the Russians headed homeward from Hainan, two Englishmen from Cambridge University were bound for the highest of all IGY outposts: the Chacaltaya Observatory, 17,100 feet above sea level in the Bolivian Andes. They, too, sought to measure the stuff of interplanetary space by means of the zodiacal light. The leader, D. E. Blackwell, believed that, by making the observations at high altitude, where the intervening air was at a minimum, the chances of solving the riddle would be greatly improved. He had already observed an eclipse from an aircraft at 30,000 feet, in an attempt to measure the density of electrons out to about eight million miles from the sun.

The little stone hut astride the Andes was still banked with snow when the Englishmen arrived in May, 1958. To their surprise, they found the station unmanned. Its cosmic-ray recorders operated automatically and only periodically did someone from La Paz come up, puffing and panting in the rarefied air, to service the equipment. The Bolivians furnished a cook, which spared the Britons from household chores, but water supply was a serious problem. Large quantities were needed to process their film and, when the snow melted in June, their only local source of water vanished with it, forcing them to haul water up from La Paz in a jeeplike vehicle. Although they discovered another source, in the shaft of an abandoned lead mine, the use of this water proved to be a mistake, for Blackwell, who was already functioning at low efficiency because of the altitude, began developing symptoms of lead poisoning.

The reward for these hardships was a dazzling view of the zodiacal light through the clear, thin mountain air. At that time of year the zodiac was vertical after sunset, rather than before dawn, and the Englishmen spent some thirty-two nights watching the last trace of day fade from the snowy peaks and then seeing the rounded pyramid of light where the sun had gone down an hour before.

Their line of attack was to see if the light's spectrum showed the same sharp black lines (Fraunhofer lines) that are characteristic of sunlight. If you look at the sun, even through the simplest vest-pocket spectroscope, the colors do not blend smoothly one into another. There are lines, as though someone had divided up the spectrum with a black pencil. The reason is that, in the light's passage through the sun's atmosphere, certain sharply defined parts of the spectrum have been filtered out. Blackwell figured that, if free electrons were responsible for an appreciable part of the zodiacal light, their thermal motion would weaken these lines. To obtain the strongest possible readings, the two men made spectograph exposures of about seven hours (actually a week-long succession of one-hour exposures), and found no evidence of electrons. Hence, Blackwell reported, there must be fewer than fifty electrons per cubic centimeter—a conclusion that was quite compatible with the Russian results.[10]

Noctilucent clouds

The other luminous puzzle that was investigated during the IGY was that of noctilucent clouds. These are said to have first been recorded in the 1880s, when they aroused curiosity because of their great height, calculated to be about fifty miles. They are a rare sight, seen primarily during summer twilight near the northern horizon in the latitudes of Canada, northern Europe, and the Soviet Union. They seem to move at great speeds. The explosion of Krakatoa, a volcanic island in the East Indies, in 1883 threw up dust that spread around the world. Hence, at first, many attributed noctilucent clouds to this eruption. The only large-scale attack on this question during the IGY was that of the Soviet Union. Some investigators proposed that these were clouds of meteoric dust illuminated, and perhaps electrically excited, by sunlight or by incoming atomic particles. The Russians took time-lapse (extremely slow motion) moving pictures of the clouds and found that they manifested strange wave motions.[11] At this writing, however, their nature is still unresolved.

CHAPTER 15
THE OCEAN ABOVE

Among the many men in the eighteenth century who thrilled to the new vision science had given them was the youthful operator of a printing establishment in Philadelphia. In hot pursuit of knowledge he once chased a whirlwind on horseback until it sent twigs and branches swirling about his head. In 1743 he looked forward to seeing an eclipse of the moon, only to be disappointed when one of those unbridled storms, a northeaster, enveloped Philadelphia in rain and clouds.

In correspondence with friends in Boston he learned that they had had a fine view of the eclipse. Although the Massachusetts city was directly upwind from Philadelphia, the storm had not reached there until some hours later. This was startling, for it had been assumed that northeasters move, with the wind, toward the southwest. The young man drew upon his knowledge of whirlwinds and suggested that such storms were huge cyclones, brewed in the Gulf of Mexico, rather than in the North Atlantic. He calculated that this one had traveled from Philadelphia to Boston at 100 miles per hour. The early inquirer into meteorology was, of course, Benjamin Franklin, then thirty-seven years old. It was a time when the new freedom of thought had stimulated men of many callings, in Europe and America, to look more keenly at the world about them—clergymen, country squires, physicians, and natural philosophers. Weather records, kept at Williamsburg, Virginia, from 1772 to 1776 (by Thomas Jefferson or Bishop James Madison) have shown the climate of two centuries ago, despite intervening fluctuations, to have been not very different from that of today.

Franklin is best known for his studies of lightning and atmospheric electricity by means of kites. He was not alone in using this technique. Dr. Alexander Wilson in Glasgow, Scotland, sent up thermometers by kite and, in 1749, obtained the first upper-air temperatures. However, before the century ended, a new and better tool for upper-air exploration had been invented: the balloon. Like the swifter space vehicles that came later, it had its early ups and downs. Among the first to attempt a flight was Jean Pierre Blanchard. As his balloon was inflated in the presence of a large multitude at Billancourt on the outskirts of Paris in 1784, a man leaped into the car with him, drew his sword and demanded to be taken along. He was finally removed by force. It was later reported that the intruder was Napoleon Bonaparte, but this was subsequently disproved. The next year Blanchard teamed up with an American physician, Dr. J. Jeffries, to make the first flight across the English channel. Jeffries, in an ascent from London, seems to have been the first to use ballooning for scientific ends, measuring temperature, pressure, and humidity during the flight.

The French, in large measure, led the way into the sky. Not only was the balloon invented there, but it was Frenchmen who did much of the early research with this vehicle. In 1804 Joseph Gay-Lussac ascended from the Conservatoire des Arts in Paris to a height of about 23,000 feet. On the ground it was a typical Parisian summer day, with the thermometer at 82°, but at the top of his flight it was a frigid 14.9°. He came down near the coast. As any mountain climber knows, the temperature drops steadily with elevation, but it had been thought that this might be due to some effect of the mountain itself. The balloon flights showed it was an inherent property of the atmosphere. The early explorers of the sky found that this rate of temperature decline was fairly constant. If it continued falling at the same rate, they calculated, it would reach absolute zero at a height of about twenty miles. Absolute zero is the total absence of heat and is 460° below zero Fahrenheit. It was therefore assumed that the top of the atmosphere was twenty miles overhead, beyond which lay the emptiness of interplanetary space.

Man's urge to reach ever higher was hampered by a major obstacle. With increasing elevation the air became too thin to sustain life. Thus, in 1862, James Glaisher of the British Association for the Advancement of Science reached an estimated 37,000 feet, but he could make no scientific observations, for he lay, crumpled and unconscious, on the floor of the basket, having passed out at about 29,000 feet.

The French came up with an answer: what they called *ballons sondes* (sounding balloons). These were unmanned and carried self-recording instruments that, if recovered, could be read to determine changes in temperature, pressure, and humidity during the flight. They were developed during the 1890s and were flown at a large number of locations in a systematic exploration of the atmosphere. The result was discovery of the stratosphere by Leon Philippe Teisserenc de Bort and his co-workers. The higher-reaching balloon flights showed that, instead of dropping steadily, the temperature suddenly leveled off, or even began to rise, at a certain elevation. This came to be known as the tropopause. It was found to be highest—about twelve miles— over the equator, sloping down to only four miles above the poles. Below it lay the turbulent, moist air in which most of our weather manifests itself (the troposphere). Above was the relatively smooth, dry stratosphere.

The chief remaining difficulty was that, unless the balloon could be found after a flight, the ascent was a waste of time. This meant trying to keep track of a speck in the sky, galloping after it on horseback in an attempt at recovery. The development of more modern methods of pursuit was helpful, but the real solution lay in the invention of a telemetering system.

As early as 1875 a Dutch instrument-maker devised a method for transmitting the readings of weather instruments by wire and in 1917 this idea was applied to kite flying. Instruments suspended from a kite sent their readings to the ground via the wire with which the kite was being flown. The invention of radio opened the way for a more practical method, and in 1921 experimenters in Europe and America began trying to send up radio transmitters. Their first objective was to develop a radio beacon for keeping track of the balloon, so that it could be recovered in cloudy weather as well as fair. It was only a short step from a radio serving solely as a beacon to one that could send coded instrument readings from aloft. The difficulty was that electronic equipment, in those days, was cumbersome, expensive—and heavy. Nevertheless in 1929–30 experimenters in Finland, France, Germany, and the Soviet Union achieved several successful flights with such *radiosondes*. They began to be sent aloft in the United States by about the end of 1934 and became a routine tool of upper-air observation two years later.[1]

These developments were of historic importance, for almost all satellite and rocket experiments of recent years have depended upon telemetering. Radiosondes added a third dimension to observations of the weather and helped to clarify a number of surprising dis-

coveries, the first of which is attributed to the German meteorologist, Johannes Georgi, who, while conducting balloon observations
from Iceland in 1926–27, discovered an extremely high wind six to
nine miles overhead. His subsequent balloon flights from a ship in
the Greenland Sea showed that this wind was extensive and apparently
not related to surface weather changes. It is said to have been his de-
sire to extend exploration of such upper air winds that prompted
him to propose the Second Polar Year.

Not until World War II, however, did the existence of these winds
become generally known. Pilots ferrying aircraft from North America
to Britain found that, if they chose the right route, they were carried
swiftly eastward on the shoulders of a powerful air current that came
to be known as the jet stream. Its core reached a speed of 200 miles
an hour or more, which was enough to bring to a standstill a small
plane that tried to buck it.

The intensive observations of the IGY disclosed that, in the autumn, another jet stream forms high in the polar stratosphere. At many
of the more than 2000 weather stations ashore extra-large balloons
were released at the same instant daily to provide a simultaneous picture of the world's weather twenty miles aloft. They revealed patterns
of pressure and temperature that were remarkably smooth when compared to lower levels where the influence of oceans, continents, and
mountains makes the picture far more complex. It was found that in
winter almost the entire flow is from west to east, focused in two intense jet streams. One, centered seven miles up at the tropopause, lies
roughly over the southern borders of the United States; the other,
with its core at an elevation of twenty miles or more, crosses northern
Canada, encircling the Arctic in what is known as the Polar-Night Jet
Stream. The latter forms the core of a great, eastward-flowing, circumpolar current termed the Polar-Night Vortex.

In spring there is a mighty shifting of gears. The Polar-Night Vortex,
including the entire circulation of the upper stratosphere, reverses direction; the more southerly jet continues to blow from the west, but
becomes weaker and moves north from the latitude of Texas to that
of the Great Lakes. There are two similar jets south of the equator,
making four in all. The southern Polar-Night Jet Stream was found
to encircle Antarctica.

The charting of the southern tropospheric jet stream was of vital
concern to the airlines. A weather man of Pan American-Grace Air-

ways reported that the IGY had led to a 50 per cent improvement in forecasting of high-altitude winds over portions of the South American routes. On December 8, 1957, an unusually violent storm appeared on the flight path across the highest part of the Andes, between Buenos Aires and Santiago. Because of the IGY network it was possible for the airline to reschedule its flights in safety. As reported by an official of the company, through the data provided on that day alone, the new network "paid for itself." [2]

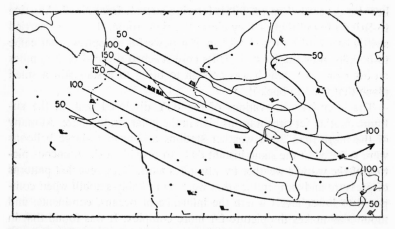

The Polar-Night Jet Stream as it was found to lie from December 31, 1957, to January 3, 1958, at an elevation of 80,000 feet. The speed along its axis was about 180 knots, with lesser speeds on the sides as shown by the other lines. The dots are stations from which balloon flights were made.[3]

The net had another important effect, as well. When combined with the other IGY activities in South America, it stimulated a sudden and significant growth of the physical sciences in that region. Not only did the United States provide modern equipment, but men were trained to use it and were given Spanish-language operating manuals.

Explosive warmings

Despite the interest in jet streams, with their obvious importance for air travelers, another upper-air phenomenon had aroused even greater curiosity among weather men. This was the so-called Berlin Warming. When a balloon was released from Berlin on February 21,

1952, carrying United States Air Force radiosonde equipment, it traced a normal pattern of temperature change. The readings dropped steadily to the bottom of the stratosphere, about seven miles up, then remained at about the same value (—94°) to a height of fifteen miles, where they became slightly warmer. A flight two days later, however, disclosed that, in the highest region accessible to the balloons, between fifteen and twenty miles up, the temperature had risen by some 81°. German meteorologists described the warming as "explosive" because of the rapidity with which it appeared. They hypothesized that the heating was the consequence of an eruption that had just occurred on the sun (although later examination showed that the high temperatures had developed over polar North America some days before the solar flare and had then drifted over Berlin).

The idea that at least part of our weather might be imposed by extraterrestrial sources of energy encouraged weather men the world over to keep a special lookout for such sudden warmings and, by the end of the IGY, a number had been observed, including one in Antarctica.[4] Two of them, involving the region between Canada and Iceland in early 1957 and again in early 1958, were of the same great magnitude as that observed over Berlin. In such cases the near-circular polar vortex became distorted, with winds from the south and north replacing those from the west. These events took place in winter, often in the latitudes of the polar night, with midsummer temperatures often recorded. The polar night vortex then was re-established briefly until it was replaced by the reverse vortex of the summer months.

The use of rockets presented the explosive warmings in a new light. On the evening of January 26, 1958, a group of men under William G. Stroud of the United States Army's Signal Research and Development Laboratory worked over an Aerobee rocket designed to explore winds and temperatures high above Fort Churchill, Canada. Theirs was delicate work, for in the nose of the rocket were nineteen large grenades, primed and ready to shoot. Only an electrical safety system that pulled away at firing stood in the way of an accidental eruption of fireworks.

At four minutes past midnight the rocket roared into the night sky and, at a height of eighteen miles, began to shoot grenades out of its nose, continuing to do so every two miles until it arched over at its summit of fifty-six miles. In front of each grenade, in the nose cone, was a hole containing a styrofoam plug that was knocked out as the grenade shot forward, driven by two small black-powder rockets. Each grenade was attached to the Aerobee by a fourteen-foot lanyard which, when it drew taut, pulled the firing pin and set off several pounds of high explosive. The grenades were designed to produce a minimum of shrapnel and a maximum of noise. In ground tests it was found that, even five feet from the rocket nose, they did no damage.

The determination of wind speed and direction in the layer between each pair of explosions was based on the fact that air movement affects sound transmission. Sound waves are carried with the wind, so that a bang in the sky, heard on the ground, appears to come from a point downwind from the actual position of the explosion. Temperature could be determined, since it affects the travel time of the sound. To make practical use of these principles, extremely precise data were needed, both on the direction from which the sound seemed to have come and on the actual position of the rocket at the time of each explosion.

This was achieved by means of a radio-tracking system known as *DOVAP*,[5] plus an array of nine microphones, laid out on the ground at thousand-foot intervals in the shape of a great cross. The time of each explosion could be determined through its effect on the radio signal from the rocket. There was a ceiling of about ninety-six miles on the use of this technique because, above that level, the air was too thin to carry enough sound for the experiment, even when a four-pound charge was exploded.

A second grenade rocket was fired twelve hours after the midnight shot to see what changes were wrought by sunlight, but it was a long time before the results could be calculated. For each shot, some 400,-000 doppler cycles had to be counted by hand before the trajectory could be calculated.

Hence it was not until about a year later that the experimenters discovered they had detected the start of an explosive warming. The two shots found that the strong westerlies typical of the winter season had broken down. Below twenty-eight miles the wind was from the northeast, but above that level it was blowing from the south, the southerly wind extending up as high as forty-seven miles. Balloon data from far to the east showed that a sudden warming had begun there, but similar observations over Fort Churchill showed no evidence of heating or of a wind shift in the lower stratosphere. In fact, no rise in temperature was observed at higher levels, where the grenades were fired. Apparently the polar vortex broke down first at very high altitude and the warming came afterward. In this case the temperature change that followed was spectacular. It was detected by another type of rocket experiment at Fort Churchill, using free-falling spheres.

The first attempt to measure upper-air density with falling spheres was in 1952, using a large inflated ball whose rate of fall was determined by tracking from the ground. The device used during the IGY required no ground tracking whatsoever. It was an aluminum sphere, developed by a group at the University of Michigan under Leslie M. Jones, with a diameter of seven inches—about the size of a melon— and a weight of eleven pounds. Inside were an accelerometer and a radio transmitter. The former determined the extent to which the ball was being slowed by air drag and the transmitter reported the results. Its antenna was packed into a groove so that it was flush with the outside of the sphere. The central element of the accelerometer was a bobbin that floated free in the weightlessness of unimpeded flight, but even the slightest drag on the sphere caused the bobbin to touch one side of its chamber, sending a signal to the experimenters. Thereupon the bobbin was quickly recaptured, automatically, and released again from the center of the sphere. The sphere was ejected from the soaring rocket at thirty-four miles elevation and its momentum carried it up to sixty miles; it reported drag both on the up-leg and the down-leg. The drag was a measure of atmospheric density, which in turn could be used to compute temperatures.

After preliminary shots during the pre-IGY period, the first spheres pitched into the sky during the IGY were sent up, by good fortune, just before, during, and just after the explosive warming of January, 1958. The initial one, thrown aloft by a Nike-Cajun rocket on January 25, found normal temperatures up to its peak at fifty-seven miles; the next, carried by the grenade-firing Aerobee at noon on January 27, still disclosed nothing unusual. It was the third sphere, shot up on January 29, that detected a remarkable heating in the region between eighteen and thirty-four miles. At twenty-five miles the increase had been 122° in the past ninety-six hours. A fourth experiment, on February 4, indicated that the temperature had dropped back, but was still not down to normal.

North American balloon data from fifteen miles up showed that the whole weather picture had been swung around. Instead of flowing in a circumpolar vortex, the jet stream cut right across the North Pole. Balloons released from Drifting Station A, near the Pole, detected winds fifteen miles overhead of more than 132 miles an hour. As an

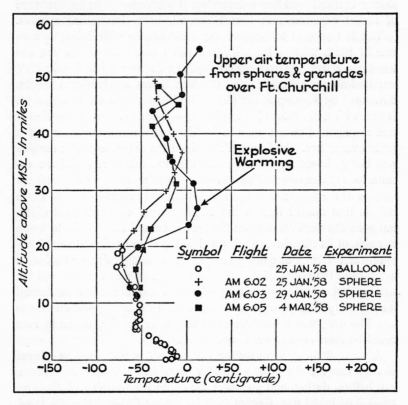

IGY rocket and balloon observations provided the first view in depth of the strange phenomenon known as an "explosive warming." This graph shows the temperatures at altitudes up to fifty miles above mean sea level as observed on various days in 1958 above Fort Churchill, Canada. Falling spheres, ejected by a rocket on January 29, disclosed a sudden and radical warming at twenty-five miles elevation. The temperature rose 122° Fahrenheit in 96 hours.

effect of the event, the Russians reported, an immense mass of cold stratospheric air shifted southward from the Arctic to a position over Europe and west Siberia.[6]

The sequence of events suggested to Stroud and his associates that the phenomenon had been propagated downward from far above the stratosphere. They pointed out that the first observed change, over Churchill, was a shift of winds in the very high atmosphere; the next was a warming at great heights; and finally the warming extended down into the stratosphere.[7] It also looked as though the effect moved westward, sloping downward in the atmosphere from west to east, since it could be observed at comparatively low levels over Greenland when it was still very high over central Canada.

Although Stroud and his men did not argue in favor of an extraterrestrial origin for explosive warmings, they did note that at least one effect of solar flares on the atmosphere had apparently been found: the correlation with changes in atmospheric density 200 miles up (discussed later in this chapter). A group of solar physicists has long fought for acceptance of the possibility that solar flares affect the weather, foremost among them being Charles G. Abbot, former secretary of the Smithsonian Institution. Walter Orr Roberts, head of the High Altitude Observatory at the University of Colorado, and his associates have sought, in particular, to correlate changes in storm tracks with solar eruptions. The skeptics have argued that the energies involved in weather events are too great to be influenced by solar flares, which produce only slight changes in the total flow of solar energy to the earth. This, they feel, would be like a mouse herding elephants, for the forces at work in the lower atmosphere are awesome to anyone contemplating "weather control." It is estimated that the thunderstorms normally occurring over the earth during a few days' time dispose of more energy than would be released by the world's entire stock of hydrogen and atom bombs.[8] The question of solar effects on weather may be resolved by the new National Center for Atmospheric Research, formed in 1960 with Roberts as its head.

Antarctic weather

Another area of concentrated weather studies was the Antarctic. Not until the establishment of IGY bases there had it been possible to map that region's weather even on the surface, nor had any winter observations been made in the continental hinterland. As had been expected, the inland plateau proved to be the coldest place on earth. On August 25, 1958, two Russians, looking somewhat like divers with their moleskin face masks, breathing apparatus, and heavy furs, tried to launch a huge weather balloon at the same moment that thousands of other scientists were doing likewise all over the globe, but for them it was a special day. The diesel fuel that kept their trailer huts warm was thick as honey and the rubbery parts of their equipment had become brittle; the temperature at their camp, Station Vostok, had sunk to 125.3° below zero—the lowest ever recorded up to that time on the surface of the earth.

Such low readings were not surprising, since Vostok and its companion station, Sovietskaya, were far higher and more remote from the sea than any others near either pole. By contrast, Wilkes Station, on the antarctic coast, had milder winters than those of Nebraska. Furthermore, a layer of warm air lay only a short distance above the inland stations. On September 18, 1957, the temperature 1700 feet over the American base at the South Pole was 74° warmer than at the surface. Another feature of weather at the Pole Station was the remarkable steadiness of wind direction there. It was almost never calm, yet only one real storm was experienced during the first year. Of the hourly observations, about 75 per cent recorded winds in the range of thirteen to twenty-nine miles an hour. On the other hand, Byrd Station—at a point in Marie Byrd Land about half as high as the Pole—had almost continuous storminess from July to September, 1957.

The reason for these differences became apparent through the work of the Weather Central at Little America. There, in a long, narrow prefabricated structure weather men from the United States and several other countries, notably Argentina and the Soviet Union, joined forces to piece together the reports sent in daily by the sixteen antarctic stations sending up weather balloons, plus a few others from ships, planes, or trail parties. To achieve the greatest possible elevation before they burst, the balloons were presoaked in some such substance as diesel oil to delay their becoming brittle in the cold. Once a balloon had been released into the blizzard-swept sky, its observations were automatically inscribed on paper moving slowly past the Weather Central's recording devices. A radar, also automatic, kept track of the rising balloon's erratic movements, which were converted into wind speeds and directions. All would go smoothly, the weather elements changing gradually, until suddenly they would all run amok. At this point the operator would rise from his stool and switch off the equipment, for he knew that the balloon, having soared fifteen or twenty miles, had burst.

A dominating factor in antarctic weather seemed to be the succession of storms whose centers moved around a racetrack encircling the continent. The most severe storms drifted westward in arclike paths several hundred miles off shore, whereas smaller storms followed the coastline. They rarely penetrated the high central plateau, where

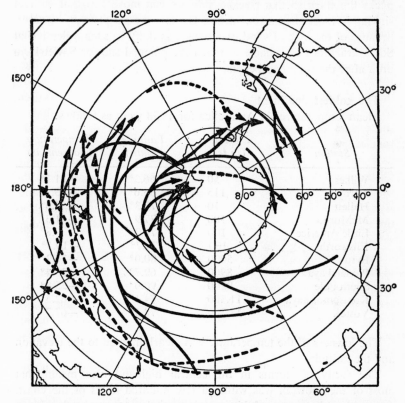

Antarctic storm tracks as compiled by the IGY Weather Central at Little America for the southern winter of 1957. The solid lines represent cyclonic systems. The dashed lines are anti-cyclones. A more detailed map of Antarctica appears on page 308. (National Academy of Sciences)

the South Pole station and Vostok were located, but they often swung into the Ross Sea off Little America. Some seemed to linger there; others swept across Marie Byrd Land to the Weddell Sea, accounting for the miserable weather at Byrd Station. The circular movement of air appeared to be centered near the highest part of the inland plateau, rather than at the South Pole. The result was that, whereas the wind blew almost constantly at the Pole, there was very little wind in the central portion of the ice sheet, where the Russian stations Sovietskaya and Vostok were situated. In most of Antarctica, wind packs the snow so that tracked vehicles can move across it without sinking in more than a few inches. On this central plateau, however, because of the lack of wind, the snow was fluffy to such a depth that Soviet tractors were unable to reach the planned site for Sovietskaya until after the IGY had begun.

The coldest continent
Mean temperatures in Antarctica for 1958 were as follows:

Station	Elevation (*in feet*)	Latitude (*south*)	Temperature (*Fahrenheit*)
Wilkes	50	66.3°	+21.7°
Mirny	115	66.6°	+10.9°
Hallett	10	72.3°	+ 4.6°
McMurdo	100	77.9°	− 1.3°
Little America	100	78.2°	− 9.8°
Ellsworth	100	77.7°	−10.5°
Byrd	5000	80.0°	−20.2°
Pionerskaya	8900	69.7°	−38.4°
South Pole	9200	90.0°	−55.8°
Komsomolskaya	11,300	74.1°	−62.5°
Vostok	11,300	78.5°	−67.7°

The lowness of the temperature was clearly related to the elevation and the latitude.

The rarity of storms in the central highland also meant that most of the snowfall was within a few hundred miles of the coast. A considerable amount of this snow is carried out to sea by the almost incessant winds sweeping down the coastal slopes. Cold air, being heavy, runs off the plateau in winds that are often of hurricane force. These winds made the launching of the balloons extremely difficult, although the Russians reported that, by April, 1958, they had missed only a single scheduled launching at Mirny, that one occasion being when a 110-mile-an-hour gale tore the covering off the tower designed to shield the balloon until it was released. At Oazis, the smaller base set up by the Russians at the snow-free "oasis" discovered by American fliers in 1947, the meteorological hut was torn apart and strewn over an area a mile long. Similar battles with the wind were fought at many of the antarctic stations. This outward rush of air from the hinterland is replaced by warm air blowing inland immediately above the surface layer, but apparently the Polar-Night Jet, flowing around the coast, acts as a barrier to prevent an influx of warm northern air at higher elevations in the stratosphere.

Thus, in the antarctic hinterland, there is far less exchange of air with warmer latitudes than occurs at the North Pole. In the north, spring warming is felt in the stratosphere in January and early February before the returning sun has reached it, whereas in the Antarctic this warming does not come until the sun has returned.

Although weather reports from the great ocean areas surrounding Antarctica were meager, it was evident that masses of cold air periodically break loose from the continent and go sailing out toward New Zealand, Australia, Africa, or South America.

As a result of their observations, the Russians made the startling suggestion that the shape of Antarctica has been determined, in part, by storm tracks. The continent, as it appears on maps, is largely not a land feature, but a great sheet of ice. Beneath it, of course, there is land, much of it above sea level, but the distribution of ice, as determined by IGY exploration, does not conform to the distribution of land. Thus the Russians found that the extent to which the continental ice sheet and its fringe of sea ice extended out from the coast seemed dependent on the patterns of storm movement. Likewise, American scientists noted that some of the thickest ice—more than two miles deep—lies along the storm path from the Ross Sea to the Weddell Sea.

Ocean areas

The gaps in oceanic coverage of weather were very large, even during the IGY. Vast portions of the earth's surface are seen only sporadically by ships or planes, and their reports are often incomplete. Two techniques were used to fill some of these holes. One was to release large balloons from Japan and let them drift with the prevailing westerlies. This was the peaceful application of a scheme the Japanese had used during World War II to send incendiary bombs to the United States. The weather balloons, forty feet in diameter, were released by the United States Navy from its air station at Iwakuni, carrying a load of 600 pounds or more. This consisted of ballast plus a radio beacon set to transmit for fifteen minutes every two hours. Radio direction-finders around the Pacific were thus able to follow its meandering flight and thereby determine wind speeds and directions over little-frequented parts of the ocean. The balloons were set to fly at either 30,000 or 34,000 feet and often reached the coast of the United States within two days.

Although they were capable of staying up a week and, perhaps, encircling the world, a timer was set to bring them down after four days lest their heavy loads imperil jet aircraft crossing the Atlantic. For political reasons the balloons were not released when there seemed a possibility of their blowing toward neighboring China, but at least one of them drifted across eastern Siberia. Others landed as far afield as the South Pacific and Greenland during the course of the project (from September, 1957, through April, 1959). Of 100 launchings during 1958–59, all but a dozen were tracked for at least a day.[9]

These free-drifting balloons were known as transosondes. The other device used to fill midocean gaps was the drop-sonde. This carried a package similar to that lifted by radiosondes, except that it was dropped by parachute from a plane instead of being sent up by balloon. Of the two routes flown for these drops, one was of special interest because it was aimed squarely across the rarely frequented breeding ground for the hurricanes that devastate the Atlantic seaboard from Cuba to New England.

All of these drop-sonde flights were made to or from Puerto Rico and all took place in connection with World Meteorological Intervals. These periods, each of ten-day duration, were scheduled every three months during the IGY. On the more northerly of the two routes, along a line between Puerto Rico and North Africa, twenty flights were made to span such a Meteorological Interval in March, 1958. On the other route, aimed a little to the south of due east from Puerto Rico, the plane, flying at 10,000 feet, turned back before crossing the ocean. On each of the four thrusts in this direction thirteen drop-sondes were released, recording among other things the heights of the trade-wind moist layer. Sometimes there were marked changes in these heights between the outward flight and the time of return past the same area. Because it was thought that some quirk in the easterly trades set a hurricane in motion, these changes were earmarked for special study.[10]

Additional oceanic observations were, of course, obtained from ships, particularly weather ships stationed along such well-traveled routes as the North Atlantic. It was in the less-frequented parts of the ocean that the major gaps lay, and there the only clues were from a few island observatories. These nevertheless helped bring to light an extraordinary IGY discovery. This was a cyclic sinking and reversal of upper-air wind streams over the equator. When Krakatoa blew up in 1883, its dust was carried from east to west twice around the earth within a month. The phenomenon was attributed to winds, nineteen miles aloft, that came to be known as the Krakatoa Easterlies. An opposite flow lay near the twelve-mile level. A study of winds aloft, observed from ten equatorial stations for the forty months ending in May, 1959, indicated that each of these currents steadily lost altitude, being replaced, above, by a flow in the opposite direction. What was particularly strange was that this cycle took twenty-six months, suggesting that it was unrelated to the change of seasons.[11]

Radiation balance

One of the most ambitious, yet simple, approaches to problems of meteorology is the study of heat and radiation balance. This is, in effect, the global approach, although it depends on the most precise observations of what is happening on portions of the earth's surface no larger than a postage stamp. It is an attempt to ignore the trees and visualize the forest. Since the sun shines upon the earth comparatively uniformly, from day to day, it must be properties of the earth itself that produce the weather. What are they? What happens to the sun's radiation as it shines upon our planet? How is it disposed of?

Studies before the IGY had shown that only 45 per cent of the sun's radiated energy is absorbed by land, water, and ice on the earth's surface. Another 18 per cent is absorbed by clouds and water vapor in the lower atmosphere, and 2 per cent is captured between twelve and thirty-eight miles overhead, where ozone is heated by the absorption of ultraviolet radiation. The remaining 35 per cent of the radiation is reflected directly back into space. The cooling of the troposphere with increasing altitude is due to the growing distance from the warm earth, whereas sun-heated ozone helps maintain the temperature at greater elevations. It was evident that any changes in this pattern could bring about radical changes in climate and weather. Special IGY programs therefore sought to observe radiation balance, particularly near the poles, as well as variations in the richness of the atmosphere in ozone and carbon dioxide.

It was known that more of the sun's heat is absorbed, in low latitudes, than is reradiated back into space, whereas the reverse is true nearer the polar regions. The movement of warm air and water toward the poles keeps the mechanism in equilibrium. What were lacking were sufficiently precise measurements of the radiation balance in various areas to spell out its role in producing weather. As part of the American program, six antarctic stations, the two drifting stations of the Arctic and the station on the Hawaiian peak, Mauna Loa, were equipped with instruments that looked either up or down to measure incoming and outgoing radiation. The incoming component proved to be the most intense at the South Pole, due to the extremely dry, dust-free air, but it had little effect, since as much as 94 per cent of the amount striking the hard, white surface was reflected back into the sky. Sometimes, when clouds hung overhead as radiation mirrors but did not cover the sun, the measured intensity at the station was greater than that known to be striking the top of the atmosphere (equivalent to two calories per square centimeter per minute).[12]

When solar radiation is reradiated upward it is on the long-wave or infra-red side of the spectrum. Such waves do not penetrate moisture and carbon dioxide with the ease of the incoming short-wave radiation. Hence, at Drifting Station Alpha, on the Arctic Ocean, it was found that summer melting was most rapid under a cloudy sky that held in the heat like the glass roof of a greenhouse. When it cleared and the sun shone brightly, refreezing was apt to occur.

Another, somewhat similar, "greenhouse effect" is produced by carbon dioxide. Because of it, some suspected that the warming of the climate during the first half of the twentieth century might be man's own doing. During the past fifty years our industry, vehicles, and homes have released large amounts of carbon dioxide into the atmosphere through the burning of such fuels as coal, oil, and gasoline. Although at least some of this was absorbed by the oceans, a study of the radiocarbon content of wood from trees that grew in preindustrial times with that in more recent trees suggested that the carbon dioxide content had increased at least 2 per cent, and perhaps as much as 10 per cent.

Hence a special IGY project sought, at some sixty stations around the world, to measure the amount of carbon dioxide in the atmosphere, to determine its distribution and establish a basis for future detection of any increase. Surface amounts were strikingly uniform as recorded by ship and at stations from Antarctica to Hawaii. On one occasion a research vessel in mid-Pacific observed a sudden increase for a few minutes, but it turned out that a ship had passed that way a short time before. Another time there was a marked increase during a violent rain squall and the carbon dioxide enrichment was found to have penetrated the ocean to a depth of at least 200 feet.[13]

There was also a study of atmospheric ozone. This is a form of oxygen in which, under stimulation such as that of ultraviolet light, each molecule picks up an extra oxygen atom. Thus the oxygen we breathe is primarily O_2, whereas ozone is O_3. Since it is largely formed more than twelve miles overhead, its distribution in the lower atmosphere at any moment is an indication of air circulation. To determine the amount of ozone in specific portions of the sky, two wavelengths of ultraviolet light were observed, one of them strongly absorbed by ozone, the other not. Comparison of their intensities gave an indication of the amount of the gas along the path of the light. Among the stations that made these measurements was Little America. When there was no sun, during the long winter night, moonlight was used, since, being reflected sunlight, it would serve the same purpose. Because the manufacture of ozone depends on the sun, it was assumed that little or none would be detected during the polar night. Instead, the quantity proved greater than in sunny New Mexico, presumably due to infiltration of air from the north.

It was hoped that the ozone studies would find the holes in the tropopause. This floor that separates the turbulent troposphere from the relatively serene stratosphere seems unbroken, yet it is obvious that, at certain places and at certain times, stratospheric air breaks through to the "floor below."

Fallout

Another project sought to make the best of a bad thing—fallout. An IGY study of this problem had been proposed by the Netherlands National Committee, in 1955, on the grounds that fallout might eventually become a menace to health and that it might even influence the weather. Meteorologists were particularly interested in fallout as a weather tracer. By painstaking analysis of a sample it was possible to determine the date—and hence usually the location—of the bomb explosion that produced it. A fallout study was endorsed by the final pre-IGY conference at Barcelona in September, 1956. Observations were to be made of particles in the air, of those falling on the ground, and of those already in the ground.

To plan the work and standardize collection methods a committee was formed at Barcelona with scientists from the Netherlands, Sweden, and the United States chosen by name. It was understood that others would be designated from three additional countries, including the Soviet Union, but when the committee held its first meeting at Utrecht in January, 1957, no Soviet delegate appeared. The Russians were participating in the United Nations Scientific Committee on the Effects of Atomic Radiation, which was concerned with health problems, but apparently the government in Moscow decided its scientists should not take part in any project that implied fallout had some usefulness.

Because it got off to a late start, the IGY nuclear radiation program did not begin until January 1, 1958, but by spring of that year a pole-to-pole chain of twenty-three stations was carrying out observations under United States auspices. It extended from Station A, on an Arctic floe, to Little America in Antarctica and in general followed the east coast of the United States and the west coast of South America. These same stations carried out many IGY tasks, from satellite tracking to observations of the weather and ionosphere.

By this time some 137 nuclear explosions had taken place, producing an upper-air reservoir of radioactive particles that was carried hither and yon by stratospheric winds. The rate at which this material was transported across the equator and the times and places where it was brought down to the ground were all of meteorological significance. At each of the stations air was drawn through a paper filter at about thirty cubic feet per minute. The filters in most cases were changed daily and sent to either the Naval Research Laboratory or the Air Force Cambridge Research Center, where they were baked into ashes. Monthly composite samples were analyzed for six types of bomb product, plus one natural radio isotope.[14]

The results showed that the world-wide spread of nuclear debris is far more rapid than many had supposed. One of the isotopes particularly useful as a tracer was tungsten-185. Within one month after the Hardtack series of bomb shots, fired early in 1958 in the Marshall Islands, their tungsten-185 by-products were collected at all the stations from South Carolina to Chile. It was concluded that there are occasional bulk movements of air across the equator in the upper

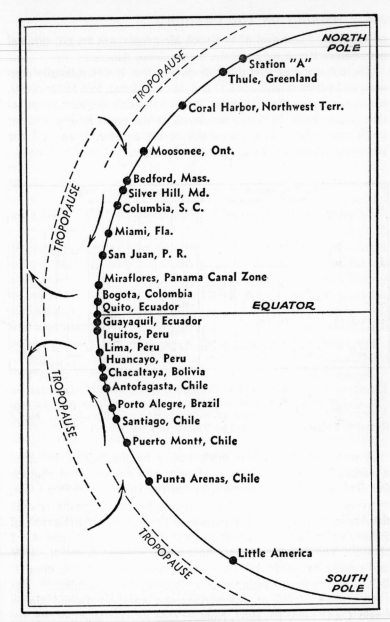

The pole-to-pole chain of fallout stations, established as part of the United States IGY program to study air movements. The arrows represent a provisional concept of the interchange, across the tropopause, between stratosphere and troposphere. (*The New York Times*)

troposphere. The travel of two such air masses was traced, through detection of tungsten-185 at the higher South American sites.

The collection of strontium-90 showed that it was primarily concentrated between latitudes 20° and 40° north and, to a lesser extent, in comparable southern latitudes. It was at a minimum near the equator. During early 1958 the maximum in the north averaged about seven times higher than that south of the equator. Even at Little America, strontium-90 was found in the snow.

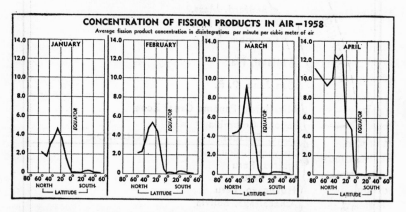

The dramatic increase of fallout during the spring of 1958. The peaks in the right-hand graph are in the latitudes of Philadelphia and Tampa. Almost none of the bomb products were carried across the equator. (Naval Research Laboratory. Adapted by *The New York Times*)

A series of observations made earlier by the British, indicated a marked increase in fallout every spring and a minimum during the fall. This and ozone measurements led the British to propose that, every spring, a large mass of air descends into the troposphere over the Arctic, carrying with it a portion of the stratospheric reservoir of fallout, which is then brought to earth by March winds and April showers. The spring surge in fallout was confirmed during the IGY and subsequent years, but its cause remains uncertain, as does its link, if any, to those harbingers of spring: explosive warmings.

One series of fallout observations was unexpected—and almost tragic. On October 10, 1957, Number One Reactor at Windscale, the British nuclear plant in Cumberland, got out of control and overheated, releasing about 50,000 curies of radioactivity into the atmosphere. Despite an initial scare, no serious harm was done. Shifting winds blew the "hot" cloud here and there until, by the time it was seventy-five miles south of Windscale, it had spread to a width greater than ninety miles. At a symposium on nuclear radiation, held during the 1958 IGY conference in Moscow, the British reported that 13,000 curies fell on English soil and that most of the remaining material vanished before it reached the Continent.[15]

Whistlers

How far out does the ocean of air reach? As noted earlier, the atmosphere once was believed to be only twenty miles thick. It has been growing steadily ever since. It took a big jump with the discovery of whistlers.

These are very low frequency radio sounds that resemble a whistle of swiftly descending pitch, somewhat like a chirp. They are said to have been heard in Austria during the last century, but it was in World War I that scientists began in earnest to look for their source. H. Barkhausen, a German, was eavesdropping on field telephones of Allied troops by capturing a small portion of the current as it flowed through the ground, then running it through a sensitive audio amplifier. He heard the chirping sounds and subsequently reported them to the scientific world. It was proposed that they originated in distant lightning flashes and L. R. O. Storey, a graduate student at Cambridge University, suggested that the impulses did not travel directly but followed the force lines of the earth's magnetic field, arching far out into space before returning to earth on the opposite side of the equator. Early in 1957 Robert A. Helliwell and his group from Stanford University effectively demonstrated this by setting up a radio receiver at Cape Horn tuned to the 15.5-kilocycle signal from NSS, the Navy station at Annapolis, Maryland. Cape Horn was thought to lie at the other end of the magnetic force line passing through Annapolis. Each signal from Maryland was heard first via the normal ionosphere-reflected path and then, about a second later, came in via the longer route that curved out some 5000 miles from the earth.

It had been thought that, at such a distance, space was a near-vacuum, but to propagate radio signals in this manner, it was calculated, there must be an average of at least 400 electrons per cubic centimeter—comparable to the density inferred (before the IGY) from the zodiacal light.

Whistlers therefore seemed to offer a tool for determining the nature of the region beyond the reach of ordinary ionospheric sounders. They were recorded by some forty stations in various parts of the world, usually paired off on magnetic meridians. The American program was extensive, with two chains of stations: Whistlers East, reaching from Greenland to Antarctica, under the guidance of Millett G. Morgan at Dartmouth College, and Whistlers West, under Helliwell, reaching from Alaska to New Zealand and the sub-Antarctic. One Whistlers East recorder was tended by storekeepers at the trading post of the Hudson's Bay Company at Frobisher Bay, Baffin Island. Another, at the Naval Research Laboratory in Washington, made 280 miles of whistler tape recordings during the IGY, the equipment being turned on for two minutes an hour.

As often happens with scientific probing, the phenomenon proved far more complicated than had been supposed. Although whistlers were recorded in Washington at the rate of more than one every two minutes, not a single whistler was seen to coincide with a lightning flash. Yet both Morgan and Helliwell reported observing such coincidences. The occurrences of whistlers and similar phenomena such as the "dawn chorus" seemed to occur in cycles. Morgan found what seemed to be a fourteen-day cycle with a subsidiary period of half that length. In Washington NRL found daily and yearly cycles with the maxima at 4 A.M. local time, and in March. Neither this time of day nor the season suggested any relationship to lightning activity. Equatorial and polar stations failed to hear whistlers, as was expected because of their positions with regard to the magnetic field, and the records obtained at the other stations suggested that the shape of the field in space was considerably distorted.

The most remarkable feature of whistlers is that they often travel back and forth between the Northern and Southern hemispheres many times before they die. Since the higher-frequency portion of the impulse travels faster, the low-pitched end of the whistle lags progressively farther behind the high-pitched part, so that after each trip to the other hemisphere the chirp becomes more elongated. When recorded on paper in terms of frequency and time, this produces a characteristic pattern that is the sure mark of a whistler. Often a dozen or more echoes are recorded in a single sequence, representing a dozen transequatorial round trips. One type of whistler produces a noselike trace on the recording paper and is known as a nose whistler. After studying these, as recorded at ten stations, Helliwell and his group concluded that there are 100 electrons per cubic centimeter at a distance of 16,000 miles from the earth's surface. This was roughly in line with other types of observations.[16]

Rockets and satellites

The implication of whistlers that a thin atmosphere extends thousands of miles into space was confirmed by rocket and satellite observations. During the thirty months of the IGY and its successor program, International Geophysical Cooperation–1959, the United States launched almost 300 research rockets and the Soviet Union sent up 175. Additional vehicles were launched by Australia, Canada, France, Japan, and Britain.[17] Some of the observations already have been described. They delved into such problems as temperature, density, winds, chemical composition, electron densities, auroral particles, radiation, and magnetism.

The United States IGY program called for 227 rockets, all but six of which were actually fired, thirty-one being sent up during the warm-up period prior to July 1, 1957. Nearly half of them were fired at Fort Churchill, Canada, which, in October, 1953, had been recommended by the Upper Atmosphere Rocket Research Panel as an ideal site for IGY shots. It was the northernmost station on the North American rail network and lay within the auroral zone. Being a military post it had housing, messing, and repair facilities, and the Canadian government agreed to make it available and to assist in the scientific program.

These were a few of the more important rocket observations: [18]

1. At an elevation of 125 miles the summer air of the Arctic is six times more dense, in daytime, than under similar circumstances in temperate latitudes. Likewise, at this height, the air is twice as heavy in the daytime as at night, and also twice as heavy in summer as in winter. Presumably this is due to heating and expansion of the atmosphere in sunlight. Balloon observations in the area below show that, when the pole is tipped toward the sun, in summer, the air twenty miles over the Arctic is warmer than at that height above the Equator. The difference on July 15, 1957, was twenty-two degrees.

2. Temperatures 125 miles above Hudson Bay were found to be

about 3000°, compared to only half that figure over White Sands, New Mexico, due possibly to the influence of particles in the outer Van Allen belt.

3. Nitric oxide is the predominant positive ion in the E-region (about sixty-five miles up).

4. Atomic oxygen is the predominant positive ion in the F-region (above 100 miles).

5. Electron measurements disclosed thin layers of greatly increased density in the D-region, between forty and fifty-seven miles. So sharply defined were they that radical changes were recorded within less than eighty-five feet. Layers identified as sporadic-E, higher up, were thicker and not so intense. Their thickness was usually a mile, and penetration of one by a rocket on both its upward and downward legs showed the layer to be at least fifty miles in extent.

6. In daylight, above Fort Churchill, there was no decrease in electron density between the E and F regions but, as expected, the F-region density was far greater than at any level below it. Thus, although the atmosphere gets thinner, it is so highly ionized at that level that there are more electrons per cubic centimeter than anywhere lower down, making the F region an efficient radio mirror. Above 125 miles rocket signals on 46.5 megacycles sometimes became erratic. According to the DOVAP tracking system on the ground, the vehicle was jumping crazily around in the sky. This was presumably due to the effect on the radio signals of "spread-F" or moving clouds of charged particles.[19]

7. Auroral displays were traced to incoming, high-energy electrons. A rocket shot through a display detected such electrons within it, but not outside it. Energetic ions, however, were observed both within and without the display.

8. A rocket shot from Wallops Island, Virginia, in late summer disclosed a wind blowing toward the southwest at 560 miles per hour at an elevation of about ninety-three miles. This was observed by releasing a sodium vapor cloud that shone in the light of the rising sun, its drift indicating wind speed and direction. A similar experiment in November found very weak winds at this elevation.

9. An ultraviolet glow, visible in the night sky from above all water vapor, is so bright in the Lyman-alpha line of the spectrum that it obscures ultraviolet emissions from the cosmos beyond. This effect was found to increase in intensity toward a point directly opposite

the sun, much like the gegenschein. The rocket fired from the USS *Point Defiance* before the 1958 eclipse in the South Pacific showed that the glow also becomes more intense in that part of the sky near the recently set sun.

These last observations encouraged the belief that the earth has an outer atmosphere of pure hydrogen, reaching perhaps halfway to the moon, or even beyond it. The glow, it was felt, could only be produced by the effect of sunlight on neutral (that is, non-ionized) hydrogen. The question was whether it came from an extension of the atmosphere or from hydrogen spread throughout interplanetary space.

One discovery concerning this outer atmosphere was a complete surprise. Luigi G. Jacchia at the companion observatories maintained in Cambridge, Massachusetts, by the Smithsonian Institution and Harvard College, was doing a routine analysis of the effect of drag on orbiting times of the IGY satellites. It was, in effect, an upward extension of the falling-sphere experiments. As Robert Jastrow, youthful head of the Space Administration's Theoretical Division, put it, this was "spadework in what first seemed to be an unpromising garden."

The decay of a satellite orbit, due to the tenuous material in its path, manifests itself not in a slowing down but in a speeding up of the orbital period. This is because the effect of the drag is to cause the satellite to fall slightly toward the earth, shortening its flight path. The work of Jacchia and others in the United States and the Soviet Union showed that the drag effect was about ten times what had been expected, but since the previous estimates had been based on rocket data obtained at considerably lower levels, this was not surprising. What struck Jacchia, however, was that the rate of decay for Sputnik II was variable, with maxima that seemed to recur about every thirty days.

Jacchia realized that this might be due to slow tumbling of the rocket-shaped vehicle. When pointed "into the wind" its drag would be far less than when broadside to it. Although this effect might, in general, be averaged out, it presumably could not entirely be eliminated. There was, however, one satellite in orbit whose shape would not affect the calculations. This was Vanguard I, the little "grapefruit" that had been the subject of considerable ridicule, particularly along the Volga. Because of its spherical shape, it was the most suitable of all IGY satellites for orbital studies. The only other one with such a configuration was Sputnik I, which stayed up for just the first three hectic months of the space age. The lifetime of Vanguard I is estimated at two centuries or more. This means the effect of drag on its orbit is slight, but its decay can be determined with great precision. Ground stations of the Minitrack system, following sun-powered radio signals from the little sphere, can determine its orbital period to within a few hundredths of a second.

Jacchia found a clear cycle in the decay rate of Vanguard I and, with its more precise orbital data, he discovered that the interval between maxima was twenty-seven days rather than the thirty days indicated by Sputnik II. The number pointed immediately to a source 93 million miles away: the sun, whose rotation period, as seen from the earth, is twenty-seven days. It looked as though certain places on the sun emitted jets of gas that "thicken" the earth's outer atmosphere. When Jacchia plotted the decay of the Sputnik III rocket for the period of his Vanguard study, he found that the changes in decay rate of both satellites ran parallel and that the drag seemed to increase sharply a day or two after a solar flare. A German radio astronomer at the Bonn University Observatory, Wolfgang Priester, read Jacchia's report and checked the records of solar radio emission obtained at the Heinrich-Hertz Institut für Schwingungforschung at Adlershof in East Berlin. The intensity on a wavelength of 20 centimeters, which he regarded as a good index of eruptive activity, showed a striking correlation, and he wrote immediately (December 18, 1958) to Jacchia, who then reached for the record of solar emission most readily available to him —the 10.7-centimeter data (2800 megacycles) provided by the Canadians in Ottawa. A comparison of the satellite curve with the Canadian data, he said, with more excitement than is usually betrayed in a scientific report, "showed a correlation which could be classified as little short of perfect." [20] Superimposed on the twenty-seven-day cycle was a general elevation of the decay rate following the two flares of July and September, suggesting that it might be due to enrichment of particles in the Van Allen belts.

Thus man studied the ocean of air above him, using satellites, falling spheres, grenades, balloons—and faithful surface observations by thousands of weather men in all nations. The volume of resulting data was formidable. At the headquarters of the World Meteorological Organization in Geneva, one of the three World Data Centers for weather, about one million IGY reports were received. To make this information manageable, each report form was reduced to miniature size so that eighty, mounted on a single file card, could be read through a special viewer. In this manner all of the data could be contained in a sixteen-drawer card-catalogue cabinet. The subscription price for this eighteen-month record of the world's weather was $5990, low enough, it was hoped, to enable a number of research groups to purchase it. At last report data had been received from ninety-two mem-

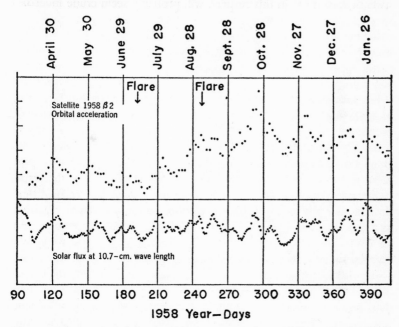

The correlation found by Jacchia between solar emissions (lower line) and the rate of decay of the Vanguard I orbit (upper line).

bers of WMO and from six nations not belonging to that organization.

Compilation of world weather maps, for the surface and for one level of the upper air, was assigned to the Union of South Africa (southern latitudes), to West Germany (equatorial latitudes), and to the United States (northern latitudes).

This was only a start toward a comprehension of events that we call the weather. Although IGY atmospheric observations overshadowed anything in the past, there were still vast gaps. As stated by Helmut E. Landsberg, head of the Office of Climatology at the United

States Weather Bureau, meteorologists were still struggling with the question of "What is there?" and were therefore in a poor position to tackle the next question of scientific inquiry: "Why?"

Satellites that view the weather from above, rather than from below, and that can cover the entire globe have begun to carry out radiation-balance and cloud-cover observations (some of them originally planned for the IGY), but a generation or so from now the efforts of the mid-twentieth century, in this respect, will probably seem crude indeed.

CHAPTER 16
LIFE ADRIFT

On November 2, 1958, twenty-one Americans, encamped on an ice floe drifting through winter darkness near the North Pole, heard a sound like that of an approaching express train. The alarming noise ran right through their camp. They hurried out of their snug buildings with lanterns and flashlights and hunted until they found a hairlike crack in the ice. It was evident that their home was doomed. A few weeks later, on December 21, a party of twenty-eight Russians, similarly camped near the Pole, found their community split in two.

These two groups of men had placed themselves in jeopardy to carry out some of the more dramatic research of the IGY. All told, there were four drifting stations on the arctic pack during the IGY. In addition to those they had on fragile floes, the United States and the Soviet Union each maintained a station on a more substantial "ice island."

The idea of entrusting one's destiny to the gentle, inexorable drift of the polar ice dated back several generations. It came with the realization that the arctic ice is not a solid cap, fixed motionless atop the world. When, in 1827, Sir William Edward Parry and his men sought to reach the Pole by dragging heavy boat-sleds over the floes from Spitsbergen, they found that their grueling daily march northward was cancelled, as they slept, by the steady southward movement of the ice. It was this southerly drift into the North Atlantic that persuaded the Norwegian explorer Fridtjof Nansen that, if he could work his ship into the ice on the opposite side of the Pole, it would be carried right over the top of the world. During his memorable voyage of 1893–96 the *Fram* was, in fact, borne across the Arctic Ocean in this manner and, although it missed the Pole by a considerable margin, it emerged from the pack close to where Parry had turned back.

The first attempt to explore the Arctic Ocean by camping on a floe, allowing wind and water to do the rest, was probably that initiated in

1918 by Vilhjalmur Stefansson. He planned to march north over the ice from Herschel Island, near the Canadian-Alaskan border, until a suitable floe could be found on which to ride across the Arctic Ocean to within walking distance of Siberia. At the last moment he contracted typhoid fever, but his subordinate, Storker Storkerson, carried out the project with four men of the expedition. They drifted for six months north of Alaska and, although they did not reach Siberia, they demonstrated the usefulness of the ice floe as a vehicle.

The introduction of aircraft made it possible to establish a full-fledged drifting station on the ice. In 1927 Sir Hubert Wilkins and Carl Ben Eielson demonstrated the feasibility of using a skiplane to land in the heart of the Arctic Ocean, and a decade later the Russians used this method to establish a camp directly at the North Pole, inaugurating a large-scale research program that, except during World War II, they have continued ever since.

The Soviet Pole camp was manned by four men until, by the following year, their floe had drifted so far down the east coast of Greenland that it had to be evacuated. This station came to be known as North Pole 1. In 1950 another floe was manned, which the Russians called North Pole 2, and this has been followed by a succession of stations. When one drifted too far south or began to break up, it was evacuated and a new one established. Since 1954 the Soviet Union has tried to keep two drifting stations in operation all the time. In addition, during the first postwar decade, Soviet aircraft made hundreds of landings throughout the arctic pack, shunning only a narrow zone extending 125 miles off the coasts of North America and Greenland.

United States research on the arctic pack did not begin in earnest until the spring of 1950, when a group from the Geophysics Research Directorate (GRD) of the Air Force Cambridge Research Center made several skiplane landings on the ice north of Barter Island, Alaska. A year later an expanded program was carried out with a C-47 twin-engine transport (the commercial DC-3) that carried equipment for various types of soundings and gravity readings.[1] The work was under the scientific direction of a young man named Albert P. Crary, who was to become one of the key figures in IGY polar research.

That same year the Air Force had its first experience with an ice-floe station, and it was not a reassuring one. On February 20 it established a camp on the pack 115 miles north of Barter Island, off the arctic coast of Alaska. Several semicylindrical Jamesway huts were set up. These structures are smaller than the Quonset huts of World War II and are covered with pads mounted on a wooden frame. The floe was large enough for skiplane landings, the Air Force objective being to see if it was feasible to set up a base on the ice from which to search for a downed plane. Less than three weeks later the floe cracked, one part of it overriding the other. By the time a rescue plane arrived, later in the day, two of the Jamesway huts were being annihilated and three days later no sign of the camp could be found. Its destruction was attributed to pressure produced when wind blew the ice against the coast, the lesson being to place such stations much farther out to sea.

Meanwhile the Air Force had discovered what was to become a more permanent station on the ice. On April 27, 1947, an Army Air Force B-29 bomber flew north of the Canadian archipelago to monitor signals from Loran radio-navigation stations recently installed in Canada. Aboard were Colonel Walter A. Wood, a veteran mountaineer who later became president of the American Geographical Society, and Sir Hubert Wilkins. The following is from the flight log that Wood submitted to Army intelligence:

> 0835 GMT—observed a great slab of "shelf ice" lying most conspicuously among the pack ice. Its size was about 4 x 6 miles, perhaps larger. . . . It could be clearly recognized as a section of shelf ice similar to that observed clinging to the north coast of Ellesmere Island. . . .

In that year B-29s began making long-range flights from Alaska out over the pack and, although they were kept secret at the time, it was later stated that their objective was to report weather in a region extending as far as the Pole. During these missions radar operators on the planes observed several platters of ice so massive that they stood out clearly from the rest of the pack on the radar screens. These landmarks were given target designations: T-1, T-2, and T-3, the last being the one that had been sighted by Wood and Wilkins.

By 1952, five years after its discovery, T-3 had drifted from close to the Canadian islands to within about 120 miles of the North Pole. It was thus a tempting platform for a drifting camp and, in March, 1952, one was established there with Colonel Joseph O. Fletcher in command and Crary in charge of the geophysical studies. Fletcher had been director of GRD and had subsequently commanded the B-29 squadron in Alaska. T-3, which came to be known also as Fletcher's Ice Island, was manned until May, 1954, when its circuit of the Arctic Ocean brought it back so close to weather stations in the Canadian Arctic that its occupation no longer seemed worth while, although the camp was reoccupied for several months the following year.

For the IGY it was decided to find a large floe likely to drift close to the Pole (to be called Station A) and to enlarge the camp at T-3, which had now drifted back close to Ellesmere Island, (to be called Station B). Colonel Fletcher was named Arctic Basin Project Officer for the program.

Station A

The search for a floe midway between Alaska and the North Pole was begun early in March, 1957, by Air Force planes flying north almost daily from Ladd and Eielson Air Force Bases, near Fairbanks. It was hoped that a floe of about fifty square miles could be found, but by the middle of the month none had been sighted and the situation was critical, for it was expected that, after early May, the ice would be too soft for landings by heavy transport planes. Some twenty prefabricated huts, plus small mountains of supplies, were waiting to be airlifted to the floe. Part of the difficulty was that, when a seemingly suitable piece was spotted, it was often impossible to find it again in the jigsaw patterns of the pack. Furthermore, the preceding winter had been so warm that ice in the area tended to be too thin. The search was shifted farther north and finally, near the end of March, a floe was found that seemed a possibility, although far smaller than had been hoped for—only a mile long and a half-mile wide, cut here and there by pressure ridges and hummocks several feet high. A ski-equipped C-47 landed on the virgin snow to take a closer look, and, as time was running out, it was decided the floe would do.

On April 23 a hulking, cargo-laden C-124 Globemaster flew over; its belly doors swung open; a platform dropped out; a cluster of huge parachutes opened and the establishment of Station A had begun. A party of engineers landed on the floe by skiplane and went to work with the airdropped equipment, including a D-4 tractor for bulldozing and dynamite with which to blast through the pressure ridges. Once a 5000-foot runway had been leveled, sea water was pumped onto it to provide a hard ice pavement and, less than a month after the first parachute opened in the arctic sky, all was ready for the intensive airlift designed to complete the job before the sun melted the runway. An attempt was made to keep the planes coming in at three-hour intervals, making the job of the unloaders a hectic one, but within four days

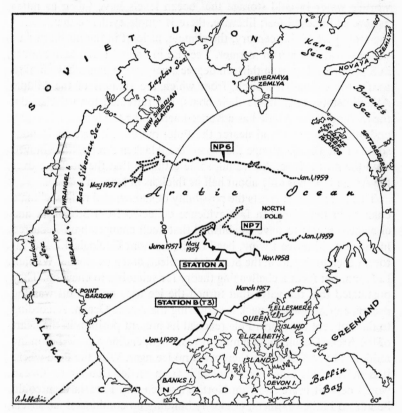

The paths of IGY drifting stations across the Arctic Ocean. Those of the Soviet stations are shown as dashed lines, and those of the United States as solid lines. The parallel patterns of NP 7 and Station A show they were subjected to the same influences of wind and current. Due to the typically clockwise drift in that ocean, Station B moved generally to the left and the others to the right.

the airlift was virtually done and, early in June, 1957, Station A was in business.

Behind a large part of the program at this station and others in the Arctic was the goal of unraveling the tangled problem of the ice ages and other long-term climatic changes. Two things were certain: During the past million years a succession of ice sheets have spread over large parts of North America and Eurasia, placing so much of the world's water in cold storage that ocean levels have fallen as much as several hundred feet; likewise, there is ample evidence that, during the early part of this century, the climate, at least in the northern part of the world, has grown warmer. The rise in annual mean temperature in Spitsbergen has been thirteen degrees; vegetation zones have moved north; the canoe-bark birch, from which the Indians of the Middle Atlantic states once made their boats, has retreated toward Canada; the treeline of the Arctic has advanced across the tundra; cod, herring, and other fish are found nearer the Pole; moose, hitherto indigenous south of the Brooks Range that spans the Alaskan Arctic, have moved onto the north slope. Above all, some estimate that the pack ice over the Arctic Ocean is only about half as thick as in Nansen's day.

This last report suggests the possibility of sudden and radical climate changes in the offing. In fact evidence collected from Station A and elsewhere seems to have established that such changes have occurred in the past. Maurice Ewing, head of the Lamont Geological Observatory, which took part in the Station A project, and a colleague, William L. Donn, put forth a challenging theory for scientists to chew on. They postulated that the valve that turned the ice ages on and off was the presence or absence of pack ice covering the Arctic Ocean. According to this concept the North Pole reached its present position in the heart of the Arctic Ocean about a million years ago, ending a period of many millions of years in which there were no ice ages. With the Pole where it is now, winds laden with moisture from an ice-free Arctic Ocean would deposit more snow on North America and Eurasia than could be melted in the summers, gradually building up continental ice sheets until the resulting drop in ocean levels cut the flow of Gulf Stream water over the submarine sill separating the Atlantic from the Arctic Ocean.

Curtailment of the warm water entering the Arctic Ocean would enable the ocean to freeze. The polar winds would become dry; snowfall over the continents would fall off radically; and summer would gain the advantage over winter, gradually wasting away the ice sheets until the rise in ocean level was enough to reopen the gates to the northward spur of the Gulf Stream. The return of warm water to the Arctic Ocean would melt the pack and start the whole cycle over again.

It was an ingenious—and controversial—theory, but however remote the possibility that all of the arctic ice would melt, the effects would be so drastic that a careful study was warranted. While the climatic effects of an Arctic Ocean free of ice in summer were imperfectly known, it was clear that the economic implications would be immense. Ports like Churchill, on Hudson Bay, would be opened to the full flow of world shipping; the little-exploited mineral and oil resources of the Canadian Arctic would suddenly become accessible. The great north-flowing rivers of Siberia—the Ob, Lena, and Yenisei —would become great arteries for development of the Soviet Arctic.

One of the most important projects at Station A was therefore to determine what was happening to the pack: what was its annual "budget"? How did it vary with the seasons and how did it respond to (or influence) weather changes? What were the energy interchanges at the critical boundary between sea and sky, between water or ice and the atmosphere? The investigation of these problems was carried out, that first year, by Norbert Untersteiner, an Austrian geophysicist working at the University of Washington. He made use, in part, of the new science of micrometeorology—the study of the weather in the first few inches, feet, and yards above the earth's surface—for this held clues to the problem of heat exchange.

Thus he measured air temperatures at 25, 50, and 100 centimeters above the ice (the centimeter equals .4 inches); at four levels within the ice and at 3 meters (about 10 feet) below the ice. He obtained a profile of air movement across the pack during periods of changing weather by measuring winds at 20, 40, 80, and 160 centimeters above the surface. By periodically weighing plexiglass pans filled with ice or snow and buried level with the floe surface, he sought to measure evaporation and, by means of two devices improvised on the spot, he recorded the over-all growth and shrinkage of the floe, top and bottom.

One of these made use of a hole bored through the ten-foot floe to the sea beneath so that the level of water in the hole represented the waterline of the floe. The rise and fall of a float in the water moved a pen that inscribed a line on a recording drum, thus disclosing even slight changes in the draft of the floe.

To find out if the floe bottom melted or grew, a wire, run down another hole, was attached to a horizontal bar under the ice. By pulling this bar up against the bottom of the floe it was possible to see if new ice had formed. The problem was that the hole froze solid. To overcome this a wire was dropped into the sea water and an electric current driven through it, into the water and back through the frozen-in wire. This heated the latter enough to free it for each reading.

Before the camp could become well established, the melting began and by July 8 the snow cover had almost entirely gone, leaving pools of water that covered a third of the floe. The twenty-odd men at the station were living a miserable life amidst a floating lake. Instead of being the most comfortable time of year, summer proved quite the opposite. Having disposed of the snow cover, the sun went to work on the ice, which melted or evaporated off the top at the rate of almost a half-inch daily throughout the rest of July. The men melted holes through the ice so that water could drain from the pools, and during one month the floe rose a foot out of the water. Finally, in August, after 11 per cent of the ice raft on which they were living had vanished, snow again began to accumulate, easing any fears that the floe might wither away altogether. Furthermore, Untersteiner was making some remarkable observations on the bottom of the floe.

The fresh water drained from its surface, instead of mixing with the sea water, had remained in large measure in reservoirs under the floe. Being lighter than sea water, it stayed on top, so that the surface pools had simply become under-ice pools. In a furtherance of this upside-down behavior, the fresh-water pools were freezing from the bottom up. Thus, when an ice auger bored through a section of the floe eight feet thick, it broke out on the bottom into what seemed a pool of fresh water, but five inches farther down it hit a layer of fresh-water ice some eight inches thick.

Untersteiner suspected that needlelike and platelike crystals of fresh-water ice had formed where the fresh water, at $32°$, met the salt water, at $29°$. These crystals floated upward, constantly replaced, until the reservoir was filled with them, at which point its bottom layer began to freeze solid. The loose crystals were presumably too tenuous to be felt when drilling. Eventually all of the fresh water solidified. Untersteiner concluded that the arctic pack lost all of its snow cover in summer and the question of whether it increased or decreased in total volume hinged on the annual accretion from the bottom of the floe.

During the early months of its occupation, Station A, with a certain number of wiggles and meanders, seemed to be making a beeline for the North Pole. In the month ending July 17, 1957, it drifted an average of five miles a day and on September 25 it was only 305 miles from the Pole—less than the distance it had traveled in the past four months. While proximity to the Pole was not important in most of the work, to reach the top of the world would have been a fitting reward for the hardships of the men at the station. Unfortunately the winds changed, apparently due to the approach of winter, and the floe began slowly to retrace its steps. This had at least one advantage. From the ocean floor, more than two miles below the floe, there rose a five-to-ten-thousand-foot mountain range. Kenneth L. Hunkins, carrying out observations for the Lamont Geological Observatory, compared its ruggedness to that of the Rocky Mountains. Once or twice a day—or at intervals of from one to three miles—a small charge of dynamite was exploded and echoes from the bottom were recorded on an array of twelve geophones laid on the ice. This made it possible to determine the slope of the ocean floor, as well as its depth. On its northward drift, the floe had zigzagged its way across the range; now it did so again and before the IGY was over it had made a third crossing, establishing the range's trend as nearly parallel to that of the Lomonosov Ridge, discovered by Soviet drifting stations in 1948.

More important, in determining the nature of past climate changes, was the sampling and photography of the bottom. This was apparently the first time photographs had been taken of the Arctic Ocean floor. The device used was one that had been developed by Maurice Ewing, co-author of the provocative ice-age theory. It could be lowered several miles by winch on a wire running through a hole in the floe. When a weight, suspended from the camera by a line, touched the bottom, the release of tension flashed a light and advanced the film one frame. By raising and lowering the camera slightly, like the activation of a baited hook, pictures could be taken in sufficiently quick succession to observe the drift of riled sediment, disclosing the speed, though not the direction, of bottom currents. The drift was found to be about six inches per minute. When one considers that the layer moving at that pace may be a mile or more in depth, this represents the movement of large quantities of water.

More than 100 photographs were taken, some in color, each covering about one square yard of the bottom, and all were remarkable for the numerous rocks that they showed. These seemed to lie on sediment of great depth and were apparently dumped there by ice that had carried them from shore. What was strange was that no rocks were to be seen on the floes. Those on ice islands such as T-3 served as evidence that these heavier platters of ice had once been attached to the coast, but as Hunkins, who made the observations, pointed out, there are probably only a few dozen ice islands in existence today and the few rocks they carry are apt to stay aboard until they escape from the Arctic Ocean and drift far enough south to be melted. The rocks therefore seem to be relics of a time when conditions in the Arctic Ocean were different.

Perhaps the most provocative discovery of this program was the incontrovertible evidence that a sudden change in conditions had, in fact, occurred at one point in the past. This was obtained with a piston corer, a device somewhat like a pile driver, developed by Ewing to bring up cross sections of the bottom. It was actuated when it hit the bottom, jamming a tube as far as possible into the ooze and sediment. Altogether sixteen cores were obtained in this manner, the longest being seven feet. They were not the first, but Hunkins believes they were the longest obtained up to that time in the Arctic Ocean; and length is critical, for each inch may represent thousands of years.

In all of these cores there were two clearly defined layers. The top one, about four inches thick, was dark in color and rich in the skeletons of foraminifera, a microscopic sea creature. Below was a thicker layer, lighter in color and relatively barren of the skeletons. Since the abrupt change in sea conditions that produced the change in sedimentation was almost certainly related to the ice ages, it was important to date it. A sample of the upper layer was obtained with an apparatus known as an Ekman grab at a depth of slightly more than one mile. The skeletons were sifted out and submitted to carbon-14 dating analysis.

This technique, which has become an important tool in many areas of research, establishes the age of any carbon-bearing fossil. Carbon-14 is a radioactive product of cosmic rays and its ratio to ordinary carbon in the atmosphere is a known quantity. When it is captured from the air to become part of a living plant or animal, its radioactivity decays at a known rate. Since it is not replenished, the amount remaining at the time of analysis is an indication of the fossil's age.

The average antiquity of the skeletons hauled up by the grab was 9300 years, with a probable 180-year margin of error, but the meaning of this date was uncertain because of doubt as to the exact depth of the sampling obtained by the grab. It was decided to seek a more precise date for the climate change by picking out skeletons from only the bottom inch of the upper layer in a sampling of the cores. The resulting date, according to Hunkins, was definitely older than 18,000 years and probably older than 25,000.

This is perplexing, for it means that the upper layer represents at least the last part (if not all) of the most recent ice age, as well as the subsequent warm period. The rain of dead foraminifera upon the bottom must have been extremely gentle to produce a deposit of only four inches over that period. Hunkins estimates it was less than .13 inches every 1000 years, which seems to be borne out by the present paucity of life in the Arctic Ocean. Plankton nets of fine-mesh material were towed beneath the floe and foraminifera were found to be about one-tenth as common as in the Atlantic Ocean. On the other hand, Charles W. Thomas, who became an oceanographer after his retirement as a Coast Guard admiral, has suggested that sediment layers on the floors of polar seas that are almost devoid of biological remains were laid down when the water was covered with solid ice so thick that little sunlight could penetrate.[2]

But if the upper layer, despite its richness in skeletons, was laid down very slowly by a rather barren ocean, what about the sandy layer below, where skeletons are far scarcer? Possibly this represents a period of rapid glacier-melting, whose torrential rivers deposited sediment on the ocean floor with such rapidity that the number of skeletons per cubic inch is perforce small.

Throughout the winter of 1957–58 the floe moved silently, imperceptibly in the continual darkness. The author, seeking to keep in touch with IGY activities, found that, from his house in Connecticut, he could talk to the men drifting aimlessly, but with a purpose, near the Pole. This was thanks to the radio amateurs who, by dint of considerable expense and long night vigils, enabled those in both polar regions to keep in touch with home. During the hours of optimum transmission (usually late at night) the radio operators would contact the polar stations, one after another, to handle their phone calls. Since the amateurs' transmitters and receivers were wired to their telephones, a man sitting in his snow-buried hut, after giving the number he wished to call, could hear the nostalgic sound of the dial tone; then the crisp, "Number please"; and finally the astonished reaction of whomever he was calling. On a few occasions the telephone operators were nonplused, professing that they would have to find out the rates "from the North Pole."

One of the most helpful and diligent amateurs, in this respect, was

Jules Madey, a high school student in Clark, New Jersey. One night in January, 1958, when he had put the author through to Station A, the men on the floe had a strange tale to tell. Two weeks earlier, they said, an Air Force plane was groping its way north under a starry sky toward the floe's radioed position, some 435 miles from the North Pole. An hour and a half before its expected arrival the men, eager with anticipation, had switched on the runway lights, but nothing happened. Armed with flashlights they went out to see what was wrong. Perhaps, they thought, their tracked vehicle, a Weasel, had cut the wires. As they trudged farther and farther from their camp, they traced the wires with their flashlights until one man cried, "Hey, what's this!"

He had found a footprint 9.5 inches wide and 7.5 inches long. Near by were smaller prints, 6 by 4 inches. Polar bears! It had never occurred to them that they might encounter bears this far from land; but if a mother and her cub were lurking near, as certainly was the case, they were likely to be extraordinarily hungry.

The men were unarmed. They hurried back to the camp for guns and then a hunting party set off along the footprint trail. "That was a big cub—but playful," one of the men said on the radio. "Apparently he went up one side of the runway and then down the other, knocking out each light."

By the time the plane arrived, the lights on one side had been repaired, but the hunters never caught up with the bears. This was perhaps fortunate, since it turned out that the cold had congealed the oil in the guns, making them useless.

Despite the surprise at Station A, bears had been seen previously in roughly the same latitude by Fridtjof Nansen. In fact, while his ship was frozen in the ice, they climbed aboard and attacked the chained huskies. One member of the expedition, who had ventured some distance in the darkness, suddenly found himself confronted by a bear. He hurled his flaming lantern at the beast and sprinted for the ship.

The men at Station A were also visited by arctic foxes, an occurrence which some zoologists thought remarkable. This animal, whose coat becomes white in winter, follows the polar bear, scavenging his scraps; but, in making his way across the pack, the bear can cross broad stretches of open water, being a long-distance swimmer. The fox presumably is not. Fox trails were also seen on T-3.

Another IGY project that was beset by bears was the rocket-launching facility at Fort Churchill, where a mother and her two cubs entered the mess hall. "Like hungry relatives," said the Associated Press, "these bears refused to take a hint. They finally had to be shot by G.I.'s standing on the outside, firing M-1 rifles through the windows." [3]

During the drift of Station A, the United States lost one of its few Negro polar specialists. Robert H. Jones, aged twenty-five, was a Weather Bureau man who had been stationed on T-3, and then had spent a winter at Byrd Station, Antarctica, whereupon he volunteered to winter at Station A near the North Pole. Because the seasons alternate, north and south, he pursued the winter night from one pole to the other, arriving at the floe on January 5, 1958, to relieve another meteorologist. A week later, after releasing a weather balloon, he felt ill and his condition deteriorated rapidly into a serious congestion of the lungs (often a symptom of heart disease). The Air Force medical corpsman on the floe gave him oxygen, but he died as a plane with physician and oxygen tent was airborne en route to his assistance.

Station A's struggle for survival began as that first winter drew to a close. During the latter part of April, 1958, great pressure developed in the pack, clamping the floe in an inexorable vise. Part of it broke off and newly forming pressure ridges advanced into the camp. All but a skeleton crew of ten were flown out, although those who remained were able to keep up the routine observations. These pertained to many of the IGY sciences: gravity measurements were made twice daily; there was a radio sounder for probing the ionosphere; an all-sky camera and spectrograph recorded auroras and airglow; magnetic records were kept; and oceanic currents were measured at various depths. In addition to the regular weather observations the station used a "wiresonde"—a captive balloon flown to study weather in the lowest level of the atmosphere (on one occasion the air was found to be 32° warmer a hundred feet overhead than it was at the surface).

On May 2—only a few days after the partial evacuation—the Alaskan Air Command, which was responsible for maintaining the camp, decided to move it to a floe about one mile away. Those who had been flown out were brought back and the Herculean task was begun. Each of the twenty-one buildings had to be jacked up and placed on runners. Routes had to be blasted or bulldozed through pressure ridges ten feet high so that tractors could drag the buildings through. Power cable had to be dissected out of the ice for removal to the new site. By May 24 the entire camp had been moved across a narrow crack between the floes and only two radar-monitored weather balloon ascents had been missed from the schedule. At the same time a runway had been leveled on the new floe.

The scientists and the Air Force men (who handled communications, messing, and operation of the camp's five tracked vehicles) hardly had time to congratulate themselves on their achievement when, on June 10, the runway cracked open and two leads of black water appeared across the air strip, severing their link to the world of trees and men.

They went to work on another runway, but by now the summer sun had turned the floe into a mire of slush and melt-water pools. They bored holes to drain the water and kept at the job until, on June 22, they were able to receive a four-engine plane. Almost immediately afterward a crack sliced through the replacement runway. It was clearly hopeless to build another airstrip until after the melting period; the station was supplied by air drop until the first landing of the winter season could be made, in September.

Meanwhile, for the first time, biologists had inspected the pastures upon which all the life of the Arctic Ocean is directly or indirectly dependent. This involved donning frogman gear, including waterproof clothing and a self-contained breathing apparatus, and climbing down a shaft through the floe to swim about underneath it. The work was done by T. Saunders English of the University of Alaska and two other swimmers. The pastures consisted of diatoms—microscopic plants— clinging to the bottom of the floe. By means of sunlight shining through the ice the plants manufactured the carbohydrates which animals must have for survival. The pastures were grazed by crustaceans, which in turn were eaten by seals, fish, and other animals to complete the food chain.

One of the goals of the swimmers was to determine to what extent the ice limited fertility of the sea by cutting off the portion of the solar spectrum necessary for photosynthesis—the manufacture of carbohydrates. They used submarine photometers for this purpose and also collected specimens of diatoms and grazers as they flippered their way here and there under the floe.

The swimmers came close to having somewhat of a surprise while below. During August a message was received by Major Joseph Bilotta, in charge of the Air Force detachment, that caused obvious excitement to those privy to its secret and generated a rich crop of rumors among the others. On the evening of August 13 Bilotta launched the camp's white fiberglass boat, started up its outboard motor and began chugging around the edge of a large pool of open water near the camp. The civilians, including Untersteiner, the Austrian-born senior scientist, and Latvian-born Arthur Assur, a specialist in the structural strength of ice, were not told the secret, but some guessed that there was more method than madness to Bilotta's endless orbiting of the lagoon. All night they waited while the major chugged in circles, but nothing happened. Then suddenly, the next morning, an immense object rose from the water in the center of the lagoon. Up and up it came, as the motorboat scurried to the icy shore. It was the USS *Skate,* the nuclear-powered submarine that was one of the first two craft to sail to the pole under the ice. Earlier in the month the *Nautilus* had completed a transpolar journey without surfacing. The reason for the mysterious performance with the motorboat then became apparent. The *Skate* had first surfaced in a pool some distance off and Bilotta offered, by radio, to operate the boat, so that the submarine could home on the sound of its engine.

The men at Station A had seen most, if not all, of their good movies. Here was an unexpected opportunity to freshen their supply. And the exchange was equally welcome to the submariners. After a brief stay the *Skate* sank from sight and was on its way.[4]

By September 1 the distance between the camp and its old site had grown to two miles, but the case history of the old floe was kept up to date. Because of the early summer, the floe lost twice as much during the 1958 melt season as it had the previous year, but did not become so thin, due to the heavy two-foot accretion of ice it had gained on the bottom during the winter of 1957–58.

It was when the polar night enveloped the camp for the second time—in the winter of 1958–59—that the final split occurred, separating the men from their airstrip. Fortunately, 2200 feet of runway remained intact on the other half of the floe and the pressure that had broken it held its parts together so that, for a time at least, it was possible to walk from one to the other. The camp was left on a chunk 1000 feet long and 800 feet wide, far too small for construction of a new runway. By this time the floe had drifted so far east that it was nearer Greenland than to the Alaskan bases. Hence rescue flights were launched from Thule, but for several days the weather made it impossible to go hunting for a floe that, in the dark vastness of the Arctic Ocean, was somewhat of a needle in a haystack.

Captain John S. Smith, the new Air Force Commander on the floe, radioed a recommendation that the C-123-J plane that was to haul them out keep its skis up and its wheels down. On skis it might skid right off the end of the short runway, whereas with brakes there was a better chance of stopping short. Meanwhile the scientists packed their precious records (the instruments had to be left behind) and joined the Air Force contingent in a feast, culled from the pick of the next year's rations, which likewise would have to be abandoned. They washed the food down with "ice skates" (pear juice and vodka) or "old rusty throats" (a form of hot buttered rum); then set up flares beside the longer fragment of the runway. When the winking lights of the plane finally appeared, according to George Cvijanovich, head of the scientific party, they were "the most welcome sight I have ever seen coming out of the air." Two days later the nucleus of the party arrived at La Guardia Airport in New York.[5]

Station B

The program carried out at Station B, better known as T-3 or Fletcher's Ice Island, closely resembled that at the floe station. Being about 150 feet thick and some 42 square miles in area, T-3 provided a far more substantial platform than the floe, although it was not the biggest chunk of drifting ice in the Arctic. T-1 was about 300 square miles in area.[6] Since its discovery in 1947, T-3 had circled the Arctic Ocean clockwise, passing close to the North Pole soon after its original occupation in 1952. By the start of the IGY it had returned to the vicinity of its presumed birthplace on the north coast of Ellesmere Island. Its reoccupation began with an aircraft landing on March 7, 1957, and during April, while an ice runway was being constructed, a succession of polar radio blackouts kept the men isolated from the rest of the world. As at Station A, their task was to hasten completion of a runway so that the airlift could be carried out before the thawing of late spring. The thaw seemed a long way off to the engineers, for temperatures of 65° below zero gummed up the hydraulic systems of their motorized equipment. The runway was essential, since buildings were being airlifted intact within the cavernous Globemasters. These structures, comparable to outsized house trailers, were lined up to form a neat "town" of about twenty buildings atop the ice island.

Knowing that the surface would tend to melt in summer, the designers of the camp provided aprons around the buildings to keep the sun from eating away their foundations, but the melting was far more than had been expected. In some undisturbed parts of the island the surface level dropped three feet, but in the camp, where the snow had been soiled and where buildings reflected additional heat, the melting was much more severe. Cargo parachutes were spread around the foundations as additional protection, but by fall each building stood precariously on a pedestal of ice eight or ten feet high.

Interest in this fast rate of melting was not limited to the engineers. It had serious implications for those seeking to measure the trend of climate change in the North. After the IGY, Crary, who had been the first scientific leader at T-3, reported that the ice island, as well as the Ellesmere Ice Shelf, had been losing ice, from the top, at the rate of about one foot per year. "This obviously could not have been representative of high arctic conditions over a very long period in the past," he said, "or the ice rises, shelves and islands would have disappeared long ago." [7]

As with the floe, replacement of surface melting was entirely by freezing onto the bottom. Thus a sponge that had grown on the ocean floor under the Ellesmere shelf was found on the surface of the ice. It apparently had been frozen into the base of the ice and then, as each summer peeled a layer off the top and each winter added one on the bottom, the sponge was slowly carried to the top. Its age, when it emerged, according to a carbon-14 analysis, was 400 years. [8]

One of the features of T-3 that strengthened the view that it had broken off from the Ellesmere shelf was the presence of deeply furrowed, parallel valleys strikingly similar to those of the shelf. In summer these valleys caught the melt water, forming streams and elongated lakes. To their surprise the island's occupants found that the little rivers in these valleys reversed direction from day to day. The reason was that changing winds imparted various tilts to the floating island.

Throughout the IGY the drift of the station was generally to the southwest, along the edge of the continental shelf and largely within 130 miles of the Canadian Arctic Archipelago. Observations made along this route detected the layer of what is assumed to be Atlantic Ocean water that was observed at great depth below all the drifting stations. This layer, which transports a little of the warmth of the tropics to the North Pole itself (and which, according to the Ewing-Donn theory, is the instrument that will precipitate a new ice age) was identified both by its temperature, which is slightly warmer than that of the water above and below it, and by its chemical composition. All through the summer of 1958 the top of this layer lay about 900 feet below the surface and its bottom was roughly 3300 feet down, yet its influence was evident in ameliorating the climate throughout the Arctic Ocean area. Although Station A was near the Pole, its minimum reading was only 57° below zero, compared to 69.7° below, recorded at Rogers Pass, Montana, in 1954 and the very much lower temperatures of the Antarctic. T-3, although farther south, was so large and thick that its influence was like that of a small land mass and its minimum was somewhat lower—65° below.

North Pole 6

This link in the long chain of Soviet drifting stations was established in 1956 on an ice island north of easternmost Siberia, and for many months thereafter it drifted in slow circles and figure eights near the De Long Islands, named for the United States naval officer whose expedition ship, the *Jeannette,* was crushed among the floes there in 1881. At length the ice island was caught in the transpolar drift toward the Atlantic Ocean. The first IGY party, under Dr. Valentin M. Driatsky, carried out a program similar to that of the American stations. The island was triangular, with a shoreline of more than twenty miles, and its thickness ranged from thirty to forty feet, except around the edges, where there was a fringe of thinner sea ice. It was channeled with parallel valleys, like T-3, and the saltiness of ice in its upper layers convinced the Russians that it had grown from the bottom.

By October, 1958, the station had drifted some 4000 miles, covering a straight-line distance of about 1000 miles.[9]

North Pole 7

By what seems to have been purely a coincidence, the floe for this Soviet station, occupied in April, 1957, was only 120 miles north of the floe on which the United States was preparing to place Station A. One of the most important men at North Pole 7, during the first year, was Dr. B. Korolev. As camp physician he not only had to perform an emergency appendectomy under difficult circumstances, but he had to deal with the medical and psychiatric problems that arise when men must sit out the winter night adrift.

The camp was equipped with one or more helicopters, prefabricated houses of foam-insulated wood mounted on runners so that they could be moved in a hurry, hemispherical tents, a radar for tracking weather balloons, and a heavy winch for trawling specimens from depths greater than 13,000 feet.

All sixteen members of the wintering party, led by V. A. Vedernikov, had been given thorough physical examinations by a medical commission and all, except two who were more than fifty years old, were classed as excellent sportsmen. Nevertheless, even before the winter night descended upon them, signs of stress began to appear, particularly among the older men who were less active physically. The monotony of the life weighed heavily upon them and, despite the efforts and prescriptions of Dr. Korolev, the number of complaints and illnesses increased.

When perpetual darkness came, the situation worsened. The expedition members complained of lack of appetite, insomnia, and lethargy. Their memory seemed weakened and their working ability was impaired. There were symptoms of vitamin deficiency, despite what the doctor considered a well-balanced diet that included fresh fruit and vegetables. He attributed the trouble to the lack of sunlight, the cold, the wind, and the mineral-free water obtained from melted snow.

Such troubles are not unusual in the North, where the symptoms are often referred to as "cabin fever," but the discussion of such subjects in Soviet literature is rare. The difficulties at North Pole 7 and the measures Dr. Korolev took to combat them were described in the Moscow periodical, *Fizkultura i Sport*. According to the English-language version published by the Department of Commerce in Washington, the doctor "even thought of the remote possibility that the drift might have to be discontinued." Some of the men had developed a rapid, irregular pulse, intestinal bloating, and were moody, easily irritated, and quarrelsome.

He noticed, however, that these troubles were primarily characteristic of those with sedentary jobs. The men who did hard work out-of-doors were less severely affected. He described the case of a twenty-eight-year-old polar scientist who felt continually "droopy," yet had strong palpitation of the heart. Dr. Korolev diagnosed it as "a progressive, functional insufficiency of the cardiovascular system." Another of the more serious cases was moody. Neither of these men responded to treatment with drugs.

The answer, the doctor found, was to put them to work. He sent the two men out on ski journeys around the floe and gave them vigorous setting-up exercises. Whenever there was heavy work to be done, he tried to arrange it so that these "weak" men would get the job. Within a few days an improvement was discernible, he reported, and after a month blood pressure and pulse had dropped to normal and the working ability of the men had been restored.[10]

Having ridden out the winter, the men at North Pole 7 were relieved in April, 1958, by twenty-eight men who were, perhaps, more fortunate than their predecessors in that they had with them A. K. Galkin, who had been chef at what is perhaps Russia's best hotel— the Astoria in Leningrad. Galkin was placed in charge of the station mess. Although their cuisine may have been good, when summer came, their living conditions were no better than those at the American floe station in that both groups had to live in the middle of floating ponds. The two stations drifted in a strikingly parallel manner. They did many twists and turns, yet rarely were much more than 150 miles apart. From their establishment until mid-September, 1957, they both drifted toward the Pole; they then reversed direction until mid-December, when they swung toward Greenland. Thus scientists on the Soviet floe observed what was presumably the same undersea mountain range as that charted by the Americans.

Meanwhile the floe of North Pole 7, which had been rather small when the station was first established there, had been nibbled at by a year of melting, collision and cleavage until it was too small to handle the planes bringing in supplies for the next year. A fleet of seventeen aircraft was assigned the job of delivering more than 300 tons to Russia's two drifting stations, including a tractor and piano, but in the case of North Pole 7 the planes had to land the material on a floe thirty-seven miles away, whence it was lifted to the camp by helicopter.

The winter that followed was even more of a trial for the men than that of the preceding year, for the floe was gradually breaking up. Both the Soviet and American floes were caught in a squeeze as the wind blew the ice against the Canadian Arctic Archipelago. On December 21, before the end of the IGY, the floe cracked, opening a fifteen-foot gap between the hydrological-ionospheric installations and the rest of the camp. The station was not evacuated, however, until the following March, when it had drifted to within 180 miles of Greenland.

In addition to their supply of the drifting stations, Soviet LI-2 ski-planes (comparable to DC-3s) placed more than twenty radio beacons on floes throughout the Arctic, many of them combined with automatic weather stations that broadcast temperature, pressure and wind speed and direction once daily (or on radio command from a plane or ground station).[11] The other beacons were monitored ashore to keep track of ice movements. At least one of the beacons was still on the air nine months later.

In reporting their results the Russians noted, in particular, their discovery of a trench cutting across the sill separating the Atlantic and Arctic oceans. This was delineated by the icebreaking research ships *Ob* and *Lena* and was said to be about 10,000 feet deep, with portions going down more than 11,000 feet. The Russians named it the Lena Trench and said it must play an important role in the exchange of water between the two oceans. Nevertheless, this breach in the shallow dam did not necessarily rule out the Ewing-Donn ice-age theory. By the time the IGY was over there may have been enough data in hand to resolve the ice-age question, one way or the other, but at this writing no clear-cut verdict has been reached.

CHAPTER 17
HELICOPTERS AND REINDEER

The world most of us know is a place of verdant landscapes and teeming cities. Only those who have flown over much of the globe, including the polar regions, appreciate what a small portion of the earth's surface is habitable. We realize, in an academic way, that most of the planet is covered with water, but few are aware that one in every ten acres of its land area is under ice. The volume of the earth's water that is frozen has been estimated at roughly five million cubic miles —about eleven times the total amount of water in the lakes, rivers, and underground reserves. By far the largest mass of ice is that which covers Antarctica, though another large ice sheet buries almost all of Greenland, the two of them accounting for 96 per cent of the world's land-borne ice. The remaining 4 per cent is to be found in the glaciers that stream from mountains in all parts of the world, even directly on the equator.[1]

We know that the volume of this ice has fluctuated radically during the past million years because of variations in climate, but the nature of these weather changes, what caused them, and how they produced a cataclysmic expansion of the glaciers are all unknown. During the IGY the problem of the ice ages was attacked on several fronts. The most obvious were in the polar regions, but of special interest were the mountain glaciers in warmer latitudes. Why are some expanding and others contracting? Why, when New England and the Great Lakes region were buried under a mighty ice blanket, was the Yukon Valley in central Alaska unglaciated and either a desert or, possibly, green with vegetation?

One of the first tasks was to inventory the ice in the world's mountains. This had never been done, for while the glaciers of the Alps, for example, had long been studied, hundreds or even thousands elsewhere had not even been mapped, particularly in such remote regions as the mountains between China and the Soviet Union, the more rarely frequented portions of the Andes, and the snowy peaks of central Africa.

In the summer of 1957 the author visited one of these areas, in the northernmost mountains of the North American mainland. This was the McCall Glacier in the Romanzof Mountains of the Brooks Range. The range spans northern Alaska from the Canadian border almost to Bering Strait. The McCall Glacier operation began in August, 1956, when Walter Wood flew north in search of a glacier suitable for a station. After his tour of duty with the Air Force, Wood had made extensive use of skiplanes in his study of otherwise inaccessible ice fields in southern Alaska and was now director of the New York office of the Arctic Institute of North America. He was accompanied by Richard C. Hubley, the project's chief scientist, and Robert W. Mason, who was to help man the outpost. They landed by float plane on Lake Schrader, a five-mile body of water cradled among treeless mountains on the north side of the Brooks Range. The lake was in a completely virgin state, for it was said that the Eskimos shunned these mountains in the belief that they are haunted by evil spirits. Fresh food was plentiful, the lake's abundant fish apparently having never seen a baited hook.

The territory which they were to examine was also unspoiled. In the early 1900s a prospector named T. H. Arey had traveled up the Jago River, which runs from the mountains east of Lake Schrader to the Arctic Ocean, and reported seeing glaciers up the tributary valleys. Wood and his companions took off on their aerial quest and, after only an hour's search, found a glacier in one of these valleys that met their requirements. They named it for John McCall, a young glaciologist at the University of Alaska who had died three years earlier, a few months after carrying out a heroic rescue on Mount McKinley.

One of the first steps taken by the IGY group, in establishing the McCall Station, was to place an emergency cache at Lake Schrader, but when the cache was visited, a few months later, it was a shambles. Tins of food had been bitten into and sucked clean. Five-gallon fuel cans had been grooved and punctured by bear claws. The tent was torn to ribbons and a case of smoke bombs, used to indicate wind direction to an incoming plane, had been broken into. The barren-ground grizzly that raided the camp had apparently bitten into one of the bombs, which ignited in his mouth, driving him berserk. Boxes had been hurled fifty yards in all directions. Consequently arrangements were made for the first provisions to be sealed inside heavy oil drums before being airdropped at the head of the glacier.

The scientific party was flown in by skiplane and, during the first week of May, 1957, the Air Force sent over a succession of C-119 Flying Boxcars to drop thirty-four tons of fuel and eighteen tons of other supplies. The operation called for both luck and marksmanship, for, when the fliers overshot the little mountaintop amphitheater of snow, their deliveries went over a cliff and were shattered on rocks and steep slopes of ice far below. By the time the author visited the camp, a couple of months later, its two Jamesway huts were up and its IGY observations had begun. The flight in was by a single-engine Cessna-180 that took off from the airstrip at Barter Island, one of the early-warning radar stations on the north coast. Behind us was the Arctic Ocean, clear of ice as far as we could see. Ahead, the mountains were partly hidden in mist and clouds. Below, the flat tundra was speckled with lakes and ponds whose glistening, in the direction of the sun, made the terrain appear completely sodden. The permafrost, or permanently frozen ground of the Arctic, inhibited drainage from the few feet of thawed ground on the surface.

We followed the braided stream-bed of the Jago into the mountains, its interwoven appearance produced by twining channels along its gravelly floor. Our first task was to swoop over the camp of a scientific party on the upper Jago, dumping out one case of supplies on each of a succession of passes. Merrill Wien, of a family of well-known bush pilots, flew so low that, when I pushed each box out the window, it fell only a few feet, then tumbled to a halt alongside the tent. Here the valley was narrow, and the tops of its walls were hidden in the clouds. Wien had to turn sharply, within the narrow defile, after each pass, and the cloud cover seemed to rule out any attempt to reach the glacier station, whose elevation was 7650 feet above sea level. Wien was not so easily discouraged. He saw a hole in the clouds overhead and soared into it, turning his plane into a tight spiral. One moment we were flying blind within the cloud; the next we would break out with sheer rock walls on all sides; then again inside the cloud, slightly dizzy from the climbing turns. For one who does not enjoy letting down through clouds in a commercial airliner, this makeshift reversal of the procedure was even less of a pleasure, but at last we broke out under a gloriously blue sky with the snowy peaks all about us.

Since the valleys were hidden, they could not be used to guide us to our destination, but suddenly there the glacier was, reaching up, as it were, with a long arm whose fingers gripped a circle of peaks and rocky passes. Because the wind was blowing up the glacier, it was necessary to fly into the rock cauldron at its head, make a sharp turn and swoop down for a landing short of a series of icefalls that dropped out of sight into the valley below. For maximum speed and maneuverability Wien kept his landing gear (a combination of wheels and skis) retracted close under the plane until the last seconds before touching down. To lower them he leaned forward and pumped vigorously on a handle, but during that brief period of pilotless flight we were headed directly toward a wall of rock 1000 feet high. Just as we seemed about to crash he sat up, swung the plane around and we landed on a shelf of almost level snow below the camp. It seemed a miracle that we had arrived safely, yet Wien and two other pilots made a number of these landings without mishap.

The station leader, Dick Hubley, explained why he and his three companions had come to spend sixteen months, including the midwinter period of continuous darkness, in this lonely spot. What they were attempting with the glacier was, in some respects, like the running of a basal metabolism on a human being. When such a test is made, a record is kept of the oxygen the subject removes from the air he breathes, as a measure of his energy consumption. Hubley and his companions kept careful track of the amount of radiation arriving from the sky, the amount reflected, the amount reradiated back to the heavens, and hence the amount absorbed by the glacier. A heat-flow transducer buried in the snow measured the progress of heat into the ice, and temperatures were recorded at various levels above the snow. All of these readings—from radiometers, solarimeters, transducers, and thermometers—were wired into a single machine (in a nearby hut) whose jiggling needles recorded the data simultaneously on one broad, moving roll of paper, making it possible to see the whole picture at a glance.

Every week eight-foot pits were dug to study the nature of the snow accumulation, seasonal changes in its structure, and its step-by-step conversion into glacier ice. This was pit-digging day and the visitors, drafted into service, found that it was hard work in the thin mountain air, especially a few feet down, where the snow had begun to turn into ice. One of the earlier pits served as a dump where the camp's refuse was gradually becoming frozen into the body of the glacier. Ultimately it will be disgorged at the bottom of the valley, perhaps a thousand years hence, confronting archaeologists of that era with evidence of a strange civilization that once built communities on glaciers.

Already the ice studies had shown, Hubley said, that the glacier grows primarily in summer, when the Arctic Ocean, near shore, is ice-free and winds from that quarter are therefore moisture-laden, producing heavy snows in the mountains. In winter, with little open water off the coast, snowfall is meager. It seems likely that a similar explanation accounts for the extremely dry, snow-free north coast of Greenland and the absence of any ice in central Alaska and large areas of Siberia during the ice ages. It takes heavy snows, as well as cold, to produce a great ice sheet, and ice-age storm paths apparently shunned such areas as the Yukon Valley.

Charles M. Keeler, who was to winter on the glacier, studied the McCall Valley and found evidence of five glacial advances, the first carrying the full length of the valley to join a main glacier flowing down the path of the Jago River. The advances that followed were successively weaker, the last being only a slight extension of the present glacier. It was evident that no great ice sheet had covered the region. The scattered boulders that it would have left at high elevations were not to be found. Marks on the valley walls showed that the upper portion had once been filled with ice to a depth of 990 feet and that, lower down, the ice had been almost 1300 feet deep, but the glaciers of that time were simply enlargements of the type found there today.

During that midsummer visit the four men seemed well prepared for the long vigil ahead of them. Hubley, with his bushy crop of hair, was a youthful specialist in the young science of micrometeorology. After his graduation from the University of Washington, he had taken part in several glacier studies and, at IGY headquarters in Washington, D.C., had helped coordinate the glaciological program in the United States and the Arctic. He was quiet and, in retrospect, perhaps somewhat preoccupied, but there was no evidence of the deep-seated trouble that later led to tragedy. At thirty-one he was the oldest of the group, the others only recently having been graduated from college: Mason and Keeler from Yale and John E. Sater from Ohio State. All of them, at this "camp in the sky," seemed determined to keep alive, intellectually, during the long period of winter twilight and darkness. On the makeshift shelf against the padded wall of their hut were works of Plato, Schweitzer, Nietzsche, Whitehead, Croce, Tolstoi, Poe, Jean Jacques Rousseau, Robert Service, and Thomas Wolfe.

Three months later, as Hubley's companions slept, he stepped out into the frigid darkness, clad only in his underwear and boots. When found, many hours later, he lay frozen on the glacier whose secrets he had sought to probe. As soon as word reached Ladd Air Force Base, at Fairbanks, the three others were evacuated and the station was closed for the rest of the winter.[2]

Most of Alaska's ice is much farther south, where moist winds from the Gulf of Alaska strike the mountains. It was in this region that the downhill race of the "Galloping Muldrow" imparted to IGY glacier research a hot-blooded tempo usually lacking in the study of specimens that creep a few feet per year. At the start of the IGY it was discovered that during the previous winter the Muldrow Glacier, near Mount McKinley, had leaped forward several miles. Previously dormant, it was now grinding down the valley at about one foot per hour. Here was an unexpected opportunity to see why glaciers sometimes take the bit in their teeth and sprint.

Two IGY teams, both under the auspices of the American Geographical Society, modified their plans so that they might study the Muldrow. One of them had gone into the mountains to map glaciers in conjunction with aerial photography by the Navy. The other was studying glacier behavior. The leader of the first group, Austin Post of the University of Washington, found that a mammoth wave of ice had swept from top to bottom of the glacier. Thus the surface of its upper portion had dropped some 560 feet and a comparable amount had been added to swell the lower portion of the glacier.

It had been suggested that this swift wave motion might have been touched off by an earthquake, but Post could find no such correlation. Rather, he said, such sudden, periodic waves seemed to be a built-in characteristic of certain glaciers, a result of their shape, the elastic properties of ice, and the configuration of the valley in which they lie. Piles of glacial debris (moraines) in the area showed that this was not the first time the Muldrow had misbehaved, he said, and it was known that other glaciers, such as the Black Rapids, have done the same thing on occasion.[3]

Coordination of the south Alaskan glacier studies was carried out by the American Geographical Society, under William O. Field, who also headed the IGY World Data Center for Glaciology at the society's headquarters in New York. The Juneau Ice Field Research Project in southeastern Alaska had been launched by the society a decade earlier as one of the most intensive investigations of an ice mass ever attempted in North America. This sea of ice extends from the Canadian border, across the narrow part of Alaska north of Juneau, to the Pacific coast. One of its outlets, the Lemon Creek Glacier, was a focal point of IGY study. To determine the recent history of the coastal glaciers, trees were examined that had been partly pushed over during glacial advances of a few decades ago. The dates could be told with precision by slicing into the tree to the depth of its healed-over scar. The number of annual rings that had grown over the scar indicated elapsed time since the damage.

Perhaps the most intensively studied glacier, in the American program, was the Blue Glacier on the slopes of Mount Olympus, across Puget Sound from Seattle. It was not large—only 2.5 miles long and .7 miles wide—but, contrary to the general trend, it was believed to be growing. A University of Washington group, under Phil E. Church, with the aid of air drops and helicopters, set up a station on a rock outcrop in the upper part of the glacier, at an elevation of about 6800 feet, the objective being to study the manner in which the glacier was being fed. Men from the California Institute of Technology, under Robert P. Sharp, worked on the lower section during the two IGY summers, seeking to arrive at a basic flow law for valley glaciers.

The upper station proved to be the wettest spot in the continental United States in that the volume of precipitation was greater than at any known site. Most of it was in the form of snow, twenty feet of which fell in December and January alone. A series of eighteen-foot stakes had been placed in the cirque—the amphitheater at the head of the glacier—to use in studying accumulation, but all except one were completely buried during this period. On many winter days, winds and thundering avalanches made it impossible for the two men at the station to leave their hut and carry out their planned observations. On at least five days in November the wind velocity rose higher than 100 miles per hour and, although the wind-recording anemometer failed in several of the fiercer storms, gusts up to 130 miles per hour were recorded. Fortunately there were a few calm periods when a small plane could fly in to relieve the two men at the hut. The four taking part in the University of Washington project took turns, two of them processing data at the university and the other pair riding out the storms across the sound.

The Cal Tech group was interested in the lower glacier as a laboratory for the study of flowing rock. Ice is an unusually pure form of rock and the response of its crystals to the stresses and strains of flow would be useful as a basis for understanding what ancient events produced the crystalline structures observed in true rocks. The ice in a flowing glacier recrystallizes, due to the stress, producing the equivalent of a metamorphic rock whose crystal structure tells the nature of the flow that produced it.

For the crystal observations to have any meaning, it was necessary to determine the flow patterns of the glacier, including variations in flow from surface to glacier floor as well as from side to side. The results of some thirty-five explosions indicated that the ice was about 920 feet deep at its thickest and two holes were drilled in attempts to reach the rock beneath it. Neither did so, but one penetrated 738 feet, after grinding slowly through a section, 690 feet down, which seemed to be a layer of rock debris. The ice at this spot was thought to be 886 feet deep. Pipes left in these holes were to be examined annually for several years to determine their deformation by the variation in flow speed from top to bottom.

Another American program sought to inventory all glaciers in the United States proper, apart from Alaska. It produced a list of almost a thousand. The results, as analyzed by Mark F. Meier of the United States Geological Survey, showed that 79 per cent of them are mere patches of ice among the higher peaks, constituting but 10 per cent of the total ice volume in forty-eight states.[4] The principal glaciers are concentrated in the state of Washington, which encompasses 77 per cent of the total ice-covered area. The largest are the ones that cling to Mount Rainier; the only others bigger than two square kilometers each are in the Olympic Mountains, the Northern Cascades, and on Mount Adams (all in Washington), and in the Wind River range of Wyoming.

According to Edward R. La Chapelle of the University of Washington, in the 1957–58 observation period (which included an unusually hot, dry summer), of those glaciers in the Northern Cascades where a trend was evident, nine were advancing and five retreating. During the previous year, including the more moderate summer of

1957, eighteen advanced and only four retreated. There was also evidence of a general advance in Oregon, a state of equilibrium in Montana, and of glacial retreat in California.[5]

The Canadians studied one of the world's northernmost rivers of ice—Gilman Glacier, forty miles northeast of Lake Hazen on Ellesmere Island. This was not far from where Greely and his men spent their first terrible winter, but the Canadians believe they were the first on the glacier except for a 1935 expedition from Oxford University. The Canadian IGY station at Lake Hazen was flown in by the Royal Canadian Air Force in a total of ten flights in April–May, 1957, and a small camp was also airlifted to the glacier. The Canadian pattern of studies resembled that of the Americans in that they observed micrometeorology, ice movements, and the annual budget of additions and subtractions from the glacier. The eight-man summer party was relieved by a wintering group of four, the new arrivals flown in by helicopters from the United States Coast Guard icebreaker *Eastwind,* which penetrated Chandler Fiord to within thirty miles of the camp. It took thirty-five flights by the 'copters to ferry in the fifteen tons of stores needed for the winter—a service that helped repay the Canadians for their hospitality at Fort Churchill.

Another Canadian group concentrated on the Salmon Glacier in British Columbia.

Of the world's major nations, probably none has so many glaciers within its continental borders as the Soviet Union, and its IGY projects in this field of science spanned that vast land from the Koryak Mountains, overlooking the Bering Sea, to Europe's highest peak, Mount Elbrus, facing the Black Sea. Elbrus is a quiescent volcano most of whose glaciers were found to have been destroyed by a geologically "recent" outflow of lava and then to have reformed. Nine teams of scientists and students worked on the slopes of the mountain and, with extensive records of its glacial cover in past years, were able to determine that it has been shrinking since the 1850s. Furthermore, in other parts of the Caucasus, the rate of recession since 1930 has been two or three times as rapid as during the preceding sixty years.[6]

Glaciers in the ranges that crisscross central Asia were of more than academic interest, for they feed many rivers upon which the life of that region depends. Large areas of central Asia are rocky deserts, but where glacial streams run forth from the mountains there is almost invariably an oasis with irrigation nets and farms.

Of special interest was the exploration and survey of the Fedchenko Glacier, almost fifty miles long and, when combined with some thirty tributary glaciers, one of the largest masses of ice outside the polar regions. It descends from a massif in the Pamirs that is dominated by the 24,590-foot summit of Mount Stalin, crowded into the corner of the Soviet Union that lies between China and Afghanistan. One of the early attempts to use photomapping in the study of a glacier was that carried out on the Fedchenko by the German, Sebastian Finsterwalder, during the German-Soviet Alai-Pamir Expedition of 1928. Further work was done there in the Second Polar Year, and a weather station was set up at the 13,700-foot level. For the IGY, the Russians invited a group of German photogrammetrists to join in a resurvey designed to see what changes had taken place in the intervening years.[7]

The expedition was a joint venture of the Academy of Sciences of the Uzbek SSR, the Institute of Geography, and the Universities of Leningrad and Moscow, with specialists from China and Poland also taking part. The logistic problems were formidable, for the town that served as the base of operations was 250 miles from the glacier and for the last forty-four miles there were no roads. When the initial party of sixty set forth in June, 1957, they had with them a pack train of eighty horses. About a hundred tons of supplies, including pre-fabricated huts, had to be carried to the glacier and, as often was the case with the Soviet IGY effort, the expedition combined the primitive with the most sophisticated. Some of the huts were of duralumin, insulated on the inside in the manner of an aircraft fuselage. Their design was streamlined as protection against high winds on the glacier. Yet these huts were heated by coal and wood. American stations of this type have long used diesel oil as fuel, since it is so much more easily handled. The pack train had to ford the mountain torrents of the Tanymas and Seldara rivers and the horses then had to pick their way among treacherous crevasses on the glacier. Altogether a dozen of them were lost, either down crevasses or in the swift rivers. Winter began to close its grip on the mountains before the supplies could all be brought in, and hence twelve tons of priority supplies were dropped on the glacier by a squadron of four planes.

On August 10, 1957, as a party was making its way up the Fed-chenko Glacier, one of its members, Professor Pronin, spotted something unusual:

> ... Somebody seemed to be standing on one of the sharp rocky eminences [he said, in an account recorded by Lucien Barnier]. We knew that this mountainous part of the Pamir was completely uninhabited; there were therefore no villages.
>
> At first I thought it must be a bear. As I got over my surprise, I began to watch the creature carefully. I soon realized that it was not a bear but a being that looked like a man. The creature walked with its two legs slightly bent. It wore no clothes. Its body was covered in thick, reddish-grey hair. It was thick-set. Its upper limbs were on the long side. I particularly noted this point. I was apparently looking at a Yeti or Abominable Snowman.
>
> It had just come out of a cave; after walking 200 yards, it disappeared behind a rock. I had been in a position to observe it for seven or eight minutes.[8]

Although the Soviet Academy of Sciences is said to have appointed a special commission to investigate the reports of such creatures, official accounts of the expedition steer well clear of abominable snowmen.[9]

The upper station was erected 4900 meters (16,170 feet) above sea level, making it the highest of all IGY stations except the one manned sporadically at Chacaltaya, Bolivia. A similar station was placed lower down, at 9900 feet. The flow in the upper part of the glacier proved to be about 1.6 feet daily and the hut there moved more than 200 yards during the IGY. The eight men who manned it for a large part of the time were led by V. Nozdryukhin, who was described as a geographer-alpinist and Master of Sports of the Soviet Union. Accounts of the expedition told of their suffering from oxygen starvation due to the elevation.

Near this station an "ice laboratory" was dug out of the glacier to a depth of twenty-three feet, in which ice crystals could be studied without fear of their thawing. Other observations included micrometeorology, seismic sounding of the ice depths, aerial photomapping, and the exploration of the many tributary and discharge glaciers, some of them previously unexplored, as well as the measurement of their water contributions to various rivers. The glacier was found to be almost 3000 feet thick in its upper part. The resulting maps, as well as ground observations, established that its snout had receded some 950 feet since the survey of 1933, and the current rate of shrinkage was estimated at 33 feet a year. Since the upper mass is flowing downward at about 585 feet a year, the shrinkage figure represents the excess of evaporation and melting over the downward flow.

In seeking to determine the date when the Central Asiatic glaciers reached their most recent maximum, growth rings were examined on trees atop the ridges pushed up by this last great advance. The conclusion was that it had coincided with a period of maximum Eurasian water volume in the fourteenth and fifteenth centuries.[10]

Northeast of the Pamirs are the Tien Shan (in Chinese "the Celestial Mountains"), a system of mighty ranges that includes those marking the border between the Soviet Union and China. When the author hiked into these mountains on the Chinese side, in 1949, they were little changed from the days of Genghis Khan, inhabited only by scattered Kazakh and Russian sheepherders. The glaciers were said to number many hundreds and, through much of the area, had never been inventoried.

Several hundred of them were visited during the IGY, the work being divided between the Academy of Sciences of the Kirghiz SSR, which concentrated on the central ranges, and the Academy of Sciences of the Kazakh SSR, which worked on the Zailisky Ala-Tau, a northern spur of the mountain system. The records of earlier studies on some glaciers of the central ranges made it possible to determine that, since 1943, one glacier, the Karakoltor, had retreated more than a mile and many of its former tributaries had shriveled until they were no longer connected to the main ice river. Another, the Davidov, was found to have been retreating at almost ninety feet a year. Yet, in perplexing contradiction, the Northern Karasay had advanced about two-thirds of a mile in fourteen years.

The Kazakh academy sent out an expedition that drilled through the Zailisky Glacier, much as the Cal Tech men had sought to pierce the Blue Glacier, to obtain a vertical cross section of the ice's flow rate. Instead of shoving a pipe down the hole, the Kazakh expedition lowered a string of electrodes. The hole was filled with water, which froze. It was then possible to measure the electric field produced in the ice by each electrode and thus determine its position. In 190 days, it was found, the surface of the glacier moved 7.5 feet, whereas its base, 172 feet below, slid only 5 feet over the rocky floor. The intervening electrodes showed a gradual transition from the faster to the slower speed. The studies there and on glaciers of the neighboring Ala-Tau and Altai ranges again used micrometeorology to assess interchanges between the ice and the atmosphere.[11]

Apart from these observations along the southern frontiers of the Soviet Union, the Russians sought to obtain at least preliminary information on the little-explored mountains in the more remote parts of Siberia. The Koryak Mountains, which flank the Bering Sea and whose extension forms the spine of Kamchatka peninsula, were photo-mapped from the air by a stereoscopic technique. It was reported that 282 glaciers had been found, with a total area of seventy square miles. Another Siberian range, the Suntar-Khayata, had been found, in a 1946 aerial survey, to harbor 114 glaciers and snowfields with an area of about sixty square miles. Their existence was difficult to explain, for they lay in a region of very meager snowfall. The Suntar-Khayata Mountains form a southern spur of the Verkhoyansk Mountains, whose north-south wall isolates northeast Siberia from the rest of Asia. The Academy of Sciences decided to establish a high-altitude station in the Suntar-Khayata to study the glaciers and the permafrost, or permanently frozen ground.

Where horses had provided the backbone of the transport on the Fedchenko, here the chief reliance was on reindeer. The airfield at Oymyakon lay less than 100 miles to the northeast, but the animals had to pick their way through unbeaten taiga—the scrubby forest of the Arctic—and over rugged mountain trails. Hence, in August, 1956, an air search for a landing strip site was made by P. F. Shvetsov, director of the academy's Institute of Permafrost Studies, and N. A. Grave, who was to head the station. As the pilot swooped low to fly down the trough of the Burgali Valley, gusts of wind emerging from side canyons almost dashed the aircraft against the rock walls. This forced them to stay higher, and they were unable to find a site. A week later, a flat bench was found alongside the Bengali River, sixteen miles from the station site and close by two large ice fields. The plane landed safely, a strip was smoothed out, and about thirteen tons of supplies were flown in, including seven months' rations for the fifteen men of the station. A team of woodcutters marched ten miles down the valley to a forest of larch, where they began felling trees to build a log house at the station and to provide firewood for the furnace of its hot-water heating system. The wood was then hauled by reindeer to the station site in a pass 6730 feet up among the barren, glacier-strewn mountains.

Before the framework of the building could be transported up the valley, however, winter snow blocked the way even for the reindeer and work had to be suspended. The men waited out the winter in this coldest region of the North and completed the station in the spring in time to begin the planned program of radiation-balance observations and other glacier studies at the start of the IGY. The glaciers of the area were found to be stable, with no signs of current recession.[12]

In addition to these mainland studies, the Russians examined some of the glaciers on islands of Franz Joseph Land in the Arctic Ocean. Atop the dome of the ice cap on Hooker Island they hollowed out a laboratory surmounted by a vaulted ice ceiling, with forty ice steps and a rope railing leading down into it from their camp building. Here their microscope remained cold so that they could study the formation of ice crystals. Those at the station consisted of seven men and two young women: Tatyana Psareva, who worked in the ice laboratory, and Lyubov Voronina, a meteorologist.

The ice cap was found to be shrinking steadily. The Churlyanis Dome, site of the main station, was lowering eight inches per year and some of the smaller domes were subsiding even faster. This was attributed not to a warming but to a chilling of the climate in the years immediately preceding the IGY. Colder weather would mean less open water in the Arctic Ocean and therefore a drier climate, with less snow.

This expedition also visited the ice cap of Hayes Island, where further evidence of retreat was found. On this island, as well, was the Soviet Union's northernmost IGY station ashore, which carried out a broad program of auroral, magnetic, and cosmic-ray observations. It also served as the Soviet counterpart of the American rocket-launching site at Fort Churchill. The buildings of the community, known as Druzhny, were set up in a semicircle around a fresh-water lake and had a clear view of the launching site for the meteorological rockets. The first launching was on November 4, 1957, and, by the following March, six of the twenty-five IGY shots scheduled to be fired from this site had been launched. The radar antenna atop a green-roofed tracking van followed their flight until the jettisoned nose cone floated down under a bright red parachute to the frozen sea, where it was recovered by ski plane or surface travelers.[13]

IGY expeditions also did research on other arctic island groups. The Poles, who, a generation earlier, had studied the bleak scenery of Spitsbergen, returned to measure the glaciers in the vicinity of Hornsund. They came to the same conclusion as the Russians in Franz Joseph Land, namely that there had been a reversal in the warming trend of the first half of this century.[14]

While a cooling might starve arctic glaciers, it would help slow the shrinkage of those in warmer latitudes. No such effect seems to have been observed. In fact, most IGY studies found the rate of recession as great as ever. The Swiss Glacier Commission reported, for its 1957–58 observation period, that eighty-three out of eighty-nine Alpine glaciers had retreated an average distance of forty-eight feet. This was an increase over the thirty-foot average for the preceding year, due presumably to the unusually dry season.

During the IGY the long-standing glacier studies of West European nations were expanded, in particular those of Norway and Sweden, as well as those in countries that include in their territory a part of the Alps. France's Expéditions Polaires Françaises, under Paul Emile Victor, continued to study the Greenland ice sheet and served as the nucleus for an international expedition that enabled glaciologists from several European nations to work in Greenland immediately after the IGY.

In many other parts of the world the IGY gave young lovers of mountaineering an excuse to venture into little-frequented regions. Mexicans scrambled up the ice-crowned volcanic cones of Orizaba, Popocatepetl, and Ixtaccíhuatl. South Americans marched high into the Andes. The Geological Survey of India sent three expeditions into the Himalayas, one of them to investigate the Gangotri Glacier, from whose mighty ice cavern flows the Bhagirathi River, one of the most sacred in India and the traditional source of the Ganges. The glacier was found to have receded 300 feet in twenty-one years. In Africa teams of students studied three great mountain masses, two of them directly on the equator. One of the equatorial ranges was the Ruwenzori, whose eternal snows, looking out across the steaming jungles of Uganda and the Congo, are thought to be the fabled Mountains of the Moon, legendary source of the Nile.

In January, 1958, a group from Makerere College in Uganda, led by F. P. Henderson, started up the Ruwenzori from the 6000-foot level to place a small hut at 15,000 feet. The hut sections, instruments, food, and bundles of winter clothing were carried as head loads by a long string of African porters. The range had been explored in 1906 by the Duc D'Abruzzi, and members of the IGY expedition took photographs which they sought to match with those made more than a half-century earlier. It was found that the ice-covered area had shrunk considerably. When the men sought to place markers in the ice for movement studies, it proved almost impossible.

> During our marking-work [Henderson reported], we discovered, as did the expedition to Mt Kenya . . . that the ice of the tropics is different in nature from that of the temperate regions. It appears to be both harder and tougher and may require the development of new drilling techniques. . . .[15]

He thought the hardness might be related to the annual cycle of two rainy seasons and two dry seasons peculiar to the region. The expedition's reconnaissance disclosed thirty-one glaciers, six or seven of which were unnamed.

This expedition had one of the smallest budgets of any in the IGY: 182 pounds sterling.

Some 500 miles due east, beyond Lake Victoria and likewise on the equator, another expedition worked on Mount Kenya. Its labors in establishing a base camp at 13,500 feet and a satellite camp at 16,000 feet were eased by a detachment of mules furnished by the King's African Rifles. The venture, sponsored by Britain's Royal Society and other groups, was led by Igor S. Loupekine, lecturer in geology at the Royal Technical College in the nearby city of Nairobi. Here, too, evidence was found of wide glacial retreat. The third expedition, from the University of Sheffield in England, studied Africa's highest mountain, Kilimanjaro, whose 19,340-foot ice-clad summit rises to the south, near the border between Kenya and Tanganyika.

CHAPTER 18
ANTARCTIC PREPARATIONS

On July 6, 1955, a conference opened at the Paris Observatory to which few except those in attendance paid much attention. Yet this meeting, held in a lecture hall near the summit of Montparnasse, set in motion a sequence of events that seems to have determined the political fate of an entire continent, resulting in precedents that may prove of great importance in dealing with the problems of outer space.

The conference was the first of several called to coordinate the IGY program in Antarctica, its chief task being to decide who should go where. The previous fall, at the CSAGI Assembly in Rome, fourteen sites had been recommended for new or reactivated scientific stations in Antarctica and its off-lying islands. In addition, virtually all existing stations maintained by Argentina, Australia, France, New Zealand, and the United Kingdom were to take part.

The most dramatic effort, as foreseen by the Rome conference, was to be the attempt to establish a United States outpost in the vicinity of the South Pole itself. No human being had set foot there except during the southern summer of 1911–12, when a team of five Norwegians led by Roald Amundsen won the famous race to the bottom of the world. The losers, five gallant Englishmen under Capt. Robert F. Scott, died en route back to McMurdo Sound.

At Rome, ten of the proposed new sites were tentatively allocated as follows:

Australia	Advanced Base (480 miles south of Mawson)
France	Pointe Géologie (reactivated); Base Secondaire (near Magnetic Pole); Îles Crozet
Norway	Peter I Island; Bouvet Island

South Africa   Marion Island
United States   Little America; Marie Byrd Land; South
                          Polar Plateau.

Four sites were left open for any nation that wished to send an expedition: the Princess Astrid Coast of Queen Maud Land, the Knox Coast of Wilkes Land, Ross Island by McMurdo Sound, and Vahsel Bay in the Weddell Sea. It was stressed that the occupation of these "gap-locations" was important for a number of scientific reasons, including their critical orientation with respect to study of the aurora and their importance in completing the proposed pole-to-pole chains of stations.[1]

When the meeting opened at the Paris Observatory, Colonel Georges Laclavère, Secretary-General of the International Union of Geodesy and Geophysics, was elected chairman. His forceful, almost militant manner helped resolve several problems that arose. His announcement, at the opening session, that the Soviet Union planned to send an expedition to the Antarctic created a sensation in the hall. The Russians, like all IGY participants, had been invited to go south, but, until Vladimir Beloussov, immediately before the conference, sent notification that he planned to attend, there had been no hint that they planned to do so. All Soviet polar efforts had been concentrated in the North, with the exception of a whaling fleet that joined in the annual operations off Antarctica. The only exploratory expedition that had ever been sent south by Russia was that of Admiral Thaddeus Bellingshausen who, in 1820–21, sailed his ships, the *Mirny* and *Vostok,* around much of the antarctic continent. However, during the antarctic crisis of 1948, Moscow asserted its right to take part in any settlement of the antarctic problem.

In that year the dispute between Britain, Argentina, and Chile over control of the Palmer Peninsula (Graham Land) had come to a head. The thousand-mile peninsula is geologically and geographically an extension of the Andes and lies on the southern flank of the only open-water link between the Atlantic and Pacific. Hence, in the premissile thinking of World War II, it had some strategic importance. For this reason, Britain secretly occupied Deception Island, off the northern tip of the peninsula, to deny the area to the Germans and Argentines. In 1948 the Argentine Navy made a show of force, sending a large task force to Deception Island. The British responded by dispatching one of their own cruisers to the scene. The United States then proposed that all seven nations claiming territory in Antarctica agree on "some form of internationalization." Despite its long record of antarctic exploration, the United States never had made a declaration of sovereignty over any part of the continent, largely on the ground that such a claim would have no legal standing unless a permanent station had been established. The seven countries who had spoken for slices of the continent and to whom the United States sent its proposal were Argentina, Australia, Britain, Chile, France, New Zealand, and Norway. Moscow, at this point, citing the discoveries of Bellingshausen and Russia's whaling activities, announced it would recognize no antarctic solution to which it was not a party. In recent years the only important natural resource of Antarctica has been its abundance of whales.

When Beloussov arrived, the third day of the Paris conference, he told the delegates that the Soviet Academy of Sciences was considering the establishment of three antarctic stations: one on the coast, one near the South Pole, and the third midway between the other two. The coastal station, he said, would be at one of two of the recommended locations—the Princess Astrid Coast or the Knox Coast. He noted that the latter was particularly desirable because it would complete the pole-to-pole station chain that bisected the Soviet Union.

At his mention of the South Pole the hearts of many in the hall sank. Everyone else there knew that this was where the United States planned to go and suspected that Beloussov knew it too.[2] It looked as though Soviet-American rivalry, which had been so carefully kept out of the IGY, was now inevitable. Furthermore, the Knox Coast was in the sector claimed by Australia and, while the Australian delegates said nothing of the matter publicly, they were clearly disturbed at having Soviet bases there—even under IGY auspices.

In all, five nations were interested in the location on the Knox Coast, almost due south of Australia. Part of the attraction was the image of "Bunger's Oasis" as a fascinating station site. In 1947 the pilot of a United States Navy seaplane, Lieutenant Commander David E. Bunger, had sighted a snow-free region an estimated 100 square miles in area, and the suggestion that it might be warmed volcanically led to its being called an oasis. A year later a survey party, landed there by helicopters from two Navy icebreakers, found the region a desert almost barren of life. Its freedom from ice was attributed to meager snowfall, high winds, and protection by the terrain from flowing hinterland ice.

The chief drawback to the site was its difficulty of access. It was separated from the open ocean by an extensive apron of sea ice. However, a few hundred miles farther east the Navy icebreakers had found a great open-water area (now called Vincennes Bay) with a partly ice-free coast that could be reached directly by ship. Laurence M. Gould, who had been second in command of Byrd's first antarctic expedition and now was director of the American IGY program in Antarctica, therefore suggested that the United States station be in the vicinity of Vincennes Bay. As it turned out, none of the main IGY stations was placed on the Knox Coast. The Russians ultimately went west of it, the Americans went east (to Vincennes Bay), and the Australians, Belgians, and Japanese, who had been the other candidates, picked sites even farther away. Later a small Soviet camp was set up at the "oasis."

During the discussions in Paris Laclavère pointed out that, although the United States was planning to go to the Pole, there was a vast cavity in IGY coverage at the center of East Antarctica (that portion of the continent lying primarily in the Eastern Hemisphere). This heartland, roughly a thousand miles from the sea, was probably the most difficult place in the world to reach and came to be known as the Pole of Inaccessibility.

When Beloussov next took the floor he said, in his mild manner, "We do not insist on the Geographic Pole," and promised to bring back to Moscow the recommendation for a station at the Pole of Inaccessibility. Also of special interest, some of the scientists pointed out, was the South Geomagnetic Pole, deep within the unexplored hinterland. Eventually Soviet stations were placed at both points.

The pattern of cooperation and accommodation that thus began in Paris continued past the end of the IGY. This applied as well to another, more emotional situation—that involving the rival claims of Britain, Argentina, and Chile.

To the dismay of the conference organizers, the Argentine and Chilean delegations were headed, not by scientists, but by ambassadors. Colonel Laclavère decided to head off trouble before it started. In opening the first meeting he read a statement that political questions had no place in the discussions and the two ambassadors agreed to endorse it.

The problem was that the British wanted to place a base at Vahsel Bay, in the southernmost corner of the Weddell Sea, where Argentina had just set up a station, in part to support its assertion to sovereignty over the area. In fact, before the conference was over, the United States indicated that it, too, might send an expedition to that region. One of the principles of the IGY was to keep the stations as far apart as possible, for maximum coverage and a minimum of duplication. However, at this and the subsequent antarctic planning conferences, it became clear that none of these nations was going to withdraw. The British considered the site essential for their proposed transcontinental journey; the United States had in mind a program that would not duplicate the work of the other two expeditions; and the Argentines were already there. Hence it was agreed that all three nations would operate at the head of the Weddell Sea, but the two Latin American representatives stated for the record that "these are temporary measures" that "do not modify the existing status in the Antarctic regarding the relations of the participating countries." [3]

One of the American proposals at the Paris conference was that an international Weather Central be established at Little America to process all the information collected daily by ships, planes, tractor parties, and stations. It would produce forecasts valuable to all the expeditions and carry out special studies of antarctic weather. As this plan matured, it was proposed that the staff of the Weather Central be international; consequently specialists from seven nations took part in its work. When the question of having a Soviet participant arose, the United States IGY Committee asked the Russians if an American could similarly be stationed at the main Soviet base. To this Moscow agreed, and nothing could have done more to allay fears and suspicions than the series of personnel exchanges that resulted from this arrangement. The men selected for these ambassadorial roles, on both sides, were obviously chosen for their tact and good humor and did much to improve relations between the expeditions.

At the conclusion of the Paris meeting, Beloussov raised two additional questions: mapping and the use of way stations in nearby countries. At that time the Russians apparently expected to fly large aircraft to the Antarctic via Australia or South Africa, as the United States was to do from New Zealand. In the end, however, they used smaller planes that were brought in by ship. Nevertheless, a resolution was passed by a subsequent meeting on the Antarctic, recommending that nearby nations cooperate in this respect.[4]

Although Laclavère was in favor of Beloussov's mapping idea, it was subsequently turned down as not falling within the purview of the IGY program. Those going south, however, were urged to collect and publish any information that would be of value to cartographers, and both the American and Soviet expeditions headed south with map-making among their goals. The operation plan drawn up by the United States Navy for its initial season of antarctic operations in preparation for the IGY called for extensive aerial photomapping, using specially equipped aircraft with enough range to reach all parts of the continent from a proposed airstrip on the ice at McMurdo Sound. Permanent stations were also envisaged "in support of United States 'rights' in the area." [5]

This introduction of a political motivation was objected to strongly by the scientists organizing the United States IGY program and such an objective was omitted from all subsequent operation plans. The ambitious American mapping program was also curtailed. The Soviet expedition, on the other hand, went ahead with its mapping. The research ships *Ob* and *Lena* sent aircraft flying over the coast, photographing sections all the way from Queen Maud Land almost to the Ross Sea, embracing roughly half the continent and all of the Australian claim. Parties were landed at some three score points, either to take celestial observations for pinpointing photographed features or to study the geology of the region.

Although it was agreed in Paris that the Soviet base would be on the Knox Coast, this probably would have been an almost impossible site, due to the extent of offshore ice. However, before the first contingents sailed south, Belgium announced that it could not occupy its assigned location at the Haswell Islets, 300 miles to the west in the Davis Sea, which usually clears of ice in the summer. The Russians decided to go there, placing their camp in an area of rock outcrops linked by semipermanent ice to the mainland. The station was christened *Mirny* (Peaceful) and the one at the Geomagnetic Pole was to be *Vostok* (East), these having been the names of Bellingshausen's two ships.

American activities began with a reconnaissance by the icebreaker *Atka,* in 1954–55, which discovered that Byrd's old base at Little

America had been partially destroyed and rendered unusable by a massive breaking off of the ice shelf. The station was on a floating apron of glacier ice that fills a gulf in the coast roughly the size of France and, at its seaward end, is about 800 feet thick. Its frontal cliffs move north at some five feet daily so that any camp on the shelf is doomed, eventually, to go to sea or be destroyed as icebergs break off.

In 1955–56 a naval task force consisting of three icebreakers, three cargo vessels, an oil tanker, and two oil barges sailed south, in Operation Deep Freeze I, to set up the two coastal stations which would serve, the following year, as steppingstones to the interior. One, at McMurdo Sound, would be the base for an airlift to the Pole, since the 850-mile surface route up a treacherous glacier and across many miles of ice sheet seemed too unreliable. Kainan Bay, to the east of the old Little America site, was selected for the IGY's "Little America Station," whence tractors would haul the supplies for the projected base, Byrd Station, near the center of Marie Byrd Land.

During the antarctic summer of 1955–56 four long-range Navy planes flew from New Zealand and landed on the bay ice covering McMurdo Sound—the first such air link between Antarctica and the outside world. After several reconnaissance flights over the hitherto unseen heartland of the continent, they flew out again. Wintering parties totaling about 163 men were left at Little America and at McMurdo Sound, in a camp near Scott's weatherbeaten shelter on Hut Point.

Meanwhile, two British expeditions had sailed into the ice-choked Weddell Sea to establish a joint base near Vahsel Bay. One was the Commonwealth Trans-Antarctic Expedition, led by Vivian (later Sir Vivian) Fuchs. The other was the IGY expedition of the Royal Society. On account of ice conditions the two groups actually picked different sites, a fortunate development from the scientific point of view, since it made for a broader distribution of data. The Royal Society camp was placed at Halley Bay, but when Fuchs arrived he feared it would be difficult for his vehicles to reach the interior from there, and he proceeded farther south to a site only twenty miles from the Argentine base at the head of the Weddell Sea. France reactivated its station in Adélie Land and the Argentines, Australians, and Chileans prepared to enlarge scientific observations at their existing camps.

The following spring—late in 1956—the push into the interior began. The first step, so far as the United States was concerned, was the preparation of a hard-ice runway on McMurdo Sound. This would enable C-124 Globemasters, the Air Force's largest operational transports, to fly in from New Zealand, make wheeled landings on the ice, and load up the heavy Polebound cargo that had been brought in the previous year by ship. At the McMurdo camp the cargo—tractors, power plants, prefabricated hut panels, and so forth—was packaged for air drop. But the big problem was the airstrip. Before the bitter cold of winter had subsided, the Navy Seabees were out on the bay, trying to prepare a suitable runway. Their various schemes for flooding, rolling, and tractor-tamping at first seemed hopelessly futile, but at length they reported that a runway was ready and in October, 1956, the planes began to fly in from New Zealand. The first to arrive was a transport with Rear Admiral George J. Dufek, commander of the military support forces in the Antarctic, on board. Then five other Navy planes, including a P2V Neptune loaded with aerial cameras, took off and headed south. It was a long haul—about twelve hours for most of the planes—with only one place to go, once the point of no return had been passed. Ahead of them lay a mighty continent —but only one runway, on a frozen-over bay surrounded by mountains, one of them an active volcano 13,200 feet high. Unfortunately, as the planes approached, the weather at McMurdo clouded over and the ceiling dropped to 300 feet. There was a ground-controlled-approach (GCA) radar van on the ice that coached the first arrival —the P2V—down for a familiarization pass over the runway. When the pilot broke out under the cloud cover and could see the bulldozed runway, he decided he could bank steeply and circle beneath the clouds without depending on the GCA. What he did not take into account is the impossibility of judging altitude in the diffuse light of a polar overcast. His wingtip hit the snow and the plane cartwheeled. Three of the men aboard the plane, including the pilot, were killed and five injured, one of whom died soon thereafter. It was a sad debut.

There were other casualties: A tractor that was hauling cargo from the ships, where they lay moored against the bay ice, to the camp at McMurdo, broke through the ice, carrying its driver with it. At Mirny, the Soviet base, there was a similar mishap, but only one side of the vehicle broke through. The driver wisely jumped out, but another volunteered to drive it out of its hole. Instead, it broke entirely through, dropping into the icy water so fast that he had no time to leap out. A movie cameraman caught the entire terrible sequence, including the headlong flight of other men escaping in all directions from the crumbling ice. At Little America a massive, thirty-five-ton tractor was grinding over a well-traveled portion of an exploratory trail into the interior when a snow bridge, apparently dislodged by repeated vibration, collapsed, dropping the vehicle and its driver into a crevasse from which neither returned. A Globemaster, swooping low to make an air drop over the joint New Zealand–American station at Cape Hallett, crash-landed on a snow slope, apparently due to deceptive lighting conditions. The heavy load of cargo tore loose, killing all but one of the seven men riding in the cavernous cargo space. An Argentine naval vessel, the *Guarain,* hastening to the aid of an ill man at one of that country's antarctic stations, foundered and sank in October, 1958, with the loss of thirty-six lives.

Such mishaps were due, essentially, to the novelty of the environment in which men and equipment had been called upon to operate. Had the nature of the hazards been fully understood, they would not have been much greater than those confronting the man who tries to dash across Fifth Avenue against the lights. The difference was that the jaywalker, however foolhardy, has usually lived with city traffic all his life. Only gradually were operating procedures worked out that cut the risks to a minimum.

One of the most hazardous tasks of the American program, the marking of a safe trail from Little America to the planned site for Byrd Station, was assigned to a highly professional Army-Navy team whose men had specialized in ice-sheet tractor operations. Led by two Army majors who had done this sort of work in Greenland, it set forth from Little America on November 9, 1956, heading initially southeast over the Ross Ice Shelf toward its junction with the continental ice. The plan was to climb onto the inland plateau and head due east another 400 miles across hitherto untraveled country to the site. Although reconnaissance flights had shown the plateau to be smooth, they had also revealed that, all along the junction between the floating shelf and the land-borne ice sheet, there were mazes of crevasses. Any flanking maneuver farther to the south was blocked by a broad, swiftly flowing stream that seemed to drain much of the Marie Byrd Land ice into the shelf. It was a morass so torn up that, from the air, it resembled the white water of rapids, suddenly frozen in its turbulence.

The author spent ten days with this trail party as it picked its way cautiously over the shelf toward the inland plateau. When one included the twenty-ton cargo sleds in tow behind the D-8 tractors, the total weight of tractor and load was fifty tons or more. Snow bridges over the crevasses might hold a man on skis or even a light vehicle, but no snow bridge could safely be entrusted with a weight like that.

Hence two light Weasels scouted several miles ahead of the thundering D-8s, one of them pushing five basins fitted to wooden spars so that they skidded over the snow in a broad pattern. Two additional basins were towed behind. Electric currents were driven through the ice between these basins and, whenever there was a sudden drop in strength (indicating a cavity beneath the surface), a buzzer sounded and a light flashed inside the Weasel. In addition, a record of the intensity on each circuit was kept on moving paper. Although this newly developed crevasse-detector was not infallible, its use on the exploratory journeys helped prevent further loss of life.

At about 7 P.M. each day the crevasse-detector swept a large circular area, which then became the campsite. The pounding of the D-8s as they drew near made the ice tremble for miles around and their smoke trailed off in parallel plumes, like those of a ship convoy. The throb of their great diesel engines seemed to say that the twentieth century was on the march—that nothing could stop it. Nothing, that is, except a crevasse. Because of the fear of these hidden chasms, the daily advances, even over the smooth shelf, were no greater than those of Captain Scott half a century before.

"The funny thing about it is," said our second in command, Major Mogensen, "that, with all this horsepower and modern equipment, we can't do any better than they did—twenty miles a day!" Palle Mogensen, a Danish-born polar specialist, later succeeded Paul Siple as scientific leader at the Pole.

Behind one of the D-8s was an orange house on runners: our messing wannigan, descended from the movable huts of that name long used by loggers in the North Woods. Two smaller, boxlike wannigans provided additional sleeping space. The messing wannigan had three tables and a seating capacity of twelve. After we had eaten, one of the tractor drivers, James E. Gardiner, who came from a place called Radium Springs, New Mexico, would, with a minimum of encouragement, take his guitar from the hook where it had swung all day as the wannigan lurched along. "I'm a poor, lonesome cowboy, and a long, long way from home," was his favorite.

Our cook, C. Norman Coleman, was a colonel in the Army reserve. One evening, as he looked from the door of the wannigan across the icescape, sparkling blindingly white in the sun, he remarked on its strange beauty, then hastily added: "But if you were here alone, you might as well be six feet down." From this interdependence there developed a special fellowship among the men on the trail which it is hard to find under less exotic circumstances.

It had been hoped that a smooth route could be found through the crevasse belt along the shoreline, but there was none. The outriders were narrow cracks across the trail. Ahead were clefts which Mogensen, after a first look, described as being as wide as churches. Even the cracks had to be examined with caution. Dynamite sticks were lowered into them and fired. Usually fragments of snow and ice would fly into the air and shower on the trail-blazers; but sometimes there would be only a thump and no geyser. This meant trouble, for the explosion had spent itself downward into some chasm.

Once an explosion opened a cavity several feet wide. Charles H. Wedemeyer, a Navy Construction Mechanic First Class, donned crampons (spikes affixed to boots for ice climbing) and, a rope around his waist, lowered himself into the hole. With his back against one wall and his feet against the other, he worked sideways toward a point under the provisional highway that had been marked on the surface with red flags. Weasels had already been using the route in safety, but Wedemeyer emerged into a purple cavern of awesome dimensions—big enough to hold an entire church, steeple and all. Its vaulted roof, about forty feet thick, lay right under the highway. A few bags of explosive caved in the bridge so that a safe route could be marked alongside it.

The crevassed area was only seven miles wide, but it seemed an almost hopeless task to get across it. In view of the possibility that an approach over the ice might be impossible, plans were drafted for airlifting a small station in place of the fifteen-building camp scheduled to be hauled in by tractor train. Then it was decided that the airlift to the Pole was using so much fuel that not enough remained for such an operation. National prestige was at stake in the establishment of Byrd Station, for the United States was committed to filling this gap in IGY observations.

From the air the crevasses somewhat resembled a succession of waves moving toward a beach. Major Merle R. Dawson, the party's leader, decided that the only hope was to try to cut through parallel to the crevasses—along the crests of the waves, so to speak. A trail was marked by helicopter, with Mogensen leaning out of the hovering craft to jab a trail flag into the snow. In this manner there was no risk of his breaking through, although once the snow dropped out from beneath the 'copter as it nimbly lifted into the air.

Crevasses that could not be by-passed had to be bulldozed full of snow. The initial journeys of the heavy tractors along the crests between crevasses were unmanned. Gardiner and Alvah G. Edwards, Construction Driver First Class, walked well behind the vehicles, holding reins attached to the controls and driving them as a plowman drives his horse.

After the trail party had expended some 4700 pounds of explosives and spent twelve days among the crevasses, the inland plateau was achieved; from there on to the site it was straight rolling. All told, it took the group five weeks to lay the 650-mile trail. Two heavy tractor trains followed close behind, hauling cargo sleds laden with the huts and other supplies. Another 240 tons were delivered to Byrd Station by the Air Force and twenty-two men were left there for the winter, among them a dozen scientists.

Meanwhile ships were establishing the various coastal stations. The icebreaker USS *Staten Island*, escorting the cargo ship *Wyandot*, penetrated close to the southwest corner of the Weddell Sea, where no ship ever had been before. The closest, in fact, had been the British ship *Endurance*, carried there involuntarily in the grip of a drifting pack that later crushed it. The American ships were unable to reach any satisfactory site on the coast and also faced the possibility that, if they persisted and found a good spot, it could not be reached another year. They therefore turned back and established Ellsworth Station thirty-five miles northwest of Argentina's Belgrano Station, which in turn was twenty miles west of the Commonwealth Expedition's Shackleton Base.

Across the continent the New Zealand contingent of the Commonwealth Expedition, led by Sir Edmund Hillary, set up Scott Base over the hill from the United States station on McMurdo Sound. Its task, the next spring, would be to lay out depots of food and fuel along the route toward the Pole that would constitute the final leg of the transcontinental journey. A group of New Zealand IGY scientists was with Hillary, and New Zealand also helped man the station the United States set up at Cape Hallett, some 400 miles north of McMurdo. The seventh American station was placed at Vincennes Bay, 1500 miles to the west, and, before the start of the IGY, expeditions from Norway and Japan established themselves on the coast of Queen Maud Land.[6]

Of all the achievements during the pre-IGY period, the establishment of the South Pole station was the most remarkable. An entire community, buildings and all, was parachuted by planes flying in a most inhospitable environment. Food, fuel, laboratories, instruments, power plants, vehicles—all came down from the sky to the spot whose achievement, forty-five years earlier, had been one of the great feats of human endurance.

Once the base at McMurdo had been established,[7] the final step before the polar airlift was to set up an auxiliary station at the foot of Liv Glacier, where twin-engine Douglas skiplanes could refuel en route back from the Pole. The station also provided weather information midway between the coast and the Pole and could be used as a base for rescue operations, if necessary. It was established on October 29, 1956. Two days later Dufek landed at the Pole in one of the Douglas skiplanes. The temperature was —58°. This, combined with the thin air at 9200 feet, made conditions appear so severe that he decided to delay the operation several weeks until it warmed up a bit. The plane's skis had frozen to the ice and only after firing all fifteen Jato bottles (for a jet-assisted take-off) did the plane break loose and climb into the air. It had been the first time men had set foot at the South Pole since Scott and his ill-fated party left there early in 1912.

The initial reconnaissance and construction party was landed as near as possible to the Pole on November 20 under the command of Lieutenant (j.g.) Richard A. Bowers, a twenty-eight-year-old Naval Reservist who had graduated from Yale and was now serving his tour of duty in the Navy's Civil Engineering Corps. Bowers was a lanky fellow with a scraggly beard, who seemed the kind of practical, commonsense man who would build a community at the South Pole if anyone could. With him were John Tuck, Jr., likewise a Lieutenant (j.g.) in the Naval Reserve, a Navy chief petty officer, five Seabees, and a team of eleven dogs. Tuck, four years younger than Bowers and recently graduated from Dartmouth, had been in charge of the dogs at McMurdo. He was later chosen to be military leader at the Pole.

This group was brought in by two of the Douglas transports on skis while heavy Globemasters circled overhead, dropping the initial equipment, including sleds and a Weasel. The latter landed so hard that its batteries and transmission case were broken. When replacements were airdropped the next day the new lot of batteries also smashed.

After a round of sun sights, Bowers found that they were about nine miles from the Pole and so, like Amundsen a half-century earlier, the group arrived on foot behind a team of dogs. Hardly had this fingerhold been established on the bottom of the world than a procession of Globemasters of the 63rd Troop Carrier Group began passing overhead, releasing a rain of supplies. More construction men were flown in, as was Paul A. Siple, who was to be scientific leader. Siple, first widely known as the Boy Scout who went south on Byrd's first expedition, was now an experienced polar specialist. By the time the IGY was over, he had possibly spent more time on the antarctic continent than any other human being.

The arrangement for dual leadership at the Pole, similar to that at the other American polar stations, north and south, derived from the reluctance of the military to take orders from a civilian scientist—and vice versa. Disputes between co-leaders were to be referred to the senior scientist and senior military officer, who, in the Antarctic, ruled jointly at Little America. If this did not suffice, the problem could be passed on to the Pentagon and the Academy of Sciences. While there were certainly disagreements at some camps, the author is not aware of any case in which outsiders had to referee.

The camp at the Pole was officially christened "Amundsen-Scott IGY South Pole Station," in honor of the heroic rivals who raced for the bottom of the world in the summer of 1911–12. By February 21, 1957, 760 tons of material had been delivered there in sixty-five missions. The construction men had been lifted out and the last group of scientists brought in, leaving a wintering party of nine IGY researchers and nine Navy men to operate the vehicles, communications, and galley, and to provide medical care. When the last plane vanished over the snowy horizon they were, as Siple put it, "eighteen men in a box." Unlike those on the McCall Glacier, they could not count on a midwinter rescue in case of trouble. Their chief fear was of fire, which could cast them out into an environment that would mean certain death. They held drills; they split the camp in two, with a wall of snow in between as a fire break and enough food for survival on either side.

They even set up a Jamesway hut 200 feet from camp with extra sleeping bags, fuel, and emergency rations. Likewise, covered galleries were provided around the snow-buried buildings to make them accessible for fire-fighting from all sides.

In March, a month after the group at the Pole began their period of isolation and several months before the start of the IGY, the author spoke to Paul Siple and John Tuck from his home in Connecticut—again thanks to the good offices of the radio amateur, Jules Madey. Admiral Byrd had died about ten days before and, even through the cumbersome phone patch, one could sense what a blow this had been to Siple, for he had been one of Byrd's most loyal friends. He said they had half-masted the flag for the last ten days of daylight. On March 22 the six-month winter night began.

I asked if they had made any trips away from the station and, when Madey switched his circuit to "receive," I could hear laughter in the snow-buried hut at the Pole. Yes, Tuck said, they had made an unplanned journey. One of the last loads dropped by the Air Force was a bundle of girders for the barracks building. Normally they pursued the descending parachutes in their Weasel so they could cut the shrouds and prevent dragging of the load. This time, however, the Weasel battery was dead and, by the time they got the vehicle started, a brisk wind had dragged the bundle beyond the horizon. It took a day to track down the girders and haul them twenty-five miles back to the base.

They reported that they had just finished a thousand-foot tunnel so that the seismic instruments could be placed well away from camp vibration. Part way out, along the tunnel, a chamber was carved in the ice for the magnetic recorders. The tunnel was made by digging a trench, then roofing it with timbers and burlap, but as winter approached the ice had become harder and harder, making the job increasingly difficult. "We bashed in the top of a crowbar with a sledge hammer, trying to drive it in two feet," Siple said.

He added that they had erected a seventy-five-foot mast for ionospheric observations—a program of special interest since some believed that, with six months of darkness, the ionosphere might disappear entirely. This would mean that the Pole Station could not communicate by radio with the outside world. Actually, the ionosphere never vanished. The E layer often disappeared, but, higher, the one F layer, typical of the nighttime sky in other latitudes, persisted throughout the polar night. When the sun was below the horizon in the direction of the magnetic and geomagnetic poles, the F layer was unusually high; when the sun was in the opposite direction, it was particularly low. Its intensity was patchy, suggesting to some that swift winds were bringing in freshly ionized particles from sunlit latitudes.[8]

As we talked, Siple said the sun was a great orange sphere, circling just above the horizon. The area of the camp already was deep in purple shadows except downwind, where vapor, generated by warm air from the many smokestacks, hung like a fog bank over the snow. The only member of the party a little under the weather, they said, was the husky, "Bravo," who had apparently eaten some glass wool. Tuck said the much-petted dog filled a big gap in their isolated lives.

Although the men felt healthy during their first weeks at the Pole, some of them lost an alarming amount of weight. Seven of the eighteen lost twenty-five pounds or more. Siple, a big man to begin with, dropped the most. When he arrived at the Pole he weighed nearly 250 pounds, but after weeks of exhausting labor, racing with sunset to ready the camp for winter, he dropped to 211 pounds. With the comparative idleness of winter, this leveled off.

When our conversation was ended, Madey asked the men at the Pole to wait while he disconnected the phone patch. "Okay," they said. "We aren't going any place." [9]

It has been estimated that it cost a million dollars apiece to place, shelter, and sustain each man at the Pole Station. Actually there is no clear-cut way to estimate the costs of the IGY stations in Antarctica, since so many government ships, planes, and personnel were involved. Had they not been committed to the Antarctic, they would have figured in some other area of the national budget. Operational losses, arising from the unusual conditions, must be taken into account, including some $2.7 million apiece for two wrecked Globemasters. Phillip Law, who has directed Australia's postwar efforts in Antarctica, estimates the total cost to all nations at well over $280 million.[10] By contrast, when the IGY ended, the American Vanguard program alone had cost nearly $112 million.

The antarctic expenditures were a long-range investment, in that they initiated a continuing program. The sudden growth in the population of that continent is shown by the rosters of its wintering parties before and during the IGY.[11]

	1955		IGY	
	Stations	*Men*	*Stations*	*Men*
ARGENTINA	7	78	8	105
AUSTRALIA	1	15	2	32
BELGIUM	0	0	1	17
BRITAIN	8	57	14	127
CHILE	4	29	4	56
FRANCE	0	0	2	23
JAPAN	0	0	1	11
NEW ZEALAND	0	0	1	23
NORWAY	0	0	1	14
SOVIET UNION	0	0	6	165
UNITED STATES	0	0	8	339
Total	**20**	**179**	**48**	**912**

In summer the population grew far more—to an estimated 5000. During the initial IGY season there were sixteen parties from eight nations on the antarctic trail; they covered about 14,000 miles. It is safe to say that never in the history of exploration has there been, in size, composition, or scope of inquiry, an effort to compare with this international assault on a virtually unknown continent.

CHAPTER 19
CONTINENT OR ARCHIPELAGO?

Maps of the world show a great white region in the far south. In the distortion of a Mercator projection it appears as an irregular ribbon along the bottom, but on a globe, or a map centered on the South Pole, it shows as a rounded continent comparable in size to Europe and the United States combined. What is represented, however, is primarily the ice sheet. Unlike Greenland, where glaciers plunge into the sea through rugged fiords, the ice sheet of Antarctica completely buries most of the true coast and in many areas has pushed far out to sea in the form of ice shelves. The most ambitious goal of the IGY in Antarctica was to look under this icy shroud.

The nature of the land beneath has long been a subject of speculation, extending even to the question of whether Antarctica is one continent or two. Griffith Taylor, a geologist on Scott's last expedition, had suggested that Antarctica might be divided into two land masses by a trough linking the Ross and Weddell seas. Some thought at first that there might be a water connection under the ice along this route, and that the strong currents observed under the ice shelf near Mc-Murdo Sound might represent an interchange of water between the Atlantic and Pacific oceans. The possibility of such a cleavage has been supported by the clear geologic separation of East Antarctica (in the Eastern Hemisphere) from West Antarctica (in the Western Hemisphere). Serving as a frontier wall for East Antarctica is the Great Antarctic Horst, the chief mountain system of the region. It extends from Cape Adare, south of New Zealand, at least to the eastern shore of the Weddell Sea, south of Brazil, and is probably as extensive as the Rocky Mountains. A *horst* is an area where blocks of the earth's crust have been lifted in a manner that has kept their layers comparatively horizontal. This one encloses the mighty shield of pre-Cambrian rock —the oldest type known—which is the basic formation of all East

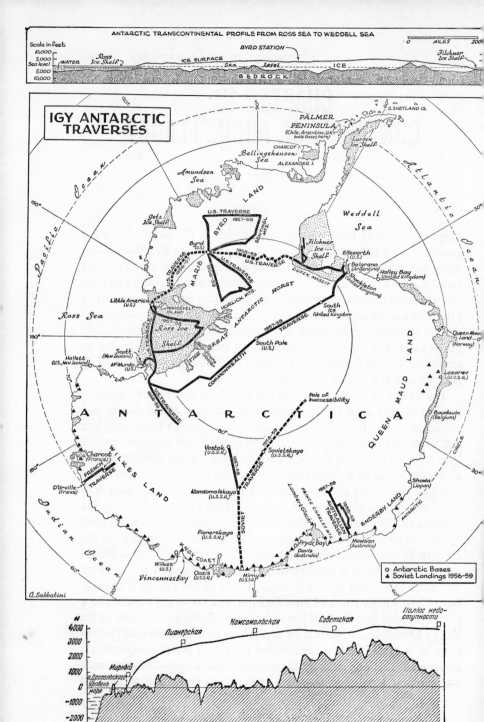

Antarctica. The rocks of West Antarctica are of various younger types, none of them related to the pre-Cambrian shield.

After taking a look at early IGY soundings of the ice sheet, the Russians went farther than the two-continent idea. Grigori A. Avsyuk, head of the Soviet glaciological program, suggested that Antarctica might not be a continent at all, but rather a string of islands holding a massive block of ice within its perimeter.[1] Such an idea seemed particularly plausible after the initial American seismic exploration, made in February, 1957. By recording the time required for the sound of an explosion to travel through the ice to its rock floor and be reflected back again it was possible to determine ice depths. This had been done experimentally by the Byrd expeditions and had been brilliantly demonstrated as a technique for charting sub-ice terrain by the 1950–52 Norwegian-British-Swedish expedition to Queen Maud Land.

The first American soundings in 1957 were made along the trail from Little America to Byrd Station and produced startling results. After the seismologists climbed from the shelf ice onto the continental ice sheet, they found that the rock below them, instead of rising as they advanced into the interior, got deeper and deeper. By the time they reached Byrd Station, which is roughly 5000 feet above sea level, they were standing on 8300 feet of ice. Thus, near the "coast," the land was less than 1000 feet below the surface of the sea, but in the heart of Marie Byrd Land it was 3300 feet below sea level. Even if all the ice were removed and the land rose, like an unloaded barge, to regain equilibrium with the rest of the earth's crust, it would still be below the present level of the sea.

The following spring three American tractor parties set forth on long, over-ice "traverses," each of them traveling in two or three

on facing page

Above this map of IGY tractor journeys in Antarctica is a transcontinental profile combining observations made on treks between Little America and Byrd Station with those on the journey from Ellsworth Station to Byrd Station. Below is a Soviet profile. The flags atop the ice sheet on the Soviet diagram mark the sites, from left to right, of Mirny (on the sea), Pionerskaya, Komsomolskaya, Sovietskaya, and the Pole of Inaccessibility. The routes of these profiles show as dashed lines on the map. It is upon such fragmentary information that the endpapers are based.

Sno-cats, a vehicle with four tracks that rotate around four pontoons. The Sno-cat cabs were long enough for the men to sleep inside them. One vehicle, in the typical convoy, was equipped with a crevasse-detector and navigational gear. Aboard another were the seismic, gravity, and magnetic instruments, and in the third were the messing facilities and the party's most powerful radio. (The other two vehicles carried smaller radios, primarily for communicating with each other on the trail.) Cargo sleds in tow behind each Sno-cat carried the supplies. As a rule these parties would travel thirty to fifty miles one day, stopping every two to five miles to take readings of gravity, magnetism, and elevation, which required only a few minutes. The following day would then be spent in one spot digging a ten-foot pit for ice studies and setting off explosions for echo-sounding.

To keep accurate track of the elevation an "altimetry leap-frog method" was used whenever possible. The altimeter, which determines elevation by measuring air pressure, is limited in its accuracy by changes in pressure due to weather. An airline pilot is told the local barometric pressure, by radio, so that he can adjust his altimeter accordingly. To eliminate weather effects on the trail, simultaneous measurements were made at a station of known elevation and at one five miles ahead. Because the weather was virtually identical at both places, the difference in air pressure was due entirely to difference in elevation.

The gravity readings indicated local configurations of the terrain. Since gravity is a manifestation of mass, and rock is three times denser than ice, local variations in gravity are indications of differences in ice thickness. It was therefore possible for those traveling across the ice to chart the buried mountains and valleys beneath them by means of a highly sensitive gravimeter. But, because of long-range gravity and instrument variations, actual ice depths had to be verified by seismic shots at intervals of about fifty miles.

The trail party based at Little America made a circuit of the Ross Ice Shelf; another party headed inland from Ellsworth Station; and the third, led jointly by Vernon H. Anderson, a glaciologist, and Charles R. Bentley, a seismologist, drove northeast from Byrd Station to an unnamed mountain near the coast, then turned right and rolled across the snow-covered ice to the Sentinel Mountains. Until this group set forth, on November 19, 1957, it had seemed possible that the deep sounding at Byrd Station was simply indicative of a fiord, but this traverse and others that followed showed that the heart of Marie Byrd Land is a great basin whose floor lies well below the level of the sea, even allowing for its "rebound" after removal of the ice. In contrast to the utter levelness of the blindingly white surface on the first leg of this journey, the land below proved to be mountainous, with at least one peak rising above sea level. At the unnamed mountain that was this group's first turning point, the summit that protruded was of volcanic rock. In fact, many of the mountains in this part of Marie Byrd Land seem to be old volcanoes. En route to the Sentinel Mountains the rock floor smoothed out into a deep basin, but when the travelers moved parallel to the range they found themselves rolling smoothly over ice-filled fiords a mile deep.

Among the surprises experienced by the men on this traverse was the sighting of fresh penguin tracks headed bravely inland at a point some 150 miles from the nearest known coast. Although the bird had left the sea, which was his only source of food, far behind him, his stride was bold and there was no sign that he was wavering. At intervals his footprints gave way to a trough through the snow, showing that periodically he had been tobogganing on his belly, using his toes and flippers for locomotion in the manner typical of penguins.

A more startling event occurred when the party was some ninety miles west of the Sentinels, at the turning point between the second and third legs of its journey. From the direction of the mountains the men heard a low, windlike noise that approached rapidly until, about ten seconds later, it arrived with the screaming intensity of a jet plane. They could see nothing. However, just as it reached them the ice quaked and there was a sharp, cracking sound. Somewhat similar phenomena have been reported before from the Antarctic, causing dog teams to panic and gripping men with fear. What apparently happens is that a hoarfrost layer some feet below the surface suddenly collapses over a wide area. The frost crystals are fragile and can carry only a certain load of snow without being squashed. After this event, the party dug one of its ten-foot pits for routine snow studies but could find no evidence of such a layer. Presumably it lay at a greater depth.

On a subsequent occasion the glaciologists were working in a pit while their colleagues were setting off a ten-pound seismic explosion two and a half miles away. The charge had been placed in a thirteen-foot hole so that it would give the ice a proper jolt. After the bang the men in the pit heard that same strange sound, coming swiftly toward them from the explosion site. As it passed, the ice sheet shook and the noise continued on, receding into the distance. They looked to see if there had been any change in the cross section of the snow in their pit, but could detect none.[2]

Six days were spent at the Sentinels, which are among the most isolated mountains in the world. Before the IGY they had been seen only twice—in 1935, on the remarkable transantarctic flight of Lincoln Ellsworth, and in 1947, during a series of long flights by Finn Ronne. In both cases the sightings were from great distances and all that could be seen was a single cluster of mountains. When the members of the IGY party reached the range, it proved to be a long and impressive chain, extending southward as far as the eye could see. To reach the ramparts of the central range would have been a major undertaking, but the party visited five outlying peaks that poked above the ice. One man, Daniel Hale, collected sixty kinds of lichen, a remarkable diversity for so remote a spot. The rocky slopes showed that, at one time, the ice had been 800 feet higher. But most important of all, the nature of the rocks indicated that these mountains were similar to the Andean formations of Palmer Peninsula. Thus the Sentinel Mountains seem to form the southern terminus of a system that extends the full length of South America and includes the highest peaks of the world outside of the Himalayas.

About 100 miles short of Byrd Station, on the return leg, the seismic shots showed a depth of 14,000 feet, believed to be the deepest ice sounding ever made. The group reached Byrd Station on February 23, 1958, having covered 1200 miles in ninety-six days.

On November 1, 1958, a new team under Bentley headed south from Byrd Station toward the Horlick Mountains, named by Byrd for the malted-milk manufacturer who had been one of his backers. Like the Sentinels, this range had been seen only from the air and its location and geography were uncertain. One advantage of visiting mountains, apart from geologic exploration, was the opportunity to extend the profile of the hidden land to a place where it rose out of the ice, thus providing a check on the soundings.

After the party had rolled 320 miles south, the purplish, flat-topped battlement of the Horlicks was clearly visible ahead, but a maze of crevasses barred the way. One cargo sled broke partly through a snow bridge but fortunately did not drop. Mechanical difficulties likewise brought the Sno-cats to a halt and, while the men waited for a plane to fly out a repairman and spare parts, two of the men—Frederic L. Darling and William F. Long—donned scarlet down-filled suits (to make them easily seen in case of trouble), slung packs over their shoulders, roped themselves together, and set off toward the mountains.

On this and subsequent visits by the traverse party the mountains were found to be rich in coal beds, with fossil tree trunks up to twelve feet long. The coal seams varied in thickness from a few inches to thirty or forty feet, with layers of sandstone or shale in between, the entire formation rising nearly half a mile on top of a massive shield of ancient granite. The structure and composition of the range showed it to be a continuation of the Great Antarctic Horst that seems to form a rampart around much of East Antarctica. Coal had been sighted previously in virtually every sector of this great mountain system that had been visited on foot. It is one of the most extensive coal fields on earth, but what makes it remarkable is its nearness to the South Pole. The beds in the Horlick Mountains were about 300 miles from the Pole, and other fossil leaves and tree trunks have been found even closer to the bottom of the world. In fact, the meager geologic evidence that is available suggests that for most of its long history Antarctica has been rich in forests and green meadows—a formidable challenge to those who seek to understand the nature of climate changes and who wonder if a role may have been played, in producing them, by slow wandering of the poles, of the continents, or of the earth's entire crust.

Bentley and his men drove their Sno-cats eastward, parallel to the range, then headed back to Byrd Station. Their soundings were of special interest, since, en route to the mountains and, again, on their return, they crossed the most likely path of the transantarctic cleavage. The terrain under the ice was generally well below sea level and, within 100 miles of the mountains, on both legs, explosion and gravity readings showed a cleft that was 4600 feet below sea level on one crossing and 3300 feet on the other.

The traverses made from Ellsworth Station on the Weddell Sea complemented those from Byrd Station in that they ranged over the Atlantic end of the hypothetical trench. The roles of military and scientific leader at Ellsworth were combined in Captain Finn Ronne of the Naval Reserve, who, on his own expedition in 1947, had sought to fly from Palmer Peninsula the full width of the Filchner Ice Shelf to Vahsel Bay. After following its ice cliffs for 450 miles he had been halted by cloud cover and had turned inland almost directly over the site later chosen for Ellsworth Station. He flew forty miles toward the interior before turning back and recorded a rise of 600 feet in the level of the ice surface, suggesting that the Filchner Ice Shelf was a comparatively narrow fringe along the southern shore of the Weddell Sea, widening to about 150 miles at its western extremity.

The traverses from Ellsworth Station showed that the shelf was vastly larger—probably greater than the combined area of New York state and New England. The rise in the ice surface observed by Ronne may have been the slope reaching toward an ice-covered island that was discovered during the first season of tractor operations. This party, led jointly by Edward C. Thiel, a seismologist, and Hugo Neuburg, a glaciologist, departed from Ellsworth on October 28, 1957, and was immediately embroiled in a maze of crevasses. After repeated aerial searches for a safe route, the group finally digressed forty miles to the east, using what was apparently the same smooth ramp as that employed by the Commonwealth Trans-Antarctic Expedition.

The tractors climbed onto an ice-covered island in the midst of the ice shelf whose snowy dome rose 3200 feet above sea level. The rock supporting it lay at the level of the sea. The party continued southwest to the Dufek Massif, a range that had been discovered on one of the reconnaissance flights from McMurdo when the base was being built there two years earlier. The mountains were reached on December 10, 1957, and were found to be about a hundred miles southwest of where they had been placed by the Navy fliers—a not uncommon margin of error after a long flight in a region with no electronic aids to navigation.

The range was about thirty miles long and ten miles wide at its broadest point. Some of its peaks were extremely jagged, and the range as a whole was marked by striking horizontal bands of black and rust-colored igneous rock, largely diorite. Although its eastern end seemed from a distance to be overwhelmed by the flowing ice, the explorers found, when they reached it, that, on the side sheltered from the flow (the north side), there were extensive snow-free areas that looked as though they had been paved with giant cobblestones. This was water-logged gravel that had been broken up into polygons by successive changes in temperature.[3] In one of these ice-free valleys there was a frozen tarn that resembled a large skating rink. The average height of the range was about 6500 feet.

The party then turned northwest in an effort to reach Mount Hassage, which had been the turning point of Ronne's most southerly flight in 1947. This appeared to be the southern anchor of the mountain system that forms the backbone of Palmer Peninsula.

The men had expected that this route would be over an inland plateau, but instead they found themselves traveling on the floating shelf. They crossed another island, much smaller than the first, and then, about eighty miles short of Mount Hassage, were told to turn back because they were getting beyond the range of their supporting aircraft. When they had completed about half the return journey, they had to be flown out to catch the relief ship that was to take them home.

Since there was sea water under the shelf, the discovery of its great extent effectively enlarged the Atlantic Ocean by an area twice the size of Lake Superior. The over-ice travelers also found what seemed to be a continuous trough in the ocean floor underneath the shelf, running south from beneath Argentina's Belgrano Station and passing close to the western edge of the Dufek Massif. The trough was crossed four times on the zigzag journey of the vehicles and in each case was about 3500 feet deep. It lay just where the adherents of a transantarctic cleavage would expect to find such a feature.

The Ellsworth Station traverse the next season completed a transcontinental profile of the continent that was far less publicized than that of the Commonwealth Expedition, but was of great scientific interest, for it ran from the Weddell Sea to Byrd Station and then to the Ross Sea, following a path parallel to that of the hypothetical split. After passing through the point where the vehicles of the previous year's traverse had been cached, the party, led by Matthew Brennan, continued west, looking for a route from the shelf up onto the plateau. It was found that the shelf extended still another 100 miles inland.

Once the men had climbed onto the plateau, an uncharted mountain range hove into view directly across their route. It was probably an extension of the Sentinels, for a reconnaissance flight from Byrd Station had shown that those mountains reached several hundred miles in this direction from the point where Ellsworth saw what he thought was an isolated cluster of high peaks. George R. Toney, the initial scientific leader at Byrd Station, who was on the flight, estimated that he saw as many as fifty peaks. They spread "as far as the eye could reach," he reported, and "cluttered up the radar" on the aircraft. Although he was about 150 miles from where the Ellsworth Station party found its peaks, they were probably part of the same mountain system. The tractor men surveyed a number of summits protruding from the ice in an east-west line which, so far as they could see, was seventy miles long. The highest was 7650 feet. However, the ice surface was from 4500 to 7000 feet high, so that most of each mountain was covered. The rock here was identified as dark gneiss and light tan biotite.

Over the remainder of the route to Byrd Station the profile of the rock floor was similar to that obtained by Anderson, Bentley, and their companions on the somewhat parallel route they had taken back to Byrd Station from the Sentinel Mountains. The Ellsworth group made its deepest sounding (12,000 feet) some seventy miles short of Byrd Station. When this was lined up with the deep soundings of the outbound and inbound legs of the Anderson-Bentley traverse, it appeared that there was a deep trough linking the Ross Sea with the Bellingshausen Sea (west of the Palmer Peninsula) rather than with the Weddell Sea (to the east of that peninsula). In places it was more than 8000 feet below sea level, so that it must have been well below the level of the sea even before Antarctica's ice load caused the terrain to sink.

The continuation of the Sentinel range this far south meant that the Andean mountain system, after snaking under the ocean between South America and Antarctica, extended as a narrow barrier between the Ross and Weddell seas to within 150 miles of the Great Antarctic Horst. It seemed quite possible, in fact, that these two dissimilar formations were joined. The possibility of a great cleft separating the Palmer Peninsula from East Antarctica had diminished. During the next two summers Edward Thiel, co-leader of the first Ellsworth traverse, sought by airborne surveys to throw further light on this question. The first season he landed at seven points between the Horst and the Executive Committee Range of northern Marie Byrd Land, observing what presumably was part of the great Ross Sea–Bellingshausen Sea depression. The second summer (1950–60) he did a survey closer to the gap between the Sentinels and the Horst and showed that, if any cleft joined the Ross and Weddell seas, it was so small that it lay between his soundings, made at roughly thirty-mile intervals.

In January, 1960, four of those who had made IGY ice soundings—Bentley, Crary, Ostenso, and Thiel—summarized their conclusions.[4] West Antarctica was divided into two geologic provinces: the Andean formation, extending from Palmer Peninsula through the Sentinel Mountains, and the formations of northern Marie Byrd Land, which were largely volcanic. Magnetic readings north of the Ross-Bellingshausen trough varied directly with changes in the depth of ice, showing that the buried rocks were magnetic, whereas this was not true over the trough and near the Sentinels—further evidence of geologic subdivision. It seemed well established that the many ranges along the coast of Marie Byrd Land are the spiny summits of an archipelago comparable in extent to the Philippines. These mountains, it should be noted, are by no means all volcanic; the Edsel Ford Ranges and Rockefeller Mountains display granites and metamorphosed sediments.

From time to time the Antarctic produces icebergs the size of Rhode Island and almost daily its ice sheet donates to the three major oceans bergs as large as New York's Central Park. These great platters of ice, striking for their flat tops and uniform thickness, are the products of ice shelves, the largest of which is the Ross Ice Shelf. The gleaming white cliff where the Ross Ice Shelf faces the sea is some 500 miles long; from there, across its floating expanse to the mountain glaciers that feed it near the South Pole, the distance is about 400 miles. Despite its hardness, ice can flow, as anyone knows who has seen the snaking path of a valley glacier. When afloat it tends to spread out to a uniform thickness, and for this reason the icebergs and the ice shelves all seem to be about the same height, rising about 100 feet above the water and reaching down 600 or 700 feet below the surface.

To the glaciologist the Ross Ice Shelf offers many challenges. How did it form in the first place? Did the gulf that it covers freeze over and never thaw again, allowing centuries of snow to build it up to its present state? Or did the ice sheet of Marie Byrd Land flow out over the water to join spearheads of ice pushed out from the mountain glaciers to form a complete ice cover? Does the shelf grow from below, by the freezing of sea water to its bottom, or does it lose fresh water ice to the currents that flow beneath it?

Before there could be an answer to these questions, it was necessary to obtain a general picture of the shelf—its volume, composition, thickness, and movement. During the period when the South Pole was the goal of valiant explorers, the shelf had been traversed primarily along two routes: one, followed by the expeditions of Amundsen and Byrd, ran due south from Little America; the other, used by Scott and Shackleton, followed the ice shelf south from McMurdo Sound, ascending to the polar plateau via the great Beardmore Glacier. The chief objective of these explorers had been to get across the shelf as fast as possible.

On October 24, 1957, a traverse party under Albert P. Crary set out to spend almost four months on a wide circuit of the shelf. Crary, who had done the early studies on T-3 in the Arctic, was scientific leader at Little America and was Deputy Chief Scientist of the American antarctic program under Harry Wexler, director of meteorological research at the Weather Bureau. Now forty-six years old, Crary had become one of the country's leading polar specialists. In fact, during his stay at Little America, he was almost carried away by his devotion to the frigid sciences.

He and Stephen T. Hartog, a young glaciologist, had gone to Kainan Bay, the harbor of Little America Station, to lower a bathythermograph from the ice-cliff shoreline and measure sea temperatures. Suddenly, as Hartog later reported, the front fifteen feet of the precipice broke off with a "tremendous roar and crash." Hartog was standing far enough back to be spared. He looked cautiously over the brink to the churning water and ice debris for some sign of the Deputy Chief Scientist. After what seemed an interminable time Crary came to the surface, "much to his surprise and mine." After a minute of desperate wriggling he got onto a small piece of ice, but, Hartog said, "he was afraid to stamp too much to keep warm for fear it would roll over or break."

The current and wind began carrying Crary and his cake of ice toward the open sea. Hartog jumped into his tracked vehicle and raced back to camp, only to find that the helicopter was dismantled for repairs. Captain Eugene H. Maher, in charge of all the Navy men at the antarctic stations, rounded up a team of rescuers and they hurried down to the bay. Crary, his waterlogged polar clothing freezing into a coffin, was getting closer and closer to the harbor mouth. They launched a five-man life raft and paddled furiously after him. He had been adrift an hour and a half before he was rescued, but apparently suffered no permanent ill effects.

Crary's circuit of the Ross Ice Shelf ran west, toward McMurdo

Sound, then south toward the Beardmore Glacier, swinging southeast to the auxiliary snow runway at the foot of the Liv Glacier, then back to Little America. Because it was important to observe slight changes in elevation of the shelf, this party faithfully used the leap-frog method and, although the shelf seems to the traveler to be utterly flat over most of its expanse, Crary's group found that its height increased steadily toward the southeast, reaching a maximum of more than 350 feet, compared with 140 feet at Little America. During the journey, which lasted 113 days and covered 1450 miles, they set off seismic explosions at thirty-four points, with the usual gravity, magnetic, and ice-pit observations as well. At thirty-one points they obtained temperature and density cross sections of the ice by drilling to a depth of thirty feet. Another drill hole went down fifty-five feet and three penetrated to sixty-five feet, piercing the snow layers of many years.

The thickness of the shelf proved to be less uniform than many had supposed. It became steadily thicker toward the southeast corner in a manner suggesting that its chief source of ice was from the glaciers in that corner and from Marie Byrd Land to the east. Where bergs broke off its façade, the ice shelf was only 600 to 900 feet thick, but sixty miles "inland" from its cliffs this increased to more than 1100 feet and, in its southeastern part, it reached 2500 feet.

The following spring Crary led a tractor party deep into Victoria Land, west of McMurdo Sound. He departed from Little America with

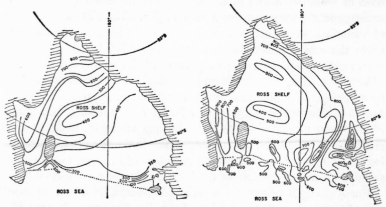

The thickness of the Ross Ice Shelf, in meters, is shown at the left, based on Crary's traverse. At the right is the water depth below the ice, determined primarily by seismic soundings. South is at the top; east is to the left. (National Academy of Sciences)

a six-man party on October 15, 1958. They followed the first leg of the previous year's traverse, then continued westward, past Minna Bluff and Mount Discovery, and up to the continental plateau via the Skelton Glacier route blazed by Hillary and his men for the Commonwealth Expedition. From the summit of the glacier Crary's Sno-cats thrust 400 miles due west, covering almost two-thirds of the distance from McMurdo to the Soviet Station, Vostok. On the ice shelf ninety miles south of the Air Operating Facility at McMurdo a seismic sounding showed the ocean floor to be 4400 feet below sea level—more than twice any of the other depths recorded under the shelf. In fact, most of the sea bottom under the shelf was from 1600 to 2000 feet below sea level, leaving, in some places, only a few hundred feet of water between the base of the ice and the ocean floor.

The great deep, only forty-eight miles south of Mount Discovery, was suggestive of a trough running parallel to the Horst, particularly since such a feature had been observed under the ice shelf across the continent. A horst is produced by "block-faulting" in which the mountains are up-lifted blocks, but often there are down-faulted blocks as well, forming a declivity parallel to the range. Crary's soundings on the shelf farther south had shown that, the nearer the Sno-cat party got to the mountains, the deeper was the ocean floor below it—instead of the shoaling that one would expect near a coastline.

The Skelton Inlet, leading to the Skelton Glacier, proved to be a fiord of great depth and at its head, where the glacier first became waterborne, the ice was about 3200 feet thick. The hinterland plateau of Victoria Land turned out to be an immense ice reservoir dammed up by the coastal mountains to a depth of 10,000 feet.[5]

Among the most unusual ice studies of the IGY was one, southwest of Little America, that sought an understanding of mountain-building by watching "ice mountains" grow. The project was carried out under James H. Zumberge of the University of Michigan at a site, north of Roosevelt Island, which he named Camp Michigan. Here the submerged island produced stresses and strains in the flowing ice, deforming it in a manner that, Zumberge hoped, would furnish an idealized, speeded-up moving picture of deformations in the earth's crust.

For Americans one of the most striking examples of the effect of crustal compression is the folding of the Appalachians. He who flies across this mountain system cannot but be struck by the exquisite symmetry of its parallel ridges, so rigidly ordered that they look man-

OFFICIAL U.S. NAVY PHOTO, MARCH, 1957

Little America Station on the Ross Ice Shelf in Antarctica. The prefabricated, windowless huts are widely separated as a precaution against fire, but are linked by a central corridor covered with burlap and chicken wire. In winter all is covered with snow except the dome housing the radar used to track weather balloons.

NATIONAL ACADEMY OF SCIENCES

The Dufek Massif, with its pinnacles and snow-free valleys, was discovered during American Navy flights preliminary to the IGY and was first visited, as shown here, during the tractor journey from Ellsworth Station in 1957–58. The nearest Sno-cat is rigged with booms that push the basins of a crevasse detector over the snow in front of it.

Mirny, the chief Soviet Antarctic base, stands among rock outcrops on the coast of

Massive Soviet tractor in a crevasse in the upper part of the Helen Glacier, Antarctica, April, 1957. The tractor—in effect a mobile hut—had a cargo sled in tow (left).

The South Pole Station as seen from the air, left, is the focus of trails made by tractors hauling in parachuted supplies. The Pole is enclosed by a ring of barrels at the right. The pattern to the left of the Pole was produced when tractors bulldozed a 45-foot hole to reach a vehicle buried when its 'chutes failed.

the Davis Sea, visible at the right.

A dynamite blast, fired by the man on the right, jars the Antarctic ice. In this manner ice depths were determined over much of the continent.

James Gardiner and Alvah Edwards use reins to drive their tractor through a crevassed area, lest it suddenly break through.

PHOTO BY N. SHUMOV, COURTESY SOVIET EMBASSY

Soviet ski plane at Druzhny, the rocket research station on Hayes Island in Franz Joseph Land, prepares to fly over Arctic Ocean floes in search of a parachuted nose cone.

Pack train carrying supplies up the fifty-mile Fedchenko Glacier in the corner of the Soviet Union between China and Afghanistan. Of the 80 horses employed in this IGY expedition a dozen fell down crevasses or were swept away by mountain torrents.

ACADEMY OF SCIENCES OF THE USSR

E. LA CHAPELLE, UNIVERSITY OF WASHINGTON

Edward C. Thiel operates a gravity recording device alongside the Blue Glacier in the Olympic Range of Washington.

Snow that fell on Greenland before Columbus discovered America is retrieved from the depths of the ice sheet by a drill rig of the oil-prospecting type. Here an ice sample is carefully drawn from the core barrel. The rig penetrated 1,320 feet into the Greenland ice and, in Antarctica, went down 1,013 feet.

SIPRE, U.S. ARMY

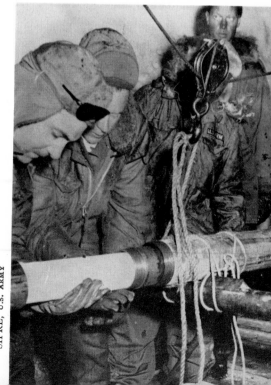

At the satellite camp inland from Wilkes Station a shaft was dug and blasted deep into the ice sheet for study of its layering.

The atomic submarine Skate *surfaced in a lagoon near the North Pole on its surprise visit to Drifting Station A, whose huts can be seen on a floe in the distance.*

Gordon Cartwright of the U.S. Weather Bureau (second from left) and some of his Soviet companions prior to a flight in the Antarctic. Sign on the plane says "Polar Aviation" with a penguin emblem.

John Swallow, aboard the Discovery II, *assembling one of the "pinging" floats of his design that led to the discovery of the countercurrent beneath the Gulf Stream.*

Following an earthquake on July 10, 1958, a 3,000-foot rock slide fell into Lituya Bay at the right, producing a wave that swept the forest from the opposite slope to an elevation of 1,700 feet. Lituya Glacier empties into the Alaskan inlet.

Wet work: bringing up a water sample from the ocean depths off Bermuda. The device is an Ekman bottle.

Oceanographer aboard the Research Vessel Vema *of Lamont Geological Observatory removing water from Nansen bottles for analysis. Such samples are collected by lowering a succession of bottles on a cable.*

JAN HAHN

made. The upward folds are known as anticlines, and Zumberge found them all around Camp Michigan, where the ice sheet, many hundreds of feet thick, was being squeezed by the pressure of 400 miles of flowing ice. The anticlines of ice were from 15 to 50 feet high, more than 300 feet wide and 2000 to 5000 feet long. Cutting across them, at right angles, were successions of crevasses ranging in width from a few inches to death traps 100 feet across. Most were bridged with snow,

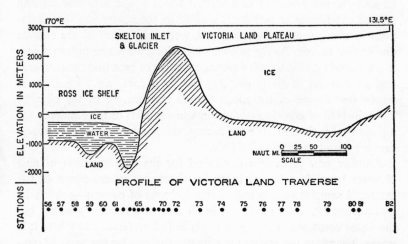

Like a great dam, the coastal mountains impound the ice of Victoria Land, as shown in this profile, obtained from the 1958–59 traverse. The numbered dots mark observation points. (National Academy of Sciences)

but when the glaciologists climbed down into the purple-lighted chasms with crampons and rope, they found the annual layering beautifully preserved. They measured the inexorable rate at which the ice sheet was being compressed. Over a measured base line of 5800 feet it was 7.6 feet in forty-two days and the rate of widening in a 7.38-inch crevasse proved to be a half inch in nineteen days.[6]

One of the heaviest items of equipment brought down by the United States expedition and hauled to Byrd Station was a drill rig of the type used in oil prospecting. The purpose was to reach back a thousand years or more into the history of Antarctica—and, to some extent, of the world as a whole.

For thousands of years the snows have been falling on Greenland

and Antarctica and remaining there, unaffected by the passage of time except in their imperceptible flow toward the sea. In each annual layer is a record of the climate, as it existed at that time, and of the composition of the atmosphere, for air is trapped within the ice sheet as new layers are added on top. The first man to dig into these "files" is said to have been Ernst Sorge, who in 1930–31 shared with Johannes Georgi, father of the Second Polar Year, the lonely winter vigil at Eismitte in the center of Greenland.[7] Sorge dug a fifty-foot pit and studied the annual snow layers, coming to the conclusion that variations in density, at any given depth, were indications of the climate during that season. As the science of glaciology became more refined, it was found that ice is such a poor conductor of heat that the temperature at a depth of thirty or forty feet in a continental ice sheet is within one degree of the mean annual temperature of the climate. Thus, instead of manning stations in various parts of the Antarctic for a prolonged period, to learn the average temperature it was only necessary for a trail party to drill a hole.

Another new procedure developed for the determination of past climates from deep boring in an ice sheet was measurement of the extracted samples of two radioactive isotopes of oxygen—oxygen-16 and oxygen-18. They are found in all naturally occurring water, but the water containing oxygen-18 tends to fall preferentially where it is warm. Therefore the cooler the climate, the smaller the ratio of oxygen-18 to its sister, oxygen-16, in any form of precipitation. By measuring isotope ratios in an ice sheet one can tell summer layers from winter layers, thus making it possible to count the years in cores drilled from a deep hole, even if the layers cannot be identified by other methods.

Even great cataclysms are filed away in the ice, for future reference. The drilling rig was first tried out 200 miles east of Thule, Greenland, and, at a depth of 105 feet, there was a tiny layer of volcanic ash. By counting the layers like tree rings, the year of its deposition was shown to have been 1912—when snow-capped Mount Katmai on the Alaskan Peninsula erupted, hurling an estimated five cubic miles of volcanic ash into the sky, burying Kodiak Island a foot deep, and tarnishing brass in Vancouver, British Columbia, 1500 miles away. In Antarctica it was hoped that ash from the explosion of Krakatoa, in 1883, might be identified. The deep-drilling project was entrusted to the Army's Snow, Ice and Permafrost Research Establishment (SIPRE), which carried out test drillings in Greenland in 1956 and

1957. The second test hole reached down 1356 feet, but below 1000 feet the ice tended to "explode" before it could be brought up. As noted earlier, contemporary air is trapped in each layer, but at such depths it is highly compressed and, with the relief of pressure, tends to burst the ice. The Greenland crew nevertheless managed to get one core up, intact, from 1320 feet.

The heavy drill rig arrived at Byrd Station, in tow behind a tractor, on October 24, 1957, and further components were air-dropped. With Ernest Marshall, a SIPRE glaciologist, in charge, a five-man drilling crew that included Lop Gooday, an Apache Indian from Oklahoma, used cold compressed air to push the fifteen- to twenty-foot core sections gently out the top, as the cylindrical drill cut downward. At first the cores failed to come up as planned. They would linger in mid-ascent until they froze to the sides of the shaft, or they would drop back. It was found that the snow, to a depth of 100 feet or more, was permeable to air, bleeding away the pressure. Thus the top 115 feet had to be cased—as often must be done in an oil or water well. From then on, by careful control of the bit speed, cores were brought up from depths that reached 1013 feet with a loss of only 2 per cent.

The cylinders of ice successfully extracted from this hole, four inches in diameter and with an aggregate length of 331 yards, constituted a historical record that, according to a preliminary estimate, extended back to the sixth-century reign of the Byzantine Emperor Justinian I. The layering was distinct to a depth of 400 feet. Below that, visible stratification disappeared, although thin ice bands could be seen all the way down to the sixth-century level. It was planned to ship the upper 400 feet to the United States intact, and split the lower 600 feet, leaving half at Byrd Station for study there. However, the band saw failed part way through the delicate job and therefore the cores from the bottom 160 feet also had to be sent home intact. The precious load was placed in refrigerators aboard the icebreaker USS *Glacier* for the long voyage across the tropics. At Boston the cores were nimbly shifted to a refrigerated truck and hauled to the SIPRE laboratories at Wilmette, Illinois.

Meanwhile, after the hole had been left for a few days to recover from changes due to the drilling, temperatures were measured throughout its length, and they were found to drop slightly, but steadily from top to bottom, the difference between 50 feet and 1000 feet being only 1.2°. Almost half of the change occurred between 150 and 250 feet, presumably indicating a more abrupt warming during that period than the very gradual increase observed during the rest of the time since the sixth century.

The weather records from Little America, when compared to those obtained there by earlier expeditions, showed a steady rise, in mean annual temperatures, of about 5° over the past half-century.

After the drill had done its job at Byrd Station, it was hauled to Little America where it bored another, shallower hole almost to the bottom of the floating ice shelf under that station.[8]

The most dramatic tractor traverse of the IGY was not an IGY project at all. This was the journey of the Commonwealth Trans-Antarctic Expedition which, although criticized in some British scientific circles as a stunt, seems to have settled the question of whether or not Antarctica is a continent. The crossing party, led by Sir Vivian Fuchs and traveling initially in eight vehicles, did seismic shots at thirty-mile intervals and gravity readings at those points and midway between them. Each shot took the better part of a day, since thirty-six-foot holes had to be dug so that the jolt would be administered within hard ice.

The Britons had much the same sort of trouble that the Americans encountered in traveling from the Weddell Sea across the heavily-crevassed ice shelf and up onto the continent. The Sno-cats were roped together like mountain climbers. This literally proved to be a life-saver, for at one point "Rock 'n Roll," the vehicle in which Sir Vivian was traveling, dangled for several hours over an abyss before the other tractors could haul it out.

After two contingents of vehicles had been driven from the coast to the expedition's advance station on the inland plateau—South Ice—the crossing party headed for the South Pole. A group with two dog teams scouted ahead for crevasses but found none. Nevertheless Fuchs had been so delayed by earlier difficulties that, in an exchange of messages that unfortunately became public, Sir Edmund Hillary recommended that the crossing party stop at the Pole and finish the trip the following summer. Fuchs declined and pressed on. At the Pole his men made a seismic sounding and obtained an ice depth of about 8000 feet, which was not substantially different from the one obtained there earlier by the Reverend Daniel Linehan, S.J., a seismologist from Boston College. However, only twenty-five miles on either side of the

Pole, the British found submerged mountains that rose to within 1500 or 2000 feet of the surface.

On January 28, four days after Fuchs and his men waved good-bye to the Americans at the South Pole Station, Geoffrey Pratt, the seismologist, was found unconscious on the floor of a Sno-cat. "His face was unhealthily pink, his eyes closed and his limbs twitching—altogether an alarming sight," Fuchs recounted later.[9] It was guessed that he was suffering from carbon monoxide poisoning, and he was immediately given oxygen from the welding equipment. This brought him back to consciousness, but there was little oxygen left and, at 10,000 feet, the thin air left him gasping. In response to a radio message, the United States Navy sent two Neptunes out from McMurdo, carrying a British doctor and two large oxygen bottles. The ceiling was down to 800 feet, but the two planes found the stalled tractor party and circled overhead during a radio discussion of the patient's condition. There was some question as to whether a Neptune could get off again if it landed at that elevation and, when it was learned that Pratt was not in danger, the oxygen was parachuted and the planes returned to base. Pratt was back on the job within two days and henceforth was careful to keep a window or door always open when the Sno-cat engine was running.

On March 2, 1958, the tractors reached McMurdo, having traveled 2180 miles in ninety-nine days. Except during the initial leg near the Weddell Sea and the final leg on the Ross Ice Shelf, virtually all of the soundings showed the buried land to be above sea level. Those patriots who felt their beloved continent had been disparaged felt vindicated.

The undertaking of the Soviet expedition, to establish an IGY station in that loosely defined region known as the Pole of Inaccessibility, some 1300 miles inland, was an ambitious one. Unlike the Americans, who used their heaviest air transports, the Russians depended primarily on tractors, possibly because they felt the elevation at their destination—about 13,000 feet—was too great for air-dropping or for aircraft take-offs.

They moved inland in stages. Once the main coastal base had been set up, in the summer of 1955–56, the expedition leader, Mikhail M. Somov, a veteran of arctic work, led a tractor party that established a small station, Pionerskaya, 230 miles inland. The men who spent the following winter there were the first to do so on the inland plateau.

The next summer it was planned to push on to the Geomagnetic Pole, where Station Vostok was to be established, but a series of mishaps repeatedly delayed the departure of this trail party. An account of this phase of the expedition has been brought back by Gordon D. Cartwright, a studious representative of the United States Weather Bureau, who spent fourteen months on the staff at Mirny, the main Soviet base on the coast. He arrived, on January 10, 1957, with the new wintering group of 180 men on the icebreaking ship *Ob* and the cargo ship *Kooperatsia.* The ships at first set their ice anchors in the apron of sea ice about a mile from the base, but summer thaws weakened this ice, threatening the safety of the tractor drivers as well as the security of supplies that might be carried to sea as the ice broke up. At length, the ice did just that, and two ships, the *Kooperatsia* and the *Lena,* had to moor directly to the cliff of continental ice, whose white parapet loomed threateningly over the decks.

Byrd had been forced to carry out a similar maneuver at Little America in 1929. On the evening of January 30 he was sitting in his cabin on the *City of New York,* tied up alongside the *Eleanor Bolling,* which in turn was moored to the ice cliff, its superstructure chipping off pieces of the ice as the ship rose to a swell. Suddenly Byrd felt a jar, followed by "a succession of terrific shocks and then a tremendous explosion." An iceberg had broken from the cliff and fallen on the *Bolling.*

> As I flung the cabin door open [Byrd wrote] I saw the *Bolling* heeling in the opposite direction to starboard. I was sure, for a moment, she was capsizing, for I saw her keel and she was still leaning. No words can fit the horror of that moment.[10]

Nevertheless the ship righted itself, tons of ice heaped on its deck. A man was clinging to a rope suspended from the brink of the cliff. Another was in the water, grasping a fragment of ice and menaced by hulking pieces of the broken berg. When the first boat was lowered too many men leaped in and it almost foundered. In the nick of time one of the rescuers jumped into the icy sea and managed to stay afloat until the man already in the water was rescued and he could be retrieved. It was close, for the polar seas drain heat from the body so fast that a man loses consciousness within a few minutes.

On February 3, 1957, the *Lena* had an almost identical experience. A great slab of ice fell onto its deck, crushing equipment ready to be unloaded and hurling men into the sea. As the ship righted itself and drifted clear, frantic efforts were made to save the men, but for two of them, N. I. Buromsky and E. K. Zykov, rescue came too late.

Although time was of the essence if the Geomagnetic Pole was to be reached, all preparations came to a halt while a burial vault was carved out of the rock on a nearby knoll. Cartwright found the burial service "dignified and moving." He wrote later:

> Strong Russian sentiment had prevailed over the Russian time sense. The great wooden platform they had built, the new coffins on their red carpeting, the catafalque drilled into the rock—no effort had been spared. Everybody who could leave the base and the ships was there. The leaders spoke, honoring the young men who had given their lives in this great scientific venture for the benefit of mankind. Friends of the deceased said their words of affection and regret. Then twenty sailors, lined up on the crest of the rocks, raised their rifles toward the setting sun for the final salute.[11]

Not long after this setback, Cartwright and some of his Russian friends were making tape recordings of his American record collection for use by the Soviet inland stations when they heard the loud clanging noise of an iron cylinder being beaten outside the mess hall. The fire alarm! A new barracks building near the sea was in flames and a fifty-mile-an-hour gale made it impossible to bring the fire under control with the meager equipment at hand. Fortunately there were no fatalities, though in 1960 another of the camp's buildings burned with a loss of eight lives. The replacement of the barracks entailed more weeks' delay, and it was not until late February that the last tractor rumbled out of camp toward the interior.

This was man's first venture into the heartland of Antarctica and traveling conditions proved almost impossible. Due to the absence of stiff winds, the snow was not packed. The vehicles sank in until they were pushing mountains of snow and dragging heavily laden sleds that likewise had become snowplows. Compounding their difficulties was the loss of power due to the elevation. At 12,000 feet the density of air feeding the heavy diesel engines was only 60 per cent of that at sea level.

The season by now was so far advanced that it was obvious the party could not reach its destination. The only alternative was to halt and camp for the winter.

> The failure was humiliating to the Russians [Cartwright wrote]. But they faced it and made their decision—to stop and dig in where they were. This caused great debate and many recriminations. In my opinion the decision was right. If they had pushed on, it might have meant great suffering or even risk of death to the men without any real scientific gain. I saw the men who came out, their hands and faces now terribly swollen with frostbite.[12]

The camp on the trail was officially commissioned as provisional station Vostok I on March 30, 1957. Meanwhile the Russians back home, their pride at a high point after the Sputnik launchings, could not accept defeat in the Antarctic. Preparations were rushed for a new effort the next summer. Tractors were built with treads forty inches wide and special air compressors for the engines. Altogether twenty-three new vehicles were shipped south on the *Ob* and *Kooperatsia,* plus dozens of sleds, including cargo carriers thirty feet long and twelve feet wide and new and larger planes to airlift fuel for the vehicles. The ships had about 6000 tons of supplies when they reached Mirny with the relief expedition in November.

A caravan of tracked vehicles had already started from Mirny on October 8 for a dash to the Geomagnetic Pole. It reached Vostok I on October 29. Additional fuel was flown in to a site, 530 miles inland, that had been selected for Station Komsomolskaya. It stood some 11,400 feet above sea level at the fork in the road. The right branch led toward the Pole of Inaccessibility (planned site for Station Sovietskaya) and the left branch toward the Geomagnetic Pole (Station Vostok). Alexei Treshnikov, who had succeeded Somov as expedition leader, joined the fast-moving tractor party. It reached the Geomagnetic Pole on December 16.

Ten days later the all-out assault on the Pole of Inaccessibility began with suitable pomp and circumstance. Ten tractors lined up at Mirny with twenty heavy sleds in tow. Unlike the big American tractors, these looked like trucks with tracks instead of wheels and a small house lashed behind the driver's cab. There were speeches as the fur-capped heads clustered to listen. There was embracing and kissing in the Russian manner. Then thirty-two men trotted to the vehicles. Engines rumbled and, as the caravan, a half mile long, started off toward the featureless southern horizon, red and green signal rockets arched in the cloudless sky above them.

At Komsomolskaya the convoy divided, part of it carrying supplies to newly established Vostok, the other breaking a trail toward the center of the continent. Even with the new tractors the deep, soft snow was an almost insurmountable obstacle. The vehicles, with a total of 120 tons in tow, sometimes sank to a depth of five feet, although as a rule the trough they left behind was two feet deep. Despite the superchargers, the engines weakened as the plateau rose above 12,000 feet. The men, led by Vitali K. Babarykin, a robust aerologist, also were affected by the elevation; at length it became clear that the Pole of Inaccessibility had been well named. On February 10, 1958, they said, like Brigham Young, "this is the place." Sovietskaya was set up about 400 miles short of the original goal. While this was undoubtedly a disappointment, it was not a serious setback scientifically, for one spot was just about as good as another on this vast, featureless plateau. The huts were arranged around a central court that was roofed to make a common room where the party's stock of twenty moving pictures could be shown—and reshown—and where they could play their inevitable games of chess and checkers. Steel radio masts were set up, the power plant wired to the various structures and, on February 16, 1958, after a party of twenty-seven men had labored six days at a temperature of $-74°$, the red flag was formally raised over Sovietskaya.

For the five men left to winter at this station, the first month was a grim experience—as was the first month at the Geographic Pole for the Americans. They suffered headaches, shortness of breath, pounding of the heart, and low blood pressure. At night they would awaken with a feeling that they were choking. The elevation was 12,280 feet and the boiling point of water was therefore so low that cooking was difficult. The camp physician, V. Konstantinov, who doubled as cook, made extensive use of a pressure cooker, but nevertheless there was a marked loss of weight by a number of the men.

Meanwhile, eleven men under V. Sidorov had dug in for the winter at the Geomagnetic Pole (Station Vostok) and it was there that the record low of 125.3° below zero was recorded. The "Cold Pole" was probably closer to the Pole of Inaccessibility, and it is reported that lower temperatures were recorded at Sovietskaya, almost 1000 feet higher above sea level than Vostok. However the thermometer at Sovietskaya was not calibrated for such extreme lows and therefore they were not official.

During periods of extreme cold Sidorov would allow no one to go out alone. Length of time outside was limited to fifteen minutes when it was colder than 112° below zero, and to ten minutes when lower than −121°. At one point a storm destroyed the aerology hut. It took the men, working in the dark with flashlights at temperatures of −103°, three weeks to repair it.

The prefabricated buildings and nonmagnetic huts (built without iron to avoid affecting the magnetic observations) used at these stations had been constructed by the Zharkovsky House-Building Combine in Kalininskya Oblast. (Panels for the Clements huts at the South Pole had been made in Danbury, Connecticut.)

When the men at Vostok and Sovietskaya went outside in midwinter, they carried 40-watt pocket-sized batteries and electric heaters that warmed their hands, feet, and chests. Subsequently the Arctic-Antarctic Institute in Leningrad designed a face mask that provided electrically heated air, but the masks used during the IGY were simply fitted with a corrugated hose that drew air from beneath the clothing. The hose also could be attached to an oxygen bottle, if the men needed it.

When the mercury hit bottom, strange things happened. Water, dropped on the supercooled ice outside, danced as though it were on a hot stove, breaking up into droplets that froze into so many tiny pearls. Kerosene looked like wet snow. Ink in the self-recording instruments froze in spite of its antifreeze. Virtually all outdoor mechanisms became immobile. During the first week of August, 1958, when temperatures were in the minus 120s at both Vostok and Sovietskaya, the sheet of cold air that hugged the plateau was extremely thin. Only six or eight feet above the surface the temperature became five degrees warmer. During this time the sky was a cloudless panoply of stars looking down on a windless snowscape.

Some 3000 feet overhead the air remained remarkably warm and constant in temperature. As a rule it varied little from −40° or −50° despite the extremes observed on the surface. This same stable layer lay some 1400 feet above the South Pole, but higher up the temperature again became extremely low. On July 16, 1958, the lowest temperature ever recorded in the earth's atmosphere, —135.4°, was measured by a balloon thirteen miles above the Pole Station.

The temperature differences between the inland stations, Vostok and Sovietskaya, and those on the coast were often extreme. Thus, on May 10, when it was —110° at Sovietskaya, it was 18° above zero at Oazis, the small station 250 miles east of Mirny. That month was a cruel one for the men at Pionerskaya, which stood, so to speak, at the crest of a dam, over which there was a constant rush of cold air down the slope to the sea. Blizzards blew past Pionerskaya every day of May. Snow built up to such a depth that it caved in the roofs of some huts and snow tunnels. Shoring timbers had to be installed, as in mines, and snow vaulting was built over weak spots in the tunnels. The constant, windblown "snow dust," according to the Russians, loaded their radio equipment and clothing with static electricity that crackled and sparked.

On September 10, 1958, a plane took off from Mirny as a harbinger of spring, laden with fish, caught in the sea off the ice cliffs, as well as fresh vegetables to be dropped at the inland stations.

Although there had been talk of trying to move Sovietskaya to the Pole of Inaccessibility, this was abandoned. Instead, a fast-moving party of eighteen men started out from Mirny in four tractors in an effort to reach that elusive destination before the end of the IGY. Planes flew fuel to them along the first part of their route, and they paused periodically to complete a chain of eighty-four gravity and seventy seismic soundings from the coast to their destination. On December 14, 1958, two weeks before the IGY ended, they achieved their hard-won goal, having covered 1360 miles in fifty-two days.

The group stayed for two weeks, making a wide range of observations and drilling two 100-foot holes in the ice. The mean annual temperature, as shown by measurements of the deep ice in these holes, was —73.3°, which was roughly 6° cooler than at Vostok. Seismic explosions showed the ice to be 9500 feet deep, under a campsite that was 12,170 feet above sea level. The annual accumulation of snow, in this region, was found to be only eight to ten inches— quite similar to the six inches recorded at the South Pole. This represents a total for the year of about one-half inch of water, hardly more than the precipitation in the Sahara, although some of the snow that fell here presumably blew north to help bury the huts at Pioner-skaya. Pits dug in Marie Byrd Land showed an accumulation for the year of twenty to thirty inches.

One of the paradoxes of Antarctica has been the question of the source of its ice. Every year it delivers many cubic miles of icebergs into the Southern Ocean, and more cubic miles of snow are blown out to sea before they catch hold of the ice sheet. Yet weather men had long thought that the hinterland plateau was a permanent area of high atmospheric pressure, with clear skies and almost no precipitation. What, then, replaces the outflowing ice? The Russians found that most of the snow fell within 400 miles of the coast and that it was here the outflow was replenished. Further inland there was little snowfall. The ice sheet was the fruit of untold millennia and lay comparatively stagnant.

One of the primary IGY objectives was to learn if Antarctica's ice reserves are growing or shrinking, since such changes would bear upon whether dramatic variations in climate or ocean level are to be anticipated. The results at first seemed contradictory. Pyotr Shumsky, chief glaciologist of the expedition in 1958, reported that the level of the ice around Mount Gauss, to the west of Mirny, had dropped an average of twenty-six feet since that dead volcano was discovered fifty-five years earlier by the Germans. He took this as evidence that the ice of Antarctica had been retreating, though at one-twentieth to one-twenty-fifth the rate observed in the eastern Alps.[13]

It may be, however, that this was a local phenomenon, for evidence reported from elsewhere suggested little recent change in the volume of coastal ice. In January, 1957, the author visited Taylor Glacier Dry Valley, a remarkable feature near McMurdo Sound that seemed to offer an opportunity to see whether the antarctic ice sheet was waxing or waning. The "hanging" glaciers that are draped over its precipitous walls and the withered remains of Taylor Glacier that lie in the upper end of this otherwise ice-free valley had been mapped and photographed by the Scott expeditions a half-century earlier. Any marked change in the outflow of ice from the interior would probably be evident, but the author's photographs, when compared with those taken earlier, showed no detectable change.[14] Troy Péwé of the United States Geological Survey subsequently carried out a far more extensive survey of the area and came to the same conclusion.

Despite these signs of stagnation or retreat, glaciologists on three widely separated expeditions concluded that Antarctica is receiving more ice, from snowfall, than it is losing through evaporation and icebergs. Shumsky of the Soviet expedition estimated in 1960 that the volume of ice is growing at about 300 cubic miles per year. The annual snowfall, he said, is equivalent to 2550 cubic kilometers of ice, but much of this snow blows out to sea—the Russians estimated it at 1,400,000 tons per kilometer of coast near their camp. Shumsky put the total loss, through blowing, evaporation, melting, and icebergs, at 1330 cubic kilometers, leaving a surplus of 1220 cubic kilometers, or roughly 300 cubic miles.

Malcolm Mellor of the Australian expedition calculated the annual accumulation at 187 billion tons, which, he felt, was about two and a half times the losses, by various means. He pointed out that little was known of the amount melted off the bottoms of ice shelves and that even the estimates of iceberg production were subject to large errors.

Fritz Loewe, who served with the French expedition, likewise proposed that the volume of inland ice was rising, although he thought it might be several centuries before the growth was felt at the coastline. Such growth, if it is taking place, must be a recent development, perhaps as a result of warming and, therefore, greater snowfall. Any substantial increase in antarctic ice would lower the oceans, whereas they have risen slightly in recent decades. The answer may be that the ocean water, because of heating, has expanded enough to cancel the losses to the antarctic ice sheet.[15]

When the Russians completed their profile of the land beneath the ice from the coast to their temporary camp at the Pole of Inaccessibility, they became convinced, as were the British, that East Antarctica is, in fact, a continent. Over a fiordlike depression south of Pionerskaya the ice was some 13,200 feet deep, yet 300 kilometers (186 miles) southwest of Sovietskaya the tractor party passed over a region where 10,000-foot mountains lay completely hidden under 3300 feet of ice. If the ice were removed, the range, relieved of its burden, would rise and be considerably higher, much as parts of the world are still rising as a sequel to the last ice age, particularly Finland, which is said to gain a new county with every century. Once the coastal region had been traversed, virtually the entire area probed was above sea level. (See profile on page 308.) This led Yevgeny I. Tolstikov, the new expedition leader, to state that Antarctica is, in fact, a continent.[16]

The nature of the heartland was further revealed by Andrei P. Kapitsa, son of the well-known Soviet physicist, who took part in a tractor journey from Vostok to the South Pole in the summer of 1959–60. He found that the rock floor was almost level and largely below sea level, but that it was sufficiently shallow so that, when not laden with ice, it would constitute a broad coastal plain. Similar observations were made by Crary in north Victoria Land.[17]

The most interesting Soviet geographical discovery was invisible, for it lay deep under the ice of the interior. It was named by the Russians IGY Valley, partly in recognition of the fact that, as they pointed out, its features had been progressively unveiled through the work of Americans, Britons, and Australians, as well as Russians. The depression channels a mighty flow of ice toward Prydz Bay, the deepest indentation on the coast of East Antarctica, forming what may be the world's largest glacier. The Australians, who have explored this river of ice for almost 200 miles—comparable to the distance from Boston to New York—have named it Lambert Glacier. It is flanked, to the west, by mountains that were sighted by American fliers in 1947, but have been explored primarily by the Australians, who named them the Prince Charles Mountains in honor of the heir-apparent to the British crown.

In the ice-buried hinterland the IGY Valley seems to be bordered on the east by the hidden mountains that the Soviet party passed over on its dash to the Pole of Inaccessibility. As the expedition progressed westward to the area in line between Prydz Bay and the Pole the soundings showed a marked slope downward. The Russians gave the valley a length of at least 800 miles and an average width of about 370 miles. Gravity readings pointed to its being a horst-type formation.[18]

In addition to exploring under the ice, the Soviet expedition mapped the coast. The *Ob* sent planes aloft to do aerial photography and, beginning on December 31, 1957, fired twenty-two rockets off Antarctica and in the South Pacific.[19] In all cases these appear to have been Meteo rockets, thought to reach up seventy miles or more. The first shot was lobbed over Mirny and the nose cone was recovered, but even when recovery failed, the results were presumably in hand, since the nose cone telemetered its observations throughout its forty-minute flight and parachute descent. By the end of February, three more shots had been fired at points where the ship pushed in alongside the coast between Mirny and Cape Adare. The remaining rockets were launched from locations in the Ross Sea, off the Marie Byrd Land coast, south of New Zealand and Australia and along the route to Easter Island.

The Soviet observations, particularly at Mirny, concerned almost all of the IGY disciplines. One of the ideas that has attracted the Russians is that electric currents in the oceans form an important and little-known part of the electrical system responsible for various magnetic aberrations. They therefore found it of special interest that the magnetic variations at their station hut were far greater in amplitude than those measured at points eight miles out on the sea ice and six miles inland. They concluded that the variations were produced by a current flowing through the ocean close to the coast.[20]

Earth-current observations were carried out both at Mirny and, to the east, at Oazis, the station set up by the Russians in October, 1956. The area, known as Bunger's "Oasis," remained free of snow throughout the winter. Strong winds blew away any that fell and the climate was so dry that few of the melt-water lakes of the region had outlets. Their water was removed entirely by evaporation and, as a result, some ponds had become so salty, in the thousands of years since the ice sheet withdrew from the area, that the water rarely if ever froze, even in midwinter.[21] An American party which camped there briefly in 1948 found that some of the "lakes" were actually oceanic inlets whose connection with the sea was hidden by a broad apron of ice along the coast. Americans and Russians both were struck by the region's barrenness of life—even the hardy lichens were scarce.

The Russians' neighbors to the west were the Australians and, despite a certain hue and cry in the Australian press at the presence of Soviet bases within the Australian claim, the two expeditions exchanged friendly visits and soon found that they had a major problem in common: the soft snow of the hinterland. A six-man exploring party led by Keith Mather, commander of the main Australian base at Mawson, drove south in the summer of 1957–58 with enough fuel in tow for a 600-mile thrust. The group ran into the same conditions that had troubled the Russians. At times the sleds had to be cast loose and a tractor driven forward alone. A cable was then payed out from a winch on the tractor and each sled hauled forward by the winch. Close to the 400-mile mark the advance was halted by a mountain range straddling the route, but the Australians returned with a profile of the land beneath the ice in the coastal area.

Their glaciologist, Malcolm Mellor, in addition to his ice accumulation work, examined how ice is delivered to the sea. His conclusions were based both on sequential aerial photographs of fast-moving ice streams and on surveys of stakes placed on the more accessible glaciers. Ice streams are currents of swift ice that cross the otherwise sedately flowing ice sheet and are apparently produced by the configuration of the land underneath. One of them, the Vanderford Glacier, which debouches into the head of Vincennes Bay, was found by the Americans at Wilkes Station to be flowing at a rate of some nine feet daily. Mellor's study led him to the conclusion that the average flow for such streams is about three feet a day, whereas the seaward flow of the ice sheet in most places along the coast is only about 1.6 inches daily. In contrast the Ross Ice Shelf, for example, moves north at about five feet a day along a front 500 miles long. Hence Mellor concluded that the number of cubic miles of ice dumped into the sea annually by the ice shelves is more than five times as great as the combined total delivered by the swift ice streams and the coastal ice sheets.[22] This seems to account for the great number of large flat-topped icebergs to be seen in antarctic waters.

Australian IGY research in Antarctica covered many disciplines, with emphasis on such subjects as cosmic rays, and was essentially an extension of the excellent work that country had been doing in the region since 1954. For the IGY a small outpost, Davis Station, was opened in the Vestfold Hills between Mirny and Mawson.

The Australians landed at a number of points along the coast to do geological work, as did the Russians, who made more than three-score landings and reported evidence of iron deposits under the hinterland ice. The Japanese said they had discovered some uranium and the author found a small vein of manganese ore (tephroite) near Wilkes Station. In view of their remoteness, none of these finds seemed to be of value. Phillip Law of Australia said, in summing up the IGY expeditions, "So far no mineral deposits of any commercial significance have been discovered." [23]

The site allocated to Japan, in Lützow-Holm Bay to the west of Mawson, proved to be extremely difficult of access from the sea. To make matters worse, the Japanese had no icebreaker. They used a

2400-ton converted lighthouse-tender, the *Soya,* which became trapped almost every time it stuck its nose into the ice. When the most powerful icebreaker in service at the time, the USS *Glacier,* stopped by in March, 1956, to reconnoiter the area for the Japanese, it was unable to penetrate the ice-choked bay. The following year the *Soya* reached the coast and, on January 29, 1957, the rising-sun flag was hoisted over the base, which was christened *Showa,* the historic name that will be applied to the Emperor after his death. When the ship sought to leave, in February, 1957, it stuck fast and had to ask for help. Two icebreaking vessels responded—the *Glacier* and the *Ob.* The former was low on fuel and had to stop in Australia, but the Soviet vessel steamed directly to the scene and led the Japanese ship into open water on March 1.

Before that month was out, a section of the coastal ice broke off at Showa, carrying six tons of the wintering party's supplies out to sea. In July one of the huts set up on East Ongul Island burned, destroying part of the scientific records. The following year the *Soya* returned with a twenty-man relief party, but again it was blocked by the ice. The icebreaker USS *Burton Island* came to its aid, but the two ships were unable to get close enough to the station to land supplies for the next year. It was finally necessary to airlift out the eleven men of the wintering party plus one husky and eight pups. Fifteen of the heavy Sakhalin huskies had to be turned loose and left behind.

The closing of the station midway through the IGY and the abandonment of the dogs created a furor in Japan. A monument to the dogs was erected in Osaka and there were grumblings in the Diet. However, when the *Soya* returned at the end of the IGY to reactivate the base, it found two of the huskies alive and well, having apparently survived on penguins and the dried fish which the Japanese had left for them. Early in 1959 the *Soya* was again stuck for twenty-six days, but finally escaped under its own power. Scientific observations were carried out on the ship, as well as at Showa, with emphasis on those fields in which the Japanese are particularly strong, such as cosmic-ray research and ionospherics.

Still farther to the west, in Queen Maud Land, the Belgians placed their station, named for King Baudouin. The base probably would never have been established had it not been for the efforts of Commandant Gaston de Gerlache de Gomery, son of the Baron Adrien de Gerlache, who, at the end of the nineteenth century, led the first expedition to winter in Antarctica. After Belgium had withdrawn from its commitment to occupy the IGY site later taken by the Russians, the young de Gerlache, who had been an RAF pilot during World War II, began goading the government, pointing out that, if Belgium was to have any say in the ultimate disposition of Antarctica, it would have to participate in the IGY program there. This political appeal struck a responsive chord, for Belgium, like the Soviet Union, had asked in 1948 to be included in any international settlement of the antarctic problem.

The result was the dispatch of a seventeen-man expedition with de Gerlache as leader and pilot of its single-engine plane. Also included were a helicopter, twenty-four huskies, and two Sno-cats. The roster of men was an imposing one. It included another flier, Prince Antoine de Ligne, a member of the royal family, and the cook was Baron Guy della Faille d'Huysse, a man in his early thirties who had volunteered to go along no matter what his duties. An American observer, Lieutenant Colonel James F. Wolaver, who rode with the two Norwegian sealing ships that landed the expedition, said the baron's cooking was magnificent.

The base was established in the closing days of 1957 and the ships departed on January 12, 1958. Before the day was out both craft had become trapped in the pack ice and the outlook was so unfavorable that the crews began hunting penguins to augment their food supply in case they were stuck all winter. A change in wind direction then loosened the pack and they escaped.

During the following November and December exploration was carried out both on the surface and by aerial photography. On December 6, de Gerlache took off on a survey flight with three companions and failed to return. At the preparatory conferences on IGY operations in Antarctica this very situation had been discussed and planned for. An international communications net had been established, routinely for weather reports, but also in readiness for an emergency. Station Baudouin sounded the alarm over this circuit, and the first to respond were the Russians. V. M. Perov, the chief aviator at Mirny and an experienced polar flier, took off, landing to refuel at the Australian base, Mawson, then continuing, via the Japanese station, to Baudouin.

After flying repeated search patterns over the area of the Crystal Mountains, 250 miles inland from the Belgian station, Perov and his men saw the Auster plane, which had crashed in a crevassed area. There was no sign of life. After picking what seemed a stretch of snow free of crevasses, they swooped down for a landing, then hiked to the plane. Happily, instead of dead Belgians, they found a note. De Gerlache and his companions had started to walk to a depot eighty miles away. It was estimated that they had only two days' food left. Perov took off again and flew a spiraling path along the route he assumed they were following. At length there they were, a group of tiny specks moving across the immeasurable expanse of snow. The rescue was swiftly accomplished and when they returned to civilization, early in 1959, de Gerlache was given a life baronetcy, and the Order of Leopold I was awarded to Perov and to the Soviet expedition leader, Tolstikov.

The next station to the west was Norway's base, placed almost directly on the Greenwich Meridian. A trail party of four led by Sigurd Helle explored the mountains paralleling the coast some 150 miles inland. They traveled with two dog teams and two Weasels, one of which fell irretrievably into a crevasse and had to be abandoned. The chief contribution of this station, from the IGY point of view, was filling a broad gap in the observations of weather, aurora, and other subjects of special IGY scrutiny. The same applied to the work done by the Royal Society expedition at Halley Bay on the east shore of the Weddell Sea, as well as to that of Argentina's Station Belgrano, farther to the south.

Because of political rivalry in the Palmer Peninsula (Graham Land) area, the three claimant nations had sprinkled the region with a dense network of stations. Britain had eleven, Argentina seven, and Chile four. A number of them conducted only weather observations; none appears to have carried out cosmic-ray studies; and only one— the British base in the Argentine Islands—was listed for seismology. Nevertheless several kept magnetic records and their collective contribution was substantial.

Three of these bases met with disaster. Two Chilean stations burned in 1958, and in January, 1959, the Argentine station at Marguerite Bay was likewise destroyed.[24] After four other such calamities, it appeared that heat, not cold, was the chief hazard in Antarctica.

The New Zealanders centered their activities at Scott Base on McMurdo Sound and at Cape Hallett to the north. In addition to the valuable stationary observations carried out at those two points, four New Zealand parties explored the Great Antarctic Horst. One of them found a vein of sub-bituminous coal exposed for two miles, as well as fossilized tree trunks two feet in diameter, in the part of the range lying west of McMurdo Sound. On the opposite side of Antarctica, in what seems to be a continuation of the same mountain system, Fuchs found coal in the Theron Mountains, overlooking the Filchner Ice Shelf. The beds were as much as two feet thick and, due to the heat emitted by ancient intrusions of dolerite, some of the coal had been altered to anthracite or, in a few places, to natural coke. The fossil leaves were of the fernlike *Glossopteris* vegetation typical of the Permian period. It is found not only in the Great Antarctic Horst but also in the deposits from that period in India, Australia, and the southern parts of Africa and South America. Its distribution has been used as an argument for the theory of continental drift. This observation by Fuchs, coupled with the American discoveries in the Horlick Mountains, meant that during the IGY coal was sighted in the Great Antarctic Horst at points covering a span of 1800 miles, giving a far larger dimension to a coal field already known to be one of the world's largest.

The French maintained a coastal base called Dumont D'Urville in Adélie Land and placed a satellite station, Base Charcot, 200 miles inland, near the Magnetic Pole. So rough was the rocky island on which the coastal station was built that platforms had to be erected on pipe scaffoldings to provide suitable foundations for the huts. In October, 1957, the expedition leader, Bertrand Imbert, and some of his men made seismic soundings from the coast to a point 100 miles past Charcot. The French already had carried out extended observations in Adélie Land, beginning in 1950, although they were suspended for several years before the IGY.

The base nearest Mirny to the east was Wilkes Station, established by the United States on Vincennes Bay. Its scientific leader the first IGY winter was Carl Eklund, a wildlife specialist who, a decade earlier, had accompanied Ronne on one of the longest dog-team journeys in antarctic history. Although bird studies did not fall within the scope of the IGY, such work was permissible where it could be carried out only because of the presence of an IGY station in some remote part of the world.

Animal physiologists long have wondered how penguins could hatch their eggs in the bitter cold of the Antarctic. Bird embryos, as a rule, will die if they cool much below the body temperature of the adult bird. Eklund's plan was to telemeter temperature from within a penguin egg to see how cold it really gets. He had brought with him a number of tiny packages developed by the Office of Naval Research for the observation of temperatures within the human body. Each, no bigger than a small shotgun shell, contained a radio transmitter, battery, and temperature sensor. Eklund had hoped to conduct his experiments on Emperor penguin eggs, which are laid during the winter night, but no Emperor rookery could be found. However, there were numerous Adélie penguin rookeries and Skua gull nests. This was Eklund's method: He sneaked up on a nest, snatched one of its two eggs, took it back to camp and cut it in two on an electric saw of the kind used in handicrafts. He placed the telemetering package within the egg, cemented the two halves together, injected albumen back inside and sealed the hole. Thus the radio equipment had, in effect, been substituted for the yolk. He then slipped the egg back where it had been and a loop antenna over the nest picked up emissions from the egg as the bird sat on it.

The Adélie proved to be a patient sitter. A bird would remain on the nest for as long as two weeks before being relieved by its mate. The temperature of the egg therefore stayed quite stable—between 84.5° and 98.2°—on the average only about eleven degrees below the body temperature of the birds themselves. The Skua proved to be an even warmer bird with an even warmer egg. The temperature of the Skua eggs ranged from 87° to 103.5°, the average body temperature of the adults being 106.1°. The only reason the eggs occasionally cooled to 87° was that the birds exchanged sitting jobs more than twice daily. Eklund felt that, in spite of the trick he had played on the birds, their incubation procedures were normal, for in each case the other egg in the nest hatched out. Still to be resolved, nevertheless, is how these birds keep so warm in such a ferocious climate.

The Soviet expedition did its own penguin studies, since Mirny was near an Emperor rookery. Like most antarctic animals, the Emperors have almost no fear of anything moving across the ice. Even the approach of a fearsome-looking tractor leaves them unmoved. The Russians found that this did not apply to something in the air. They sought to obtain an accurate count, at their rookery, by means of an aerial photograph. An estimated 20,000 birds were there at the time, each hatching an egg in the folds of loose skin of its lower abdomen. When the plane came over, they panicked and the ice was covered with scrambled eggs. Attempts at aerial photography were abandoned.

One of the most interesting studies at Wilkes Station was an attempt, by recording distant earthquakes, to resolve the question of whether or not Antarctica is a continent. The seismologist with Eklund that first winter was Gilbert Dewart of the California Institute of Technology. Dewart subsequently returned for a second winter as the American exchange scientist at Mirny. He and Frank Press, head of the Seismological Laboratory at Cal Tech, analyzed the travel times, to Wilkes Station, of surface-type earthquake waves that passed through Antarctica (Love and Rayleigh waves, as opposed to the deep-traveling P and S waves). Knowing, from observations elsewhere, where and when each quake originated, they could tell whether the passage of the wave was retarded in the manner typical of a transcontinental route, or whether it was more rapid, as is characteristic of a path beneath the floor of an ocean.

The results indicated that the continent is only about three-quarters as big as it looks on the map. The only path that seemed to be completely continental was one that crossed East Antarctica to Wilkes Station from the vicinity of Cape Hallett. The conclusion reached by the two seismologists was that a considerable portion of the earth's crust beneath the ice sheet was of an oceanic rather than a continental nature.[25]

The New Zealanders at Hallett and McMurdo Sound obtained similar results on earthquake waves moving in the opposite direction, from the southeast and southwest Indian Ocean. Crustal thicknesses of twenty-two miles, which are typically continental, were obtained on both these routes across East Antarctica.

Gravity readings made on the traverses in Marie Byrd Land showed a continental-type crust, but it was unusually thin in most of the region, being on the average about nineteen miles. It thickened markedly toward the Horst, and, surprisingly, did so as well toward the Sentinel Mountains. This hinted at a link between the Sentinels and the Horst. If they are, in fact, tied together, the Sentinels and Palmer Peninsula constitute the world's longest peninsular structure, which, if the ice melted, would emerge as a spine, snaking the distance from New York to Texas. (See the endpapers.)

The gravity readings by both the American and Soviet expeditions showed Antarctica to be in isostatic equilibrium; that is, the land has subsided the full amount required to compensate for its ice load. The Russians estimated the amount of subsidence at 2500 feet on their side of the continent, while the Americans put it at 1600 feet in most of Marie Byrd Land, with a maximum of 3300 feet in the deepest part of the central basin. Thus the 10,000-foot mountains buried under 3300 feet of ice near Sovietskaya would rise to about 12,500 feet if the ice melted. Likewise, Antarctica must have been one of the world's highest continents in the days when it was covered with forests—a factor that, combined with its polar position, made it an efficient breeder of ice sheets.

Thus data obtained in very different ways—from gravity observations, explosion soundings, and earthquake recordings—helped piece together a picture of the one continent still hidden beneath the mantle of an ice age. The picture was not complete, but the continental character of East Antarctica was well established. The great depths of ice recorded by the IGY expeditions had more than geographic significance. They increase by a large margin the amount of water known to be in cold storage at the bottom of the world. Earlier estimates that its melting would raise the oceans a hundred feet or more now had to be doubled, making it easier, as well, to understand how, for long periods in the past, such broad portions of the continents have been under water.

CHAPTER 20
THE WATER PLANET

Ours is the only water-covered planet, with the possible exception of Venus. If the elevations were smoothed out, there would be no dry land at all. Even as things are, an astronomer on another planet, viewing the earth when the Central Pacific was turned toward him, would see no land except for a few shadowlike fringes around the edges. The inhabitants of land are all children of the sea, for at some point in the remote past their ancestors climbed out of the water.

Ever since that time, millions of years ago, we have been preoccupied with the land. Our maps focus attention on the continents to such an extent that we forget that 71 per cent of the earth is covered by water. There are said to be more mountains between New York and London than between New York and San Francisco, but because they are under water they have never been charted. Echo sounders, groping through the stygian darkness of the ocean bottom, have shown the general location and character of the Mid-Atlantic Ridge, but that is all.

The seas, as a whole, are estimated to be more than twice as productive per acre as the land. In some areas the annual "crops" of plants and animals far exceed those of the richest Iowa cornfields or the densest Brazilian jungles.[1] If we can but learn to farm and harvest the seas, we need not fear starvation, even though the world's population should increase sevenfold.

Recent generations have become less conscious of the oceans rather than more so. First swift ships and then jet aircraft have helped us leap across the inconvenient barriers between our own and other lands. Now rockets, ever bigger optical telescopes, radio telescopes, and nuclear accelerators draw our attention outward into space and inward to the core of the atom.

But for the efforts of three men, oceanography, the science of the sea, might have been far more neglected in the United States than it has been.

In 1926 Columbus O'Donnell Iselin II, son of a well-to-do New York family with a yachting tradition, graduated from Harvard and bought a captured rum-runner at auction for $1800. He rounded up a crew of vacationing Harvard men and headed north on a 5000-mile voyage to Labrador. The journey had its collegiate moments—as when some of the adventurers exploded firecrackers in the bunks of their shipmates—but by the time they had returned, forty-five measurements of temperature and salinity had been taken at depths as great as 2000 feet. Iselin had demonstrated that valuable scientific work could be done by amateur sailors in a seventy-seven-foot schooner. Iselin's inspiration at Harvard had been Henry B. Bigelow, a professor of zoology who obtained a Rockefeller Foundation grant to found the Woods Hole Oceanographic Institution on the southern elbow of Cape Cod. Iselin ultimately became its director.

In 1929 another future oceanographer, Roger Revelle, was graduated from Pomona College. That same year the world's only nonmagnetic research vessel, the *Carnegie,* blew up while loading gasoline at Apia in Western Samoa. Some of the cores that the ship had brought up from the Pacific floor escaped the disaster and were brought to the Scripps Institution of Oceanography at La Jolla, California, near San Diego. Revelle, who had gone to the Berkeley campus of the University of California to do graduate studies in geology, was invited to come down and work on them. He began to make long voyages on the institution's small research craft and, in 1951, became its director. He has been described as "an enormous man (6 ft. 4 in.) who looks as if he were specially designed, both physically and temperamentally, to study the Pacific Ocean." [2]

The third member of this seagoing triumvirate is W. Maurice Ewing, director of the Lamont Geological Observatory, operated by Columbia University at Palisades, New York. In January, 1954, the observatory's 202-foot research schooner *Vema* was running before mountainous seas en route to Bermuda when a wave broke over the stern and swept four men, including Ewing, overboard. Ewing's back was hurled against a fitting as he went over the side and when he tried to swim he found himself half paralyzed. He could hear another man drowning near by, but was helpless. Don Gould, the *Vema*'s skipper, and Fred McMurray, its sailing master, brought the schooner about in the angry sea and rescued Ewing and two others. Ewing's paralysis cleared up after a period of quiet at a hospital in Bermuda, but he never fully recovered from that blow.

These men, accustomed to living with salt in their hair and their lives in jeopardy, typify oceanography as it was in the United States at the start of the IGY—a science pursued by barefoot youths in ragged shorts and greasy shirts on the wave-swept decks of sailing ships. What a contrast to the surroundings of other IGY explorers— the men on the launching pads at Cape Canaveral, or those with their instruments mounted in multijet aircraft!

The IGY program in oceanography delved into problems extremely remote from one another. Revelle likes to describe the oceanographer as "a sailor who uses long words," arguing that his field is not a science as such, since it embraces any kind of research that must be done from a ship. This ranges from biology (in the study of oceanic life) to geotectonics (in examination of the earth's crust beneath the ocean). It was this last subject which drew Ewing out to sea. He grew up in Texas so far from water that it had to be hauled in by wagon for the family wash, and his first contact with the sea was in the use of underwater explosions, off the Texas coast, to hunt for oil deposits. To Ewing the water is an impediment to the exploration of the ocean floor that is his chief interest.

Long-range IGY objectives in oceanography were probably best summarized by SCOR—the Special Committee on Oceanic Research —which was born at Woods Hole in August, 1957, and became one of the continuing international bodies to emerge from the IGY. In outlining its objectives, midway through the IGY, SCOR stressed the importance of investigating the deep oceanic basins to elucidate the structure and history of the earth. With regard to the oceans as a whole, it listed three long-range problems that, it said, "may be critical to the future welfare of mankind." [3]

The first of these concerned the use of ocean deeps for the dumping of radioactive wastes. When atomic power comes into general use, it has been estimated that the world's reactors will annually produce radioactive material equivalent to that from 10,000 megaton fission bombs.[4] How can it be disposed of with iron-clad assurance that it will not leak out of its containers and poison our water supplies (if buried on land) or produce radioactive fish, such as those brought home by Japanese fishermen after a series of Pacific bomb tests? Some of the early measurements of water composition in certain hollows of the ocean floor suggested the water there might be prehistoric, isolated from the general circulation that gradually brings bottom waters to the surface. Such spots might serve as dumping grounds where the concrete-lined "coffins" of atomic waste could lie until the radioactivity within them decayed to negligible levels. In such spots, even if one coffin fell on another and cracked it open, the released material would stay put and not contaminate the waters to which the world looks hopefully for ever-increasing food supplies. But did such reservoirs of ancient water really exist? It was hoped that the IGY would provide an answer.

The second problem cited by SCOR was the urgent need for protein food to sustain the world's rapidly growing population. There is a great variation in the fertility of the sea. The transatlantic voyager rejoices when the murky waters of the Grand Banks and other coastal areas have been passed and the ship cleaves midocean azure. These gorgeously blue portions of the sea are deserts by comparison with the regions where upwelling of deep water brings nutrients to the surface, making a rich plant life possible. The fish, shrimps, and other creatures know where these pastures of the sea are to be found; so, to some extent, do the sailors and birds that pursue them. But the mechanics and chemistry of this plowing of the sea are little understood. The currents responsible for bringing up fertilizer from the bottom are subject to change and, in terms of present knowledge, it is change without notice.

In testimony before Congress on the IGY, Revelle gave an illustration:

> Ten or twenty years ago one of the major industries of California was the sardine fisheries. It was the largest fishery in the United States, something like 500,000 tons of sardines were caught a year. Then just after the war, the sardine crop went down and down and down until [in] 1951 only about 3,000 tons of sardines were caught.[5]

Many explanations were advanced, he said, including overfishing and an observed drop in ocean temperatures. Then, during 1957–58, after the temperature in coastal waters had gone up two to four degrees, he reported, there was an immediate rise in the number of sardines. However, similar warmings off Peru have had disastrous effects. Peruvian waters are among the richest fishing grounds in the world, due to a cold current that is fed by the bottom waters of Antarctica. The current picks up organic debris that has sunk to the ocean floor and brings it to the sunlit surface off the west coast of South America. There microscopic plants thrive, as do the tiny animals that feed on them, and hence there is abundant food for fish. Sea birds devour the fish in such quantities that their guano has become a pillar of the Peruvian economy. But occasionally a warm current, known as *El Niño,* sneaks down along the coast from the north, riding over the cold water and driving the fish to greater depths. Dead anchovies litter the waves; there are torrential rains and floods in Peru; and the shoreline is heaped with guano birds that have starved to death.

Greater knowledge of the currents and of oceanic chemistry should make it possible to harvest the seas methodically, instead of haphazardly, and even to undertake artificial enrichment of the water in certain areas.

The third field of investigation listed by SCOR was the role of the oceans in climate change. To underline the importance of this aspect of IGY research, Revelle told Congress:

> A slight shift of the isotherms [lines of equal temperature] . . . and the lines of equal rainfall—a shift of only about 100 miles—would make southern California, instead of being practically impossible to live in as it is now, quite impossible. This would affect literally 10 million people, a very large part of the people of the United States.[6]

In comparison with the atmosphere, the ocean has a tremendous capacity for absorbing, storing, and releasing heat. It has been calculated that, if all the heat of sunlight over a two-and-a-half-year period were stored up in the oceans, their temperature, in the depths, would rise only about one degree.[7] Hence the oceans have been described as the stabilizing "flywheel" of the climate. Yet buried within them, by the same token, may be the seeds of future change, slowly moving to the surface with irresistible momentum.

Roughly half the earth is covered with more than two miles of water. When the IGY began, little was known of this oceanic realm below the skim of its surface. To fragile man the lower depths were a fearsome place of incredible pressure, complete darkness, near-freezing cold and strange monsters, including an eighty-foot flat worm (*Lineus longissimus*) and the largest of all spineless animals, the fifty-foot *Architeuthis princeps,* or giant squid. Although ocean currents carry heat as well as nutrients, making northern Europe livable, it has, until recently, been impossible to fathom the general circulation of the oceans. An imperfect knowledge of the surface movements was possible, but there was no adequate way to measure currents lower down.

Winds and the earth's rotation clearly affect the speed and direction of surface flow, but what happens in the depths? There were a few clues. About 150 years ago measurements of the bottom water in the tropical Atlantic showed it to be so cold that it clearly had flowed there from the polar regions. The early measurements were perforce crude, one of the first techniques being to bring up samples of the deep water in insulated containers and measure its temperature on board ship. Then thermometers were devised that shoved markers up and down to record the maximum and minimum readings on their long descent. For many years the early investigators were misled into believing that the bottom water near the Antarctic was seven degrees above freezing instead of being close to freezing temperature, as one would expect. It was not until later that someone realized a systematic seven-degree error had been introduced by the squeezing of the thermometers under the extreme pressure at such depths.

In the 1920s the German research ship *Meteor* sailed back and forth along east-west lines traversing the South Atlantic, making measurements of temperature, salinity, and oxygen content all the way to the bottom. It was found that these elements did not vary in a smooth manner. There clearly were layers, indicative of water movements in different directions. During the postwar years a veteran of the expedition, Georg Wüst, knowing that oceanic circulation had to be in equilibrium, sought, on the basis of the *Meteor* data, to balance the amount of northward-flowing surface water with an equal flow in the opposite direction. This led him to postulate a massive southward movement below 5000 or 6000 feet.[8]

A somewhat similar conclusion was reached in the theoretical studies of Henry Stommel at Woods Hole during the decade prior to 1956. He first proposed that the intensification of currents along the western shores of the oceans was due to the rotation of the earth.

This helped account for the great flow of the Gulf Stream, which, every second, transports about seventeen cubic miles of water past any point. For reasons of symmetry one would expect a similar current in the Southern Hemisphere, flowing south along the coast of Brazil. There is a Brazil Current, but it is a paltry weakling compared to the Gulf Stream. Stommel finally came to the conclusion that, for some reason, surface water subsides to the bottom in the subarctic and rises from the bottom in the subantarctic, thus rounding two corners, north and south, in a circulation pattern that spans the equator. This, ideally, would call for a northerly surface flow along the entire western shore of the Atlantic and a deep southerly flow beneath it. Stommel calculated that the effect of the prevailing wind off Brazil, blowing against a northerly flow, would be just enough to produce the observed weak surface movement to the south. The whole mechanism, he thought, was driven by differences in water temperature and salinity.

His proposal gained some encouragement from the evidence of a subantarctic upwelling reported by G. E. R. Deacon, head of Britain's National Institute of Oceanography, based on observations by the RRS *Discovery II* on a series of oceanographic cruises from 1929 to 1939. Deacon in Britain and the Americans at Woods Hole were eager to test Stommel's hypothesis, but the measuring of deep currents was far more difficult than observing wind layers overhead, for instruments sent up by balloon could be seen—at least for a considerable distance—and could be tracked by radar. More important, the observer was at a fixed reference point. In oceanic work the instruments had to be dropped from a ship, whose drift was unpredictable, into depths impenetrable even by radar.

Among those who tackled this problem was John C. Swallow of the National Institute of Oceanography. This establishment, housed in what had been a wartime radar research center in the hills of Surrey, carried on a tradition of ocean studies that prided itself in such exploits as the voyage of HMS *Challenger,* 1872–76, whose fifty volumes of scientific results are one of the monuments of oceanography.

Swallow first experimented with a sonic transmitter suspended from a string of parachutes, hoping the device would sink slowly enough for a ship to keep track of it as various water layers carried it hither and yon. It was, in effect, a radiosonde in reverse. The scheme proved impractical, but he kept trying and finally lighted upon a novel idea. He enclosed his equipment in sealed aluminum scaffold tubing, which is less compressible than sea water. Although water is highly resistant to compression, it does become denser with depth. Therefore Swallow was able to arrange his device so that, at a predetermined depth, the increased water density would surpass the overall density of his equipment, which would then stop sinking and flow with the current. As a beacon it carried a battery-powered sonic pinger.

This device, which came to be known as the Swallow neutral-buoyancy float, led to a discovery that gave IGY oceanography an exciting send-off. After about twenty trial runs, Swallow and his colleagues decided to tackle the Gulf Stream. Two ships took part: the Institute's *Discovery II* and the *Atlantis,* a 142-foot ketch especially built for the Woods Hole Oceanographic Institution. They met at Bermuda in March, 1957, and set forth together in quest of the postulated deep countercurrent. The British and American oceanographers decided to look in the deep water off the eastern edge of the Blake Plateau, which is a comparatively shallow region east of the Carolinas. A swift tributary of the Gulf Stream, the Florida Current, hugs the coast, riding over the submarine plateau, but earlier temperature and salinity measurements by the *Atlantis* suggested that the lower layer suspected of being a countercurrent flowed in the deeper water farther out to sea. If so, the ships could wallow in comparatively stagnant surface water while looking for the deep current.

The *Discovery* successively tossed seven of the floats over the side and listened to their pings through hydrophones suspended from bow and stern. Loran stations of the electronic navigational system ashore made it possible to keep track of the ships' positions to within a quarter-mile, a degree of precision necessary in determining the true motion of the floats. Those hovering at a depth of 6500 feet were almost stationary, but those set to float at 9000 feet moved south at eight miles daily. This southerly flow extended all the way to the bottom, where another device, developed in Britain by A. S. Laughton, was used. This consisted of a celluloid ball suspended from a frame that held it eighteen inches above the bottom and displayed a compass needle. The rig was photographed from above, revealing the direction and strength of current by the direction in which the ball was tugged by the water and the extent to which its suspension was deflected from the vertical. This showed that, at a depth of 10,500 feet, the current was still five miles per day toward the south.[9]

Thus any notion that the oceans are comparatively stagnant except at the surface had to be discarded. With the neutral-buoyancy float and other devices used during the IGY, the deep sea came alive. The movements involved far more water than was needed to compensate for windblown currents on the surface. It was evident that another force—heat—drives massive circulation of the ocean, much as it circulates the atmosphere.

The Atlantic studies were probably the most intensive in the IGY oceanographic program. Another Woods Hole ship, the 125-foot former Coast Guard cutter *Crawford,* ran seven east-west profiles across the Atlantic, stopping repeatedly on each crossing to make measurements of temperature, salinity, oxygen content and dissolved chemicals down to the bottom, sometimes more than 18,000 feet below. At certain of these points, observations made by the *Meteor* a quarter-century earlier were repeated to see if any changes had taken place. The *Atlantis, Chain,* and *Discovery II* made additional east-west profiles, covering the entire ocean at latitudinal intervals of no more than eight degrees from 32° South (between Argentina and South Africa) to the region between Canada and Europe.

A parallel study in the North Atlantic was the Polar Front Survey which sought to observe, from top to bottom of the ocean, the movement of warm southern water into the polar seas and the southerly flow of cold arctic water. The project was initiated by the International Council for the Exploration of the Sea, and a score of vessels from nine nations bordering the Atlantic took part. The *Gauss* of the German Hydrographic Institute in Hamburg, for example, did a profile from Newfoundland to the Azores, and the Soviet ship *Lomonosov* did concentrated studies in the Greenland Sea.

Another intensive hunting ground for submerged currents was the equatorial portion of the Pacific. In 1951 the United States Fish and Wildlife Service sent one of its ships west of the Galapagos Islands to experiment with a Japanese technique for catching deep-swimming tuna. This consisted of attaching a large number of fishing lines to a rope several miles long, stretched between the ship and a buoy. The experiment was carried out in the South Equatorial Current—the same westward flow that, in 1947, carried the raft *Kon-Tiki* from off Peru to the central Pacific—but, instead of drifting west with the ship, the lines pulled sharply to the east. Townsend Cromwell of the Fish and Wildlife Service recognized this as an easterly current beneath the well-known westward flow, but its extent was not explored until the so-called Dolphin Expedition of 1958, when two ships traced it for some 3500 miles. They were the *Horizon,* a converted

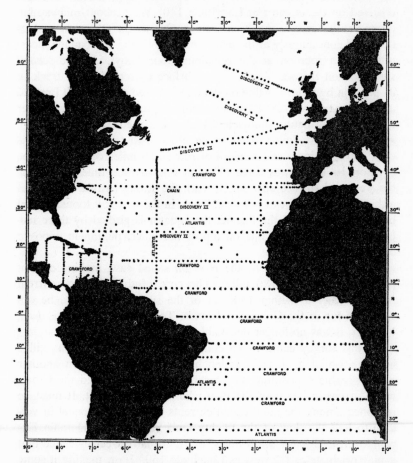

The British-American survey of the Atlantic, carried out between September, 1954, and July, 1959. Each dot represents a point where water samples were obtained. The *Atlantis, Crawford,* and *Chain* were operated by the Woods Hole Oceanographic Institution; the *Discovery II* by Britain's National Institute of Oceanography.

143-foot ocean-going tug of the Scripps Institution of Oceanography, and the *Hugh M. Smith* from the Pacific Oceanic Fishery Investigations of the Fish and Wildlife Service.

Lacking any fixed reference points from which to measure flow, they anchored five taut-wire buoys in water almost three miles deep. These markers were spaced seventy miles apart along a north-south line centered on the equator at Longitude 140° West, about midway between South America and New Guinea. One or the other of the ships remained continuously at the center buoy while the other made measurements in rotation at the remaining four buoys. As the second ship rode on the westward-moving surface current, it kept track of its position by radar-ranging on the buoy. At the same time it lowered a propeller-type current meter to depths as great as 660 feet. Farther down Swallow neutral-buoyancy floats were used.

The eastward flow proved to be about 700 feet thick, with its core 300 feet down and a width of some 250 miles centered on the equator. Its speed was three miles an hour—three times as fast as the westward surface current. Beneath the strong eastward flow was a third, weak current to the west. Thus, in the first few thousand feet below the surface of the Pacific, the equator is girdled by three ribbons of moving water, one on top of the other, pulling in opposite directions.

After these observations the *Horizon* sailed east, making current measurements every 180 miles. The core of the eastward current rose gradually to within 140 feet of the surface and could be observed as far as the Galapagos Islands. To the east of those islands, however, it was no longer detectable.

As this survey came to an end, Townsend Cromwell was killed in the crash of a plane in which he was traveling to join another oceanographic expedition. The eastward flow was named the Cromwell Current in honor of the man who first identified it. It must be reckoned among the great ocean currents of the world, equal in volume to half the flow of the mighty Gulf Stream. The Dolphin Expedition traced it for 3500 miles, but there is indirect evidence that it may originate as far west as Longitude 160° East, making it some 7000 miles long.

A subsequent IGY cruise by ships from the Scripps Institution, the Doldrums Expedition, discovered that another easterly flow, the Equatorial Countercurrent, was far more massive than had been supposed.

Three great surface rivers traverse the Pacific Ocean parallel to the equator. In the center is the eastward Equatorial Countercurrent, flanked by the westward North Equatorial and South Equatorial currents. For reasons of symmetry one would expect the countercurrent, in the center, to lie directly on the equator, but the whole system is displaced to the north and it is the South Equatorial Current that lies along the equator.

At a depth of about 360 feet in the area of the countercurrent there is a sharp temperature drop (or "thermocline"). Using this and other measurements, the Norwegian oceanographer, Harald U. Sverdrup (who preceded Revelle as head of Scripps), postulated that this was essentially the bottom of the current, with a gradual diminishing of the flow to stagnant water 760 feet down. The Doldrums Expedition anchored a buoy at midocean depths south of Clipperton Island and used the same technique that had been employed in measuring the South Equatorial Current. On the basis of a dozen current-meter observations and data from a half dozen neutral-buoyancy floats, the flow was found to be swiftest at depths between 160 and

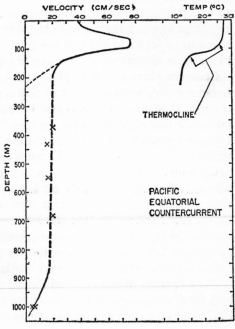

Changes in water velocity and temperature, with depth, in the Pacific Equatorial Countercurrent. The solid line forming the upper part of the velocity profile is based on twelve measurements with a current meter. The X markings lower down are observations with Swallow floats. The line of short dashes shows the previously postulated profile, in which the current was confined to surface layers. The temperature profile, on the right, is based on bathythermograph observations. (National Academy of Sciences)

360 feet, but was still detectable 3300 feet down. The eastward movement of water in this current was therefore estimated at twelve cubic miles per second—at least double the previous estimate. When this is combined with the eight cubic miles per second in the Cromwell Current, it constitutes a massive easterly movement of water across the Pacific that must, in some way, be balanced by an equivalent flow in the other direction.[10] When the IGY was over, it was clear that we have barely begun to fathom the awesome forces at work beneath the surface of the sea.

In addition to Scripps and Woods Hole, three other American academic institutions joined in the IGY exploration of the sea. The schooner *Vema* of the Lamont Geological Observatory was at sea almost continuously during this period. The Texas Agricultural and Mechanical College, which was an IGY World Data Center for oceanography, sent its research ship, the *Hidalgo,* to study the channels linking the Gulf of Mexico with the Caribbean and Atlantic, as well as into nearby areas of the ocean. The University of Washington dispatched its motor vessel *Brown Bear* on cruises off the Aleutians and the west coast of the United States, carrying out observations of water composition from top to bottom at a number of points, including eleven at which the *Carnegie* had done similar work a short time before its explosion in 1929. It was found that, during the summer of 1958, warm tropical waters had moved unusually far north.

Oceanographers also rode Navy and Coast Guard icebreakers to Antarctica and, when the press of ship schedules permitted, the vessels paused to make observations. Perhaps the most interesting result was a new explanation for the so-called Antarctic Convergence. This is a boundary line encircling Antarctica about a thousand miles offshore, where warm water to the north gives way to cold polar water to the south. The convergence is evident even to the casual voyager who finds that, south of it, the air is raw, whereas to the north it is comparatively mild. The line also represents a boundary so far as aquatic life is concerned. The classic view of the convergence is that it marks the region where northward-moving cold water slips beneath the warmer surface layer of more temperate latitudes.

Temperature measurements from the icebreaker USS *Glacier* and the New Zealand frigate HMNZS *Pukaki* showed the convergence to be a local upwelling of cold water from depths greater than 600 to 1000 feet. It occurred in a narrow region only about seven miles wide.

Farther south there was markedly warmer water down to the limit of the observations. Harry Wexler of the US Weather Bureau concluded that the convergence was actually a "divergence" produced by strong westerly winds that push apart the surface waters into less windy areas, north and south, bringing cold water up from below.[11]

A major area of IGY oceanographic study was centered about the many rhythmic changes in sea level, varying in their periodicity from a few seconds to many months. Although there were some 500 tide gauges in operation throughout the world at the start of the IGY, few were on islands away from coastal influences, and there were large gaps in coverage. For the IGY an additional 200 to 250 sea-level measuring stations were established. Most of the oscillations studied lay between the short-period waves produced by winds and the tidal motions resulting from the pull of sun and moon.

The American program for island observation of sea-level changes was largely carried out, in the Atlantic, by the Lamont Geological Observatory and, in the Pacific, by the Scripps Institution of Oceanography. One of the more interesting series of observations was made at the ill-fated air defense radar platform, in the sea eighty-five miles southeast of New York City, whose stilts collapsed in 1961 with a loss of twenty-eight lives. During the IGY, in a search for possible correlations between air waves and sea waves, atmospheric oscillations were recorded there and at the Lamont Observatory, overlooking the Hudson River, by instruments designed to observe slight changes in barometric pressure (microbarovariographs). In this way air waves were detected with a crest-to-crest period of from four to twelve minutes, moving eastward at about forty-five miles per hour. These appeared to be coupled with ocean waves likewise moving eastward and it was postulated that both might be generated by a jet stream high overhead.[12]

At many of the stations there were long-period ocean waves with rhythms characteristic of the locality. At Bermuda the interval was six to eight minutes; at the Azores, eight to ten minutes; and at Iceland, sixteen minutes. At Point Barrow, Alaska, and at Arorae, Canton and Hull Islands in the mid-Pacific, the crests were four days apart.

The waves that came at intervals of several days may have represented sloshing in oceanic basins. When one sits down in a bathtub, such a wave flows back and forth from one end of the tub to the other for a considerable time. If this was the nature of the ocean waves, there remained the question of what started them.

In all cases they were small in amplitude—often little more than one inch. Hence they could be observed only by averaging out the far larger wind waves, a job that could be done mechanically. The chief problem was to measure the waves without destruction of the observing equipment. One method, used in Iceland, consisted of anchoring pressure recorders in about thirty feet of water as much as a thousand feet off the end of a pier. Even waves of only a small fraction of an inch produced observable pressure changes. The pier in Iceland stood ten feet above mean water level, but was so open to the sea that winter storm waves often broke over it. An armored cable led from the pressure gauges to the pier and thence was linked to recorders in the office of the local fishing industry at the village of Thorlakshofn.

On the Pacific islands, wells were blasted in the coral or in coastal rocks and connected with deep water by plastic garden hose. Changes in water depth, with the passing of each wave, were communicated by the hose to produce water-level changes in the well. These, in turn, were observed by a float linked to an automatic recorder. A half-dozen of these installations were put in by a three-man team from Scripps, flying from island to island with equipment that included a plastic skiff and aqualung diving equipment. The team took about ten days to set up each station and train local men to operate it, the sites ranging from Takaroa in French Polynesia to such Central Pacific islands as Marcus, Wake, and Canton. Another group set up a recorder on Pitcairn Island, where it was tended by a descendant of one of the mutineers from HMS *Bounty*.

Every effort was made to place the recording equipment where it would be protected, but, without exception, all of the installations were damaged during storms. One hurricane sent waves completely over the atoll at Takaroa, damaging the station beyond repair. The maintenance of some gauges (at Marcus, Takaroa, Hull, and Jarvis) proved impracticable due to repeated damage and transportation problems, and they were abandoned. Several stations produced perfect records for only about a third of the time, and the situation at Jarvis was further complicated by the death of Otto Hornung, who manned the station there alone. In October, 1958, he reported, on his regular radio contact with his headquarters on Fanning Island, that he felt ill. From then on he failed to make his scheduled radio appearances and, upon request, a British naval vessel went to investigate. A distress signal was seen flying from the island and a landing party was told by the only other inhabitants, a Gilbert Islander and his wife, that Hornung had died of a heart attack on his way to make an instrument reading. He was buried on the island.

Many other nations cooperated with Scripps in the Pacific program: the Dutch at Hollandia, New Guinea; the Japanese at Hachijo-jima and Eno-shima; the French at Takaroa; the Chileans at Easter Island and Juan Fernandez; the Ecuadoreans at the Galapagos; and the British and Mexicans at other sites.[13]

In the Arctic Ocean, sea-level changes were recorded by American, Canadian, and Soviet stations as well as by a Finnish group in Spitsbergen. In addition to the usual type of trouble (for example, the washing away of the gauge at Cape Prince of Wales, Alaska), these stations had to contend with the destructive movement of ice along the coast and their recording wells had to be heavily salted to keep them from freezing.

A subject of special interest was the seasonal change in sea level. Shortly before the IGY it was reported that, during spring in each hemisphere, the mean sea level is eight inches lower than in the fall. Since water shrinks slightly when cooled, the level could be expected to drop in winter, but this did not seem to account for the entire effect. It looked as though about twenty trillion tons of water commuted north and south with the seasons. Hence measurements were made periodically to a depth of about a thousand feet so that the sea level could be corrected for temperature and salinity variations. The gauges set up on mid-ocean islands for the IGY brought in data free of coastal influences. In a preliminary analysis of the results, June G. Pattullo of Oregon State College found that in March the seas were below their annual mean almost everywhere in the Northern Hemisphere. South of the equator they were, on the whole, below average. Exceptions included the Bay of Bengal, Arabian Sea, Gulf of Siam, and the waters near Mexico, Central America, Australia, and the northeast tip of Siberia. In September the situation was almost exactly reversed. She concluded that these seasonal changes did not result, to any extent, from north-south movements of water, but rather from its expansion and contraction, due to such factors as temperature, salinity, and atmospheric pressure. Thus the weight of water and air resting on the earth's crust at any one point does not vary substantially during the year.[14]

Another area of inquiry embraced the surges that beset Barbados and nearby islands. These waves are not high, usually less than four inches, but they move at great speed and, when they strike at high tide —especially at spring tide—they sweep over the protecting reef and smash against the shoreline in a high and damaging surf. The speed of a wave increases according to the distance from crest to crest (the speed proportional to the square root of the wavelength). Since the interval between surge waves is from half a minute to an hour, they may travel at fifty miles per hour, continuing to beat Barbados for a day or more.

The observation of four of these episodes during the IGY led to the discovery that they were produced by severe storms 2500 miles away in the North Atlantic. It therefore became possible to predict their arrival at Barbados two days or more in advance.[15]

When the IGY was over, some of those who had been seeking out the veins and arteries of the oceanic circulatory system felt the attention of the world had passed them by and was focused on space. They argued that knowledge of the seas amidst which we live is at least equal in importance to exploration of the heavens. The IGY had thrown objects into the sky that were expected to orbit for years—in one case for centuries. G. E. R. Deacon of Britain noted wryly that the oceanographers had done somewhat the same thing in sprinkling the deep waters with Swallow floats, their pingers now silent (like the radios of dead satellites), wandering around the world's aqueous envelope at their predetermined depths.

CHAPTER 21
THE DEEPEST DEEPS

Between six and seven miles below the rolling waves of the western Pacific are the blackest and most inhospitable places on the face of the earth. These are the deep trenches that slice into the ocean floor parallel to island chains from the Kuriles, north of Japan, to the Kermadecs, north of New Zealand. There are about two dozen such trenches throughout the world, but most of them, including all the deepest ones, lie along the western edge of the Pacific basin. Few features of the earth's surface are more challenging than these knife-like gashes, whose sides slope steeply down, yet whose narrow floors are often strangely level. The deeper trenches are almost of identical depth, suggesting that some characteristic of the earth's crust limits the cleavage.

When the IGY began there had been relatively few glimpses of these deeps. Until the echo sounder came into use in the 1920s, the only clues to the nature of the deep ocean floor were obtained by the laborious lowering of wires several miles long. Thus the true nature of half the earth's surface—that portion lying beneath more than two miles of water—was virtually unknown. As more and more ships became equipped with sonic sounders, their crisscrossing tracks began to provide a rough picture but, as is often pointed out, we still know less of the topography of this vast region than we do of that side of the moon exposed to our telescopes.

The Russians, who probably sent as many research ships to sea as any of the IGY nations, carried out a systematic exploration of the trenches that line their side of the Pacific Ocean. Of some seventy vessels taking part in IGY oceanic research, thirteen were from the Soviet Union, including nine designed primarily for research. United States institutions sent out eight ships, and fisheries research craft also cooperated on some of the cruises. American vessels en route to and from the Antarctic likewise carried out observations whenever possible.

The Soviet research fleet included several ships considerably larger than any used by western nations. The flagship was the 6000-ton *Vityaz,* carrying about sixty-five researchers (half of them women) plus a crew of comparable size. The *Vityaz* did most of the trench exploration, and in the course of this work it found the deepest spot hitherto sounded in the oceans. Because of the uniformity in depth of the trenches, it is quite likely that the record will be broken a number of times—in each case by a margin of only a few feet.

The record sounding, made in the Marianas Trench, was 10,990 meters (36,056 feet or 6.8 miles). A primary question was what sort of creatures—if any—lived down there, where the pressure is roughly 900 tons per square foot. Another problem was to learn if the water deep in the trenches was stagnant enough to make them suitable for the dumping of radioactive waste. Earlier studies of oceanic life had shown a steady drop in population with increasing depth. The rate of decrease was such that some believed there was no life at all in the deepest areas. The total absence of sunlight below 1000 feet made it impossible for most plants to grow, and without plants (or animals nourished by plants) there could be no animals. Furthermore, if water lay on the bottom for centuries, it would probably contain little or no oxygen, likewise a necessity for most life.

Nevertheless, no matter how deep man reached, he always seemed to bring up a handful of life. In 1901 the Prince of Monaco obtained a haul from 3.75 miles down. In 1948 a Swedish expedition on the *Albatross* brought up specimens from 4.7 to 4.9 miles on the slope of the Puerto Rico Trench; and in 1951 the Danes aboard the *Galathea* obtained four hauls from between 6.1 and 6.3 miles in the Philippines Trench, proving that life existed even that far down. Two years later the *Vityaz* began the program of trench exploration that reached its climax during the IGY.

Having found the "deepest" spot, the Russians were eager to see if it was inhabited, but the dragging of the narrow trench floor was no easy task. The wave-tossed ship had to lower a cable seven or eight miles long into a crack one mile wide. On its first attempt, August 15, 1957, the wind was blowing at right angles to the trench, making it extremely difficult for the ship to stay in position. The trawl hit the side of the trench about five and a half miles down, bringing up a concrete-like slab of sediment barren of life. Laboriously the trawl was lowered again. This time it failed to hit bottom at all. For the third attempt the largest winch was used, although it was so slow that the lowering and hoisting, plus one hour of trawling, took more than twelve hours. The equipment was dragged along the bottom seven miles down and one mile astern. After long hours of careful heaving in, it could be seen through the clear water, slowly nearing the surface, the trawl pocket filled with precious sediment from the bottom. But the trophy was not hauled out quickly enough. At the critical moment, as it broke water, a wave swept through the pocket, carrying off a muddy cloud and leaving only a few claylike chunks. Whatever living things there may have been sank slowly back into their primeval habitat.[1]

There must have been Russian oaths on the Pacific breeze that day, but when the *Vityaz* reached Vladivostok the following February it came home far from empty-handed. No further bottom trawls were attempted in this deepest spot, but from the Kermadec Deep, 6.7 miles down, fifteen different species were brought up. Another haul, from a depth of 5.6 miles in the Kurile-Kamchatka Trench, brought up about a thousand specimens, likewise representing a considerable variety of organisms. A new 20,340-foot trench was found north of the New Hebrides, adding another link in the western Pacific chain of such gashes. To see what creatures lived at various levels in these chasms, nets were lowered that closed at fixed depths, bringing up "snout-fish" with special organs of illumination and "telescopic" eyes. The density of life proved to be meager, compared to that in shallow locations—a thousand times less at ten kilometers' depth than one kilometer down—but what was remarkable was that there were any living things at all. The inhabitants included mollusks and such minute forms of crustaceans as the copepods. Despite their small size, those animals brought up were, as a rule, far larger than their shallow-water cousins. It was as though the great pressure, or some other factor, had caused the tiny creatures to grow much larger than normal. It has been proposed that larger species may also grow to monstrous size but are too elusive for present-day nets and trawls. Revelle likes to cite the example of an eel that has been seen only in its larval form. The larvae of ordinary eels are about three inches long, but those of this species are sometimes four or five feet in length, implying that the adults may be of sea-serpent dimensions.

By exploring the oceans with bathyscaphs and other deep-traveling submersibles it should be possible to determine whether or not there are monsters in the deep. A French bathyscaph, the *FNRS III,* made several descents off Japan during the IGY, but not until January 23, 1960, was an attempt made on the deepest place in the oceans. On that date the bathyscaph *Trieste* made its historic descent into the Marianas Trench not far from where the *Vityaz* obtained its record sounding. The submersible had been developed by the famous Swiss balloonist and deep-sea explorer, Auguste Piccard, and his son Jacques, and had been bought by the United States Navy. Jacques Piccard accompanied Lieutenant Don Walsh of the Navy on the descent. A bathyscaph is a heavy, pressure-resistant steel sphere suspended from a blimplike container subdivided into compartments, most of which are filled with gasoline. To initiate the descent, the empty compartments are flooded with water. For return to the surface, metal ballast is dropped and, since gasoline is lighter than water, the vessel rises. During the four-and-a-half-hour descent, Walsh and the young Piccard (who is six feet seven inches tall) crouched in the chamber, only five feet eight inches high.

After they had entered the realm of total darkness, below a thousand feet, they switched on an exterior flood light and, through their porthole, watched what looked like upward-falling snow—the plankton and oceanic debris they passed on their downward journey. As they neared the bottom of the trench they dropped ballast to slow the descent. The steel sphere, its walls three and a half inches thick, was squeezed by the pressure until the paint flecked off and, at one point, with a terrifying sound, one of the portholes cracked (although it remained watertight). As the gray-white floor of the trench came into view, a flounder-like fish about a foot long swam by. Both its eyes were on one side of its head, indicating that it was a bottom feeder (although eyes were certainly of limited use at this depth). When the bathyscaph hit bottom, about 35,800 feet down, a great cloud of silt rose up and, within it, the two men saw a bright red shrimplike animal roughly one inch long. By a special telephone that transmitted through water they notified their tender, the Navy tug *Wandank,* that they were at the lowest point on the earth's surface. They released two tons of iron and rose to the top in three and a half hours.

Thus it was shown that fish and crustaceans live even in the most terrible environment on earth. The *Vityaz* and *Galathea* found more than 250 species of living things in the deep trenches of the western

Pacific. It would appear that there is no place on earth—unless it be the fiery cauldron of a volcano—where life is not found, at least sporadically.

From the point of view of evolution, the life in the trenches was younger than many had expected. It had been proposed that these chasms might harbor a lost world of species exterminated elsewhere. It was reasoned that the trenches were isolated from environmental changes that killed off many species during the process of evolution. Instead, the species proved in large measure to be ones that had emerged in the past few million years, not those dating back many hundreds of millions of years. At the same time the trenches had developed their own species, and in some cases their own families, of animal. The fauna was quite different from that which was found on the surrounding ocean floor, a mere one or two miles underwater. Yet the creatures in one trench closely resembled those in another. Identical species, for example, were found in the Kermadec Trench and in the Philippines Trench, 5000 miles apart, but nowhere in between.

Despite their youth in terms of the earth's history, these species seemed to be older than the trenches themselves. The Lamont Geological Observatory's ship *Vema,* in its study of the ocean floor, found an extension of the South Sandwich Trench that had been filled with sediment. All of this suggested that the trenches are a transient feature of the earth's crust along the boundary of the oceanic basins and that, as they open and then close or silt up, the creatures that inhabit them move along the fault lines into newly developing trenches.

It was clear that animals in the trenches were not isolated from the rest of the ocean. The food chain reached from the plankton pastures at shallow depths down to the very bottom of the Marianas Trench. Nor was the water barren of oxygen, as would have been the case after long stagnation. In short, the ocean floor did not appear to be a good place to dump radioactive materials if there was even a small chance of their escaping into the water.

Other evidence for the constant, though slow, circulation of bottom water to the surface came from analysis of the distribution of radium in various levels of the sea. Ionium (thorium-230) sinks to the ocean floor, where it slowly decays into radium, its half life being about 80,000 years. The velocity with which this radium is then distributed through the ocean can be determined. On the basis of this and other data it was found that the total surface layer of the Atlantic Ocean is renewed by bottom water in about 300 years, whereas a similar turnover takes about 1500 years in the Pacific.[2] Obviously, however, the bottom water in some areas must come to the surface much faster than that.

The remaining problem presented by the trenches was to find out what produced them. Their locations, at the edge of oceanic basins and alongside volcanic, earthquake-ridden island chains, make it apparent that they are manifestations of great forces at work within the earth's crust. To understand them, it was necessary to look deep into the earth by means of the science known as seismology. When the IGY began, a study of shock waves produced by earthquakes and man-made explosions already had brought to light a fundamental difference between continents and oceans. Continents appear to be massive blocks of granite, resting, perhaps, on a lower layer of basalt, with a total thickness of twenty or thirty miles; the ocean floor is a crust only about three or four miles thick. These two formations do not, as a rule, meet at the beach line, which is a transient boundary, subject to the whims of sea-level change. The outer margin of the continental structure is the edge of the continental shelf, where the ocean depth suddenly drops from a few hundred feet to one or two miles.

The world is thus divided structurally into two distinct provinces—continental and oceanic. One of the goals in the IGY was to try to find out why. A large part of the American oceanographic program therefore involved tossing explosives overboard to detonate under water and create miniature earthquakes. This work required two ships, one dropping the charges and the other recording shock waves refracted or reflected from the bottom at a succession of distances out to fifty or sixty miles. At such extreme ranges, it took several hundred pounds of TNT to produce an adequate shock wave, whereas at close distances only one pound was used. The waves observed were P (pressure) waves, which resemble those of sound. Unlike the catastrophic vibrations of an earthquake, the explosions did not produce any significant S (shear) waves, where particles along the wave path move sideways.

The seismic measurements made use of either reflection or refraction. Reflection measurements are, essentially, echo soundings and are useful primarily in determining depths to sediment layers close beneath the ocean floor. The listening ship has to be comparatively close to the firing ship to receive the reflected wave with clarity. Refracted waves follow the top surfaces of the various layers. The velocity of the waves tends to increase with each deeper, denser layer, and it was in terms of these various speeds that the interior of the earth was charted, bringing to light the layers of this planet's crust: the massive granite of the continents, the thin sediments of the ocean floor, and the underlying basalt.

Combined, these various layers still constitute no more than a thin veneer over our planet. Below them is the mantle, a region of unknown composition, comprising some 84 per cent of the earth's interior.

The characteristic travel velocities of the upper layers, given in the customary kilometers per second (one kilometer = .62 miles), are:

Continental granitic layer	6
Ocean sediments	2
"Second layer" (below ocean sediments)	3 to 4
Basaltic layer	6.5
Upper mantle	8

The transition from crust to mantle is marked by a clear jump in wave velocity known as the Mohorovičić discontinuity, for the Yugoslav who pointed out its worldwide occurrence. More popularly it is "the Moho"; a proposed submarine drill hole to that depth is known as the Mohole.

The mantle extends down 1800 miles, its wave velocity increasing steadily until it reaches 13.7 kilometers per second. Then the velocity drops to 8.2 k.p.s. in what is presumed to be the earth's liquid core. Still farther down there appears to be an inner core where the material is in a solid state, due to the extreme pressure.

All three of the major American oceanographic institutions did seismic work, their vessels ranging over a large part of the world's oceans. The *Vema* of the Lamont Geological Observatory continued an intensive study of the Caribbean begun before the IGY, the objective being to determine the nature of island arcs, with their volcanoes, parallel trenches, and lines of earthquake centers. Clearly, in arcs such as those that enclose the Caribbean, the Scotia Sea, or the Sea of Japan, the earth's crust is in a state of comparatively rapid transformation. Some felt the arcs manifest emergence of new continental areas; others thought they are places where fragments of continents are sinking into oblivion.

Altogether thirty-eight seismic profiles were obtained in the Caribbean, most of them shot in both directions along the line to eliminate errors. Between Cuba and Colombia both oceanic and continental types of crust were found under the sea and it was not clear whether the area was in the process of rising or sinking. Beneath the Cayman Trough there was a particularly thin section, consisting of about 1650 feet of sediment over two miles of rock.[3]

The *Vema*'s chief IGY cruise, however, was a ten-month journey that began on November 8, 1957, and took it from New York, down the east coast of South America, around South Africa, and home via the Red Sea and the Mediterranean—a total distance of 34,000 miles. Off South America, the Brazilian vessel *Forte de Quimbra* and the Argentine ship *Saraviron* helped in the shoot-and-listen operations, which obtained more than seventy profiles along the Argentine coast. In some areas, such as Beagle Channel near Cape Horn, the *Vema* charted layers of shallow sediment without stopping or firing a shot. This was done with a "sub-bottom sounder" dragged a few feet below the surface in the water astern. Its periodic discharge of sparks produced low-frequency sounds that penetrated through as much as 450 feet of sediment on the ocean floor, producing echoes that delineated in detail both the sediment layers and the configuration of the rocks beneath them. It was hoped that analysis of these layers would show whether or not the glaciers discharging into those waters from the

Cross section of the Caribbean from Cuba to the continental slope off Colombia. The small numerals represent the velocities of seismic waves as determined by shipboard observations. The rock structure is an estimate based on these observations. The vertical scale is in kilometers. The map on the right shows the location of the seismic observations and of the profile (straight line). (National Academy of Sciences)

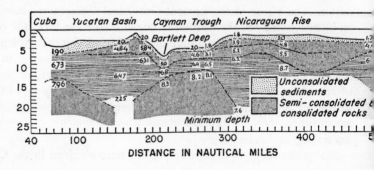

southern Andes were at their maximum at the same time as the ice sheets of the North.

Before crossing to Africa, the *Vema* studied the Scotia island arc and its associated trough, the South Sandwich Trench. It was then joined by the *Vrystaat* of the South African Navy for the observations off the African coast. After operating in the Indian Ocean and the Gulf of Aden, it sailed up the Red Sea in company with the *Atlantis* from Woods Hole, probing with explosives to seek the nature of the cleft that runs the length of that narrow body of water. Beneath the sediments was a high-velocity material (7.1 k.p.s.) which was thought to be a mass of igneous rock that had flowed upward in a molten state when the earth's crust split apart in this region. The configurations of the Red Sea and Persian Gulf have suggested to some that they are lines of cleavage where Africa has swung away from Eurasia, partly pulling Arabia with it.

By the time the ship reached New York in September, 1958, it had occupied eighty hydrographic stations on the high seas—points where it lowered sampling bottles to obtain temperature, water composition, and oxygen content from top to bottom of the ocean. At sixty-two stations it had dropped its camera for bottom photographs. Cores were obtained with Ewing's piston-coring device. When it touched the bottom, a 1200-pound weight fell a dozen feet, jamming the tube as deep as possible into the sediments. Where there was ooze, rather than rock, cores were obtained up to sixty-three feet in length.[4] Some seventy-five drumfuls of water were hauled up from various depths

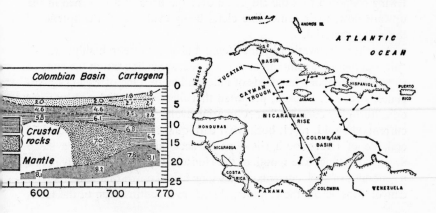

in different locations for carbon-14 dating of the time since the water had been at the surface. A fluxgate magnetometer, towed 400 feet astern, kept a continuous record of the earth's magnetism. This procedure was necessary so that the instrument would be as far as possible from magnetic metals on the ship. The explosion of the *Carnegie* in 1929 had deprived the United States of its one nonmagnetic ship; the only such vessel in operation during the IGY was the Soviet Union's *Zarya.*

When Maurice Ewing reviewed the results of the *Vema* observations, on this and the cruises that preceded and followed it, he was struck by the peculiarities of the ridges that seemed to run down the middle of the oceans, in particular the Atlantic. Detailed observations with echo-sounders showed them to be jagged, mountainous areas, almost invariably with a deep cleft down their center-lines. The plotting of earthquake origins, over the years, had shown that a large number of shallow quakes originate along the ridges. These features seemed to him to support a theory put forward by Vening Meinesz of the Netherlands, a leading authority on gravity and the earth's interior. Meinesz believed that the material deep within the earth, heated by radioactive decay, rises to the surface, spreads out, cools, and then sinks again. These movements, which may be spasmodic, constitute "convection currents" similar to the air movements produced by a stove. The rising motions, according to Meinesz, occur under the oceans and the descending movements under the continents, leaving the lighter continental rocks on the surface as a sort of solid scum. Ewing proposed that the ridges lie over the lines of divergence in the upward flow, their center-line clefts being evidence of the spread of the rising material.

Another observation by the *Vema* and other research ships was of "abyssal plains" as smooth as a glassy sea, spreading out at the ends of submarine canyons hundreds of miles in length. One of Ewing's associates, Bruce C. Heezen, proposed that these were produced by periodic "turbidity currents," or submarine avalanches of mud. Such mud-currents, he said, result both from earthquakes and from the periodic collapse of river-mouth silt deposits accumulating close to a steep downward slope. The mouth of the Hudson River may once have been a generator of such currents. It has long been known that a submerged canyon runs across the continental shelf as a continuation of the Hudson River Valley, but more recent soundings in oceanic depths of two miles or more have shown that the canyon continues for another 200 miles toward the mid-Atlantic, with an abyssal plain at its end. Heezen believes this could have been carved only by turbidity currents. In 1929 an earthquake dislodged submarine avalanches off the Grand Banks, severing about a dozen transatlantic cables. The timing of the breaks suggested that the mud had shot out across the ocean floor at express-train speed.

Meinesz' idea that hot material is slowly inching its way upward under the midocean received support from observations in the Pacific by the Downwind Expedition, which left San Diego October 21, 1957, and returned four months later. It consisted of two ships, the *Horizon* and *Spencer F. Baird,* both operated by the Scripps Institution of Oceanography. They carried a special device that could be dropped to impale itself in the ocean floor and measure the flow of heat from the bowels of the earth into the water. At forty-two locations it was put over the side, with complete success in thirty-two cases. This was believed to be more than the total of all previous heat-flow measurements on the Pacific floor. The results were not unexpected until the ships sailed over the Easter Island Rise, which runs north and south somewhat as does the Mid-Atlantic Ridge. At several points on the Rise the heat flow was five times normal and at four locations in this same area repeated seismic shooting reached no layer with a velocity greater than 7.5 kilometers per second. Elsewhere on the Rise, where there was no unusual heat flow, crustal conditions were normal, with the higher-velocity Moho plainly evident. It was suspected that the upward movement of heat and absence of the Moho might be related to an ascending convection current.

The flow was by no means volcanic in intensity, amounting to about 6.4 microcalories per square centimeter per second. The heat of sunlight is 875,000 times greater. Nevertheless, two islands of volcanic origin have been thrust up from this rise: Easter Island and Sala y Gomez, both of which belong to Chile.

Earlier soundings by casual passers-by had shown shallow points between Easter Island Rise and Peru. The Downwind Expedition found this to be a steep-sided submarine mountain range, rising 10,000 feet from the ocean floor and, in places, to within only 700 feet of the surface. Roger Revelle estimated its length at 1000 miles and its greatest width at 200. "Just imagine," he told Congress, "a discovery of a major feature of the earth's surface in the year 1958 as big as that—a major mountain range." [5]

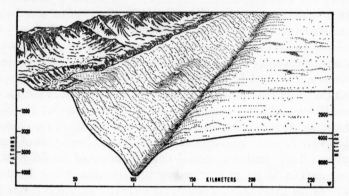

Trench off the coast of Chile (Courtesy Roger Revelle)

The two ships of the expedition also did a careful study of the trench that hugs the west coast of South America, like a downfold to compensate for the upfold of the Andes. Unlike most trenches, whose floors are flat (possibly due to sedimentation or landslides), the bottom of the Peru-Chile trench was almost knife-sharp, as though its formation were in full swing. Off Antofagasta, Chile, seismic shot-lines were run parallel to the trench on its inshore slope, down its center-line, and on its seaward side. The crustal thickness to seaward was 3.7 miles; on the trench axis it was 6.5 miles; and on the inshore slope it was 12.4 miles. Thus the trench lay directly on the transition zone from an oceanic to a continental crust structure. The same sort of measurements were made, spanning the trench off Callao, Peru, with similar results. What particularly interested Revelle was that the heat-flow measurements near the trench were very low—only about one-thirtieth what they had been on the Easter Island Rise. This led him to believe that the trench was produced by a downward creep of cold material that had flowed out from the ocean center and was now slipping down under the granitic mass of the continent:

> We think that this [the Easter Island Rise] is a growing ridge; . . . that there may be . . . a very slow movement of rock upward from the bowels of the earth under the ridge

and a downward movement under the trench—the trench
is actually being pulled or sucked down by the downward
movement [he said].[6]

Such were some of the oceanographic journeys of the IGY. Since
an estimated eighty ships from more than twenty nations took part,
their labors can only be touched upon. They found the topography of
the deep ocean floor to be quite different from anything seen on land.
It is a region divided by cloven ridges and marked here and there by
smooth abyssal plains. Gashes several miles deep slice into the sea
bottom. Canyons zigzag across it. In some areas the floor is encrusted
with an almost solid covering of nodules rich in manganese, copper,
cobalt, and nickel.[7] Strange, truncated peaks known as *guyots* rise
from the bottom. Here and there mountain masses stand as high above
the ocean floor as Everest does above central Asia. All of these features have a story to tell—a chapter of the earth's history. Between
them are the sediments, the fruit of countless years of oceanic life that
has rained its debris upon the bottom. Here there may lie buried the
evidence needed to fill the greatest missing link of all—the first half
of evolution. For some reason, the record of life's development preserved in the continental rocks goes back only to the Cambrian period,
500 million years ago, when the plants and animals had already
reached a rather advanced stage. Most of the phyla—the basic divisions
of the plant and animal kingdoms—had emerged, with the important
exception of the vertebrates. It is estimated that evolution, by then,
had run half its course to the present. The missing record may lie in
the 3000 or 4000 feet of sediment that has accumulated on the ocean
floor. Below this, in many areas, is the "Second Layer" which some
think may be earlier sediment that has solidified. Underneath these
layers is the rock, whose surface, for some unknown reason, is a poor
reflector of seismic waves. It has been suggested that this is the earth's
primordial crust, littered, like the moon, with meteoric debris that
scatters shock waves. Below the crustal rock is the mysterious Moho.

One of the boldest schemes to emerge from the IGY was an American plan to bore down through the sediments and rock to the Moho,
using a floating drill rig in midocean. The ocean site was proposed
because the crust there is so thin. The scheme, with its possibilities
for delving into such problems as the history of climate, the nature
of early life, and the origin of the oceans, continents, and the earth itself,

excited geophysicists throughout the world. Zenkevitch, chairman of the Oceanographic Committee of the Soviet Academy of Sciences, doubted the practicability of drilling from a floating platform (though he conceded that it might succeed on a one-time basis). He preferred the idea of a drill rig resting on the bottom, tended by a small school of self-propelled bathyscaphs.[8] Whichever scheme is finally successful, it seems likely that, by piercing the floor of the ocean, man will soon know far more about his planet—and the history of the life upon it— than he does today.

CHAPTER 22
THE WORLD TREMBLES

On December 4, 1957, Sangidorzh, chairman of the executive committee of Barun Bayan Ulan, was riding his camel along the foot of the northeast slope of Baga Bogdo Mountain, on a spur of the Gobi-Altai Range of Mongolia. It was a frosty day, but here and there on the lower slopes sheep, goats, horses, and camels were still grazing, for winter had been late in coming. North of Ikhe-Bogdo, at 12,400 feet the highest peak of this range, the seventeen-mile expanse of Lake Orok Nur was covered with almost two feet of ice. Desert grasses on dunes near the lake moved gently with the wind. In a nearby valley the Uliasutai River, fed by mountain snows, ran between groves of trees that stretched dainty, leafless branches toward the sky. The river was flanked by two craggy peaks: Halsan Hustin Shovh to the east and Maihan Tolgos to the west. To Sangidorzh, flexing to the rhythm of the camel's gait, the scene was one of great tranquility.

Then suddenly it was as though the world were coming to an end. Camel and rider were thrown to the ground, both stunned and unable to rise for several minutes. The tops of the two mountains, with an awesome roar, tumbled into the narrow valley of the Uliasutai, forming a new mountain on the valley floor 1100 feet high. The dammed-up river penetrated under the mountain to the east and broke out on the other side in a ten-foot waterfall. Landslides stripped the valley of its trees and, with a terrifying sound, the crust of the earth cracked open from Baga Bogdo, where Sangidorzh lay prostrate, to the Bakhar Range, 150 miles to the west. The cleft was six feet deep and from six to twenty feet wide. Another chasm a hundred feet wide opened along the south shore of Orok Nur and the ice on the lake cracked in a number of places, the ice on the southern part of the lake riding twenty feet over the ice to the north. The whole Ikhe-Bogdo Massif, fifty miles long and thousands of feet high, was lifted seven to twenty feet and moved from ten to twelve feet eastward.

As Sangidorzh got to his feet, buried boulders as big as yurts—the collapsible felt huts of the Mongol herders—popped out of the convulsed mountainside and rolled downhill like herds of charging elephants, annihilating the grazing animals. Landslides on Ikhe-Bogdo swept cattle and herders to their deaths. Wintering camps and entire villages vanished under the rubble; wells filled with rocks, plugging the only source of water in entire communities; panic-stricken goats, following each other in headlong flight, fell one after another into the great cracks, then were crushed.[1]

Meanwhile, at the Institut pour la Recherche Scientifique en Afrique Centrale, near the shore of Lake Kivu at Lwiro in the highlands of the Congo, an African was changing the roll of photo-recording paper in a Press-Ewing seismograph.[2] This was a highly sensitive instrument, for instead of inscribing oscillations with a scratchy, friction-retarded pen, it did so with a pinpoint of light, directed onto photographic paper via a mirror. The long-period earth waves produced by distant quakes moved the mirror imperceptibly, making the pinpoint of light shift a detectable amount across the paper. The African had been instructed, after inserting a new roll, to make sure the point of light was properly aligned before closing the cameralike apparatus. To his dismay he could do nothing with the light. It was zigzagging wildly back and forth across the entire instrument. He went to look for Jean Claude De Bremaecker, who was in charge of the seismic observations. De Bremaecker saw in an instant that this was no instrument misbehavior. In some distant place Mother Earth was wreaking terrible destruction.

A quite different sort of instrument had been emplaced in an abandoned gold mine near Isabella in the foothills of California's Sierra Nevada. Devised by Hugo Benioff of the California Institute of Technology, it was capable of measuring compression and stretching of the earth's crust equivalent to a tenth of an inch in 2000 miles.

The apparatus consisted of a horizontal rod of fused quartz some hundred feet long, one end of which was fixed to a pier set into the rock. The rod was suspended by wires in a manner that prevented its sagging but did not impede its horizontal motion. At the unattached end another pier was set in the rock as a reference point. Even an extremely slight horizontal motion of the rod with respect to this second pier could be measured electrically (through changes in relative positions of a magnet and an electric coil).

This device, known as an extensometer or strain seismometer, was able to observe the daily "breathing" of the earth's crust caused by the gravitational pull of the moon and sun—the twice-daily earth tides. These tides alternately stretch and squeeze the crust to a sufficient degree for this device to measure the push and pull on the rock of the tunnel. Since passing earthquake waves also produced strains in the rock, the extensometer could record them as well.

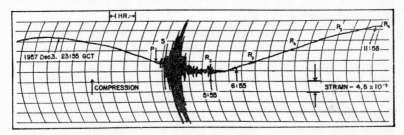

The Gobi-Altai earthquake of December 4, 1957, as recorded by the extensometer in a gold mine near Isabella, California. The smooth curve of the trace shows the strain and relaxation of normal earth tides. For more than eight hours following the quake, Rayleigh waves, circling the earth in opposite directions, could be observed (marked "R").

During the evening of December 3, California time, the rock base of the Sierra Nevada sighed, so to speak, as the tension of the semidiurnal tide was relieved, and this was reflected by a smooth descending curve on the recording trace of the extensometer. Then, about 13 minutes after Sangidorzh bit the dust on Baga Bogdo, there was a slight wiggle, representing a *P* (or compressional) wave that had followed a comparatively direct route via the earth's mantle. (A straight line from Mongolia to California does not pass through the core.) Ten minutes later the arrival of the *S* (or shear) wave, also via a deep path, made more of a wiggle, and then the surface waves began squeezing and stretching the rock, causing the trace to sweep radically from side to side. These waves were of two distinct types: Love waves and Rayleigh waves. In the first, named for their nineteenth-century discoverer, A. E. H. Love, each particle of rock moves sideways, at right angles to the direction of wave motion and in a horizontal plane. The Rayleigh waves, identified by Lord Rayleigh in 1900, move in a vertical plane, each particle rotating backward in an ellipse. The bather who stands waist-deep off a beach and watches a bit of loose seaward as a wave passes will observe this motion, except that the rotation is forward.

The first surface wave to reach California was a Love wave that came from the northwest, flowing through the crust by the shortest route (6500 miles). It was soon followed by a Rayleigh wave. Two hours after the quake, however, a Love wave reached California from the opposite direction, having traveled the long way around the world, via China, India, the Indian Ocean, the seas off Antarctica, Cape Horn, and the southeast Pacific—about 18,300 miles.

Some twenty minutes later a slower-moving Rayleigh wave arrived by the same long arc. By this time the trace had almost smoothed out again, but the crustal waves produced by the initial shock did not stop. They continued their round-the-world journeys in opposite directions, repeatedly passing through the point of their origin and through the Sierra Nevada. The Rayleigh wave approaching California from the south made its second pass five and a half hours after the quake and its third some eight and a half hours after the catastrophe.

Thus did the so-called Gobi-Altai Earthquake, the most destructive of the IGY, manifest itself around the world. Probably no major quake in history had been so widely observed with such a variety of instruments. Seismology, during the IGY, had many objectives. It was used, as has been seen, to measure ice thicknesses in Antarctica and to study the earth's crust beneath the oceans. Seismic studies and observations of gravity and magnetism were the only tools for determining the nature of the earth's deep interior. Finally, it was hoped to learn what causes earthquakes. Prevention does not seem likely, in view of the forces involved, but prediction might be possible if enough were known about them.

In this connection Benioff's strain-measuring instrument was of particular interest for those living in earthquake-ridden areas. Not only was it able to measure passing shock waves and tidal changes in tension, but it could record long-term variations in strain. Presumably an earthquake is preceded by a build-up of stress that continues until the breaking point is reached, whereupon rocks shear and the stress is relieved. The maintenance of long-term records at a number of stations may make it possible to learn the characteristic changes that precede quakes in a certain locality, although such studies may have to continue several centuries for sufficient data to be compiled.

For the IGY Benioff's instrument was installed at two points along the earthquake belt that follows the west coast of South America. In each case a Y-shaped tunnel was dug into the igneous rock so that two quartz rods could be mounted at right angles to one another in the two 100-foot arms of the Y. This provided two-directional information on the crustal strain. One of the installations was excavated by the University of Santiago at San Cristobal, in the outskirts of Santiago, Chile. The other was dug by the Peruvian National Committee for the IGY at Chosica, a small settlement twenty miles from Lima.

Fused quartz was used in the rods because it expands and contracts very little in response to temperature. A special effort was made to limit year-round temperature variations within the tunnel to less than a fraction of a degree.[3]

Another IGY seismic program sought to see how deep are the roots of the Andes. In general the thickness of the earth's crust increases in proportion to the elevation of the surface. The lowest area, on the ocean floor, has the thinnest crust. The thickest part of the crust lies beneath mountain ranges. All portions of the crust are thought to "float" on the underlying mantle, much as ice floats on the sea. A floe one foot high draws about eight feet of water; an iceberg 100 feet high extends 800 feet below the surface. Thus, it was thought, the Rocky Mountains, whose height exceeds that of the Appalachians by thousands of feet, should have foundations that are deeper by many miles. However, prior to the IGY, a puzzling discovery was made by expeditions of the Carnegie Institution of Washington. In 1954 a Carnegie field party, working in Arizona, New Mexico, and Utah, recorded strong reflections of *P* waves from the Moho under the high Colorado Plateau and found that the crustal thickness there was not substantially greater than that under the much lower plains and mountains of the eastern United States. The next year a similar situation was found on an expedition that studied the even higher mountains of Alaska. The crust was only eighteen to twenty-two miles thick. The "floatation" of the earth's crust had been well established in terms of the widely observed rebound after the melting of an ice sheet. Why, then, didn't these great mountain ranges sink into the mantle? It was suggested that they had roots—perhaps networks of narrow veins of the lighter crustal rock that penetrated some 100 miles into the mantle.

The copper mines of Peru and Chile offered what seemed an excellent opportunity to see if any evidence could be found of such roots underneath the Andes. At these mines single shots of forty to sixty tons of dynamite are fired almost daily, providing artificial earthquakes. The Andes were of particular interest in that, like the Rockies, they are associated with a large plateau area, the Altiplano. This means that thousands of cubic miles of rock lie high above the normal level of the continent.

The Carnegie Andes Expedition assembled at Lima on August 14, 1957, with six trucks and eight men. In the next three months recordings were made at more than 200 sites in the mountains of Peru, Bolivia and Chile. Shock waves from close to sixty mining blasts were observed, using radio to signal the exact time of each shot. Most of the blasts were at the Toquepala Mine of the Southern Peru Copper Corporation, but a number of the recorded shots were also fired at the Chuquicamata Mine of the Chile Exploration Company. Both mines are more than 10,000 feet above sea level.

Seismic recorders were set up, at one time or another, along ten lines radiating from the Peruvian site—an operation made particularly difficult by the many truck breakdowns on remote high Andean trails. What was strange, however, was that, despite the extremely heavy

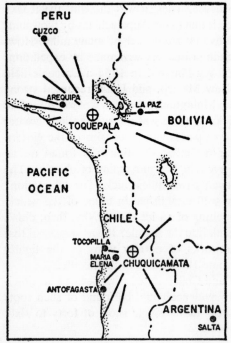

Regions in Peru, Chile, and Bolivia investigated during Carnegie Institute Andes Expedition. Observations of seismic waves from explosions in mines at Toquepala and Chuquicamata were made approximately along the radial lines. (National Academy of Sciences)

blasts, no reflections or first refractions were obtained from the base of the crust beneath the mountains or the Altiplano. The same was true of the observations along some seven lines radiating from the Chilean site, which is one of the world's largest copper mines. The only region where such refractions were obtained was on the western flank of the Altiplano, where the profile lines ran parallel to the structural grain of the mountains. In this area a crustal thickness of thirty-five miles was calculated.

Some so-called second-arrival refractions from directly under the Altiplano suggested a depth of forty miles under Peru and forty-three miles under northern Chile, but this result was viewed with suspicion. The failure of such heavy blasts to produce adequate reflections or refractions off the Moho was, the Carnegie group reported, "without precedent elsewhere." [4] It was proposed that this might be due to the volcanic structure of the mountains whose countless interfaces, at random angles, dispersed the shock waves until they were unrecognizable.[5]

When the Carnegie Expedition had completed its work, it gave most of its trucks and equipment to the Geophysical Institutes of the University of Chile and of San Marcos University in Peru for further IGY observations.

The Carnegie group, led by Merle A. Tuve, decided, when the IGY was over, that the problem of deep mountain roots had, in large measure, "evaporated," not through the discovery of such roots, but by a reassessment of the mantle density.[6] An iceberg floats deep because it is only slightly less dense than water. If it were placed in mercury, which is an extremely dense liquid, it would ride high. By

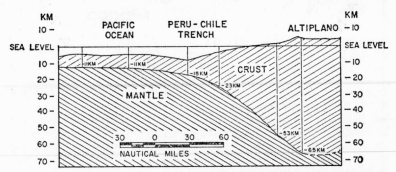

Cross section of transition zone between South America and Pacific basin, based on data from the Scripps and Carnegie Expeditions. (National Academy of Sciences)

1959 a number of geophysicists had come to the view that the earth's mantle is far denser than had been supposed (an upper-mantle density 3.27 times that of water, compared to 2.5 or 2.6 times water density for the crustal rocks resting on it). If this is so, the observed crustal thickness under the Rockies and the Alaskan mountains is not far different from what it should be, without any need for deep-reaching roots.

Seismic profiles in North America during the IGY. The Calgary and Ripple Rock profiles were part of the Canadian IGY program; the Great Salt Lake and Nevada measurements, by the University of Utah and the United States government respectively, were not in the IGY program but are of interest because they help fill in the crustal-structure picture for North America; all other profiles were part of the United States IGY program. (National Academy of Sciences)

Extensive IGY seismic exploration was carried out in North America by the University of Wisconsin under the direction of George P. Woollard. Two profiles were run, at right angles to each other, across Wisconsin and part of Michigan, another was done in Arkansas, and a fourth in Mexico. Canadian studies were carried out near Calgary and in connection with the blasting of Ripple Rock, a submerged hazard to navigation straddling one of the channels leading to Vancouver, British Columbia. Demolition of the rock on April 5, 1958, was achieved by one of the largest nonnuclear explosions to that time.

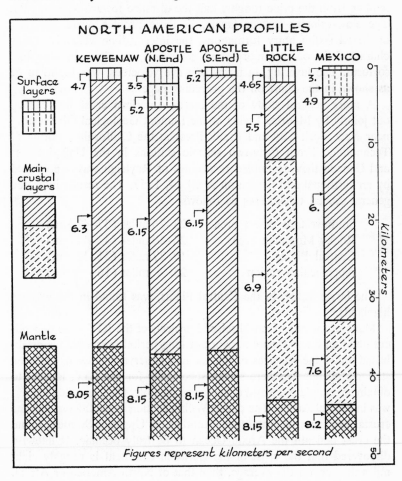

Thanks to the assistance of a Coast Guard craft, the Wisconsin group was able to fire many of its shots under the waters of Lake Superior, thus achieving an excellent energy coupling between the explosion and the earth's crust. The jolt imparted by 750 pounds of nitramon could be observed at distances greater than 170 miles—in contrast to the situation in the Andes, where sixty-ton shots could not be detected beyond about 140 miles. The Mexican profile was based on blasts in open-pit mining near Durango, midway between Mexico City and Arizona, and the observations were made along a line extending from the mine roughly half the distance toward Mexico City. The slow-velocity surface layers, in these profiles, were generally unaltered sedimentary formations, the intermediate velocities being characteristic of metamorphosed sediments, granites, basalts, and so forth. The layering, in terms of wave velocities, was found to be as shown in the chart on the preceding page.[7]

A more general study of the North American crust was carried out jointly by Maurice Ewing at the Lamont Geological Observatory near New York City and Frank Press at the California Institute of Technology. From forty-two seismic stations in the United States and Canada they assembled recordings of Rayleigh waves produced by an earthquake in Samoa on April 14, 1957. The results indicated general crustal thicknesses as follows:

Southwestern desert area	23–26 miles (37–42 km.)
Rocky Mountain area	26–30 miles (42–48 km.)
Central Plains	19–27 miles (31–43 km.)
Appalachian region	25 miles (16 km.)

The larger value, in the Central Plains, was found in the western highlands.[8]

Many of the most fruitful seismic projects of the IGY were dependent upon an international network of long-period seismographs established under the auspices of the Lamont observatory. Of its eighteen stations, all but five were set up specifically for the IGY, located to obtain as complete a world coverage as possible. One, as noted earlier, was in central Africa. The one at Wilkes Station helped determine the crustal thickness of Antarctica. Another, at Uppsala, Sweden, found the crust beneath the Arctic Ocean to be truly oceanic. It likewise discovered that the crust of the Eurasian continent is roughly eight miles thicker, on the average, than that of North America or Africa.

This seismograph also observed one of the most remarkable earthquakes of recent times. On July 9, 1958, three trolling boats, each about forty feet long, were anchored in Lituya Bay on the coast of southeastern Alaska. Between them and the open sea was a mile-long spit of land and a narrow harbor entrance. About 10:18 P.M., which was close to sunset, Howard G. Ulrich and his seven-year-old son were awakened by a violent rocking. Soon after he ran on deck there was a "deafening crash" at the head of the bay, six miles to the northeast. As calculated later, some 90 million tons of rock had fallen from a mountain into the bay, knocking off the end of Lituya Glacier and producing a wave that swept 1720 feet up a mountain spur on the opposite shore. Ulrich saw to his horror that a wall of water 100 feet high was sweeping down the bay, denuding the slopes on either side down to bed rock. The wave front seemed to be very steep, but the boat, after snapping its anchor chain, rode it out.

Another of the boats, manned by Mr. and Mrs. William A. Swanson, was carried completely across the spit of land and smashed on the ocean floor. They escaped in a skiff. Mr. and Mrs. Orville Wagner, in the third boat, were trying to reach the entrance, but the craft and its occupants vanished.

At this time, on the beach at Khantaak Island, about 100 miles up the coast, John Williams, the postmaster of Yakutat, and his wife were saying goodbye to Mrs. Jeanne Welsh Walton, president of the Bellingham Canning Company. They shoved off in their boat and Mrs. Walton turned to walk up the beach to Robert Tibbles of the Federal Aviation Agency and his wife. The party of five had been berry-picking on the island. As Williams headed for Yakutat, his wife called to him that the trees on the island were swaying. They looked back and saw a wave coming toward them so high that it hid the trees on the island. Williams gunned the engine and the wave diminished before it overtook them. The three left standing on the shore—and the shore itself—were never seen again. A boat from Mrs. Walton's company reached the island two hours later and found that part of it had vanished. The crew measured seventy-five feet of water in the area where Mrs. Walton had last been seen.

Meanwhile, as the earth heaved, the great rolling hangar doors at Yakutat airport banged against each other like giant cymbals. A moving picture was being shown at the Coast Guard loran station near by. The picture began swinging up and down, showing first on the ceiling, then on the floor. The viewers, trying to escape, were thrown from side to side against the corridor walls. At Strawberry Point, to the east, Mrs. Edith Renner heard her small son screaming and trying to crawl up the beach toward her. Big waves were approaching, but because of a rotational movement of the ground she could not move toward her child. On the East River Mr. and Mrs. Rudy Isler and Mr. and Mrs. John Lowenstein found themselves amidst fissures that opened and closed rapidly on all sides. Mrs. Lowenstein tried to run toward the river, but a crack opened before her. She turned back, to find another behind her. Mr. Isler fell into a crack four feet deep, but could not get out because of the violent ground motion, despite his fear that the cleft would close on him. Along the coast and river valleys countless thousands of sandblows erupted like so many geysers, produced by the accordion-like motions of the earth's crust. Each left a crater of sand. Sheets of water shot up from cracks. Rivers drained dry one moment, then flooded the next. In some places water spouts were so numerous that the landscape seemed to be boiling.

Almost immediately after the quake a number of scientists began to study it. Don J. Miller of the United States Geological Survey flew over Lituya Bay the next morning in a float plane, but the water was so filled with logs and other debris that a landing was impossible. Some later dismissed as incredible the report that the wave reached an elevation of 1720 feet on a mountain alongside the bay. However investigators climbed to the top of the denuded area and found that large trees, stripped of bark, had been hurled upward by the water, which had partially crossed the spur and flowed down the other side. It was thought to have been the highest "wave swash" on record.

The quake was clearly caused by movement in the Fairweather Fault that parallels the coast for 115 miles. Near the head of the bay it was found that the oceanic side of this fault had moved, jerkily, 21.5 feet to the northwest, relative to the opposite side, and had risen 3.5 feet. The lateral movement, at one point, was clearly shown by a strip of grass, one end of which had been displaced that distance.[9]

The long-period seismograph at Uppsala, which was capable of detecting waves whose crests flowed past at intervals as great as ten minutes or more, was able to record Rayleigh mantle waves originating at Lituya Bay that made six passages around the world. The wave rhythm suggested that the earth had been jarred into free vibration, like a ringing glass—a phenomenon that had been predicted by theoretical studies.

Another product of the long-period seismographs was the discovery of a low-velocity layer in the mantle, extending about 125 miles beneath the continents and thirty miles under the oceans. Thus, the differentiation between oceans and continents reaches far more deeply into the earth than was previously supposed.[10]

The IGY initiated a long-overdue expansion and modernization of earthquake observations. The great powers' need for monitoring each other's nuclear explosions stimulated the postwar establishment of secret seismic networks, but the IGY led to the setting up of more than 100 new stations, raising the world's overt total to 334, operated by fifty-five nations. Many of the new ones were in areas that had been completely devoid of seismographs—a dozen in the Arctic and eighteen in the Antarctic. The science had come a long way from the day in April, 1889, when an instrument in Potsdam, Germany, recorded a Japanese earthquake—the first such long-range observation.

In addition to the building of new stations, old ones were reactivated, among them the former French observatory at Phu-Lien, noted for its research on typhoons before it was destroyed in the Indo-China War. The Poles sent an IGY expedition to work with the new Soviet-oriented regime in North Vietnam. The Phu-Lien observatory was expanded into a seismic base as well as a weather station. Members of the expedition hiked up through the tropical rain forest, accompanied by a score of Vietnamese, to reconstruct an abandoned weather and magnetic station at Cha-Pa in the Annamite Cordillera. Three bamboo huts were erected to shelter the men and instruments.

The mainland Chinese, in spite of their official withdrawal from the IGY, carried out a greatly expanded program of seismic observations since it was essential to know the distribution of earthquake centers in planning construction of the dams, bridges, and other structures so necessary to Chinese industrialization. This mapping of "seismicity" was an important objective of the IGY program. Some 80 per cent of all quakes occur around the rim of the Pacific, and most of the rest originate along well-defined lines, such as those of the East Indies, the Himalaya-Caucasus-Mediterranean axis, and the midocean ridges. In some cases an examination of computed earthquake centers suggested the existence of still-undiscovered ridges in less traveled parts of the ocean. There also proved to be hotbeds of earthquake activity, such as an area, twelve miles in diameter, that is situated 137 miles beneath the mountains of the Hindu Kush and has generated 100 major earthquakes in half a century.

Another area of inquiry was that of microseisms—tiny tremors apparently imparted to the earth by storm waves at sea. How waves on the surface transmit their energy to the earth's crust, several miles below, is still a mystery to those studying ocean dynamics. Microseisms were monitored by 137 stations, some of them linked into triangles in an effort to compare their records and locate storms at sea.

The Soviet program in seismology was one of the most ambitious undertakings of that country during the IGY. Extensive use was made of explosions, both at sea and ashore. The Russians were driven by two powerful motivations: one was to map the entire crust of the earth beneath their territory as a guide in their search for natural resources; the other was to gain an understanding of the stupendous forces at work along the boundary between the Pacific Ocean basin and the Kurile-Kamchatka frontier of the Asiatic land mass. This was a region of deep-seated crustal movements that produce devastating earthquakes, tsunamis (tidal waves), and volcanoes that explode with little or no warning. It was one of these movements that leveled Tokyo on September 1, 1923, with the loss of 143,000 lives. On March 30, 1956, Bezymyanny, a volcanic mountain on Kamchatka, blew two cubic miles of rock from its summit, sending a dust cloud more than twenty-five miles into the sky. Bolts of lightning jabbed wildly at the terrain—a phenomenon typical of such events—and the falling ash combined with steam, rain, and snow to produce avalanches of mud that raced fifty miles down a nearby valley, sweeping all before it. It was such a mud flow, descending Mount Vesuvius at about sixty miles an hour, that is believed to have caught the inhabitants of Herculaneum in A.D. 79.

The Russians studied *S* (shear) waves traveling from Japanese earthquakes through the roots of the massif of which Bezymyanny is a part. Since such waves do not traverse a liquid, they could be used to locate the reservoir of molten lava beneath the mountain. The Russians reported that it extended to a depth of about thirty-five miles.

The compilation of earthquake records over many years showed that the sources of quakes along the periphery of the Asian continent slope downward from the trenches on the ocean floor, where quakes are quite shallow, to beneath the mainland, where they originate at depths of 400 and 450 miles. This is well down within the mantle, indicating that, whatever the nature of the margin between oceans and continents, it extends to great depth. To adherents of the convection theory this slope of earthquake centers seems to mark the area where the downflowing mantle scrapes against stagnant rock under the continents. Such slopes have been observed elsewhere on the Pacific perimeter—for example, along the coast of Chile.

The directions in which seismogram traces first move—the so-called first motion—make it possible, as a rule, to determine the fault plane and the direction of motion when it ruptures. About 80 per cent of the quakes originating around the Pacific basin appear to be by horizontal "strike-slip" faulting. This has led Hugo Benioff to make the startling proposal that the entire Pacific basin may be rotating in a counterclockwise direction, like a backward-running gramophone turntable. The Alaskan earthquake of 1958 was, in fact, produced by just such a movement. Benioff estimates that the annual faulting around the Pacific perimeter is sufficient for the ocean floor to complete one revolution in 3 billion years.[11] The proposed rotational motion also calls to mind the calculations of Stommel, who explained the concentration of ocean currents along the western shores of the oceans in terms of the earth's rotation. Might this principle, applied to the earth's crust, explain the depth of the trenches along the western edge of the Pacific basin?

The direction of first seismograph motion, as observed at widely scattered stations, is also significant in the all-important question of distinguishing underground nuclear explosions from natural earthquakes. A considerable portion of IGY seismic work was applicable to this problem, which stood as a primary obstacle to the conclusion of an agreement banning all nuclear blasts. During the IGY large underground explosions that provided seismic data were fired in both East and West. On September 19, 1957, the United States detonated the "Rainier" explosion, an atomic bomb in the range of one to three kilotons set off at a depth of 800 feet in a Nevada hill. The Canadians fired the Ripple Rock blast, mentioned earlier, and the Russians set off two nonnuclear explosions in the same energy range as Rainier. One, consisting of 1000 tons of ammonite, was detonated in an abandoned mine shaft that ran 130 feet into clay deposits near the city of Tashkent. It blew a crater more than 150 feet deep and 300 feet wide when fired on December 19, 1957. Seismologists from the Mathematics and Mechanics Institute of the Academy of Sciences of the Uzbek SSR calculated from the results that Tashkent stands on loess and other soils three miles deep, underlain by nineteen miles of granite and nine miles of basalt.[12]

Hugo Benioff's compilation of earthquake movements along the fault lines that encircle the Pacific. He believes the ocean floor is rotating counterclockwise in respect to the surrounding land masses at a rate of roughly one revolution per three billion years.

The second big Soviet shot, fired the following March 25, was designed to excavate a 3600-foot river channel at Pokrovsk-Uralsky in the Ural Mountains. In this case 3100 tons of ammonite were distributed among thirty-one pits dug thirty to fifty feet into the rock. This shock was recorded at points in Europe, Asia, Africa, and the United States. The most distant site that detected a *P* wave was

Eureka, Nevada, 5580 miles away via the direct route through the earth's interior.

The Russians found that there was no difficulty in distinguishing explosions of this magnitude from natural earthquakes.[13] However, at the time, American scientists had not come forward with the "de-coupling" idea that threw the Geneva talks on a cessation of nuclear test explosions into turmoil. The Wisconsin group, by firing its shots under water in Lake Superior, had gained a highly efficient coupling between the energy of the explosion and the earth's crust, but it was found that, by firing in a cavern, the reverse could be achieved—a de-coupling that would muffle the explosion so that it produced only a fraction of the jar that it normally would. On the other hand Teak and Orange, the hydrogen bombs fired above Johnston Island, were clearly recorded by the long-period seismographs at the Lamont observatory. This was a remarkable coupling, for enough energy was delivered from space to the Pacific Ocean floor to send a crustal wave as far as the Hudson River Valley.[14]

Until the IGY, seismology had been one of the more academic— and neglected—of the sciences. Its chief practical objective seemed to be the prediction of earthquakes that, occasionally, wipe out an entire city. Then, suddenly, specialists in this sleepy science found that their help was urgently needed in preventing a holocaust that could destroy all cities. The issue of a test suspension—and, indirectly, of disarmament and a stable peace—seemed in the 1960's to hang upon the ingenuity of seismologists. It was their task to find a way to detect underground nuclear blasts sufficiently reliable so that no one would risk being caught in a violation.

CHAPTER 23
OUR PEARLIKE PLANET

At any point on the earth a rock falls faster at one hour of the day than at another. Likewise, as a rule, a plumb line does not hang precisely straight down. A 200-pound man weighs one pound more at the North Pole than he does at the equator. Twice daily the entire city of New York, from the clustered towers of lower Manhattan to the George Washington Bridge, moves up and down several inches. These seeming deviations from the rules of nature are evident through careful measurements of gravity and are manifestations of irregularities and changes in the shape of the earth.

Gravity is by far the weakest of the four fundamental forces in nature. The most powerful is the "strong interaction" that holds together the nucleus of the atom. Electromagnetic force ranks second in strength; the "weak interactions" between nuclear particles rank third. Gravity is so weak that it requires a lump of matter as big as the earth to exert the force that makes a baseball fall back to the outfield.

During the IGY gravity was measured in three different ways: through precise timing of pendulum swings, through measurements of gravity-induced tension on a spring (as in a spring scale), and by study of satellite orbits. Prior to the IGY, S. P. Worden of Houston, Texas, had developed an instrument which measured gravity with great precision by spring tension—the Worden gravimeter. It was easily carried and a reading could be made in five minutes. Originally designed for oil prospecting, a modified version was developed for scientific gravity surveys. A highly sensitive gravimeter could detect changes of about one-billionth the force of gravity at the earth's surface, making it possible to record tidal movement of the crust amounting to only one-twelfth of an inch. On a test run in Hawaii it observed a daily earth tide of about four inches. It was this type of instrument that was used by the expeditions in Antarctica to chart terrain under the ice.

One of the Worden gravimeter's weaknesses was a slow relaxation of its spring. This "instrument drift" had to be corrected by checking against standard gravity measurements at fixed locations, and one of the objectives of the IGY was to establish a network of such standards, primarily at airports, where they would be readily available. During the IGY gravity standards were established at some 3000 points in eighty-five countries, although large gaps remained.

The pendulum was the most reliable device for such work since, although it could not be read with the great precision of the gravimeter, it was independent of the vagaries of a spring. Pendulum measurements were tedious, taking about two days at each site. The apparatus used by the United States consisted of two pendulums, swinging in opposite phase to minimize sway in their support. They were suspended on knife-edges, and the atmosphere within their airtight cases was kept dry and at constant pressure and temperature to avoid variation in air drag and in length of the pendulums. The timing was done with a crystal-regulated chronometer, checked against radio time signals from Washington and read from an electronic digital recorder.[1] The equipment for such pendulum observations weighed 700 pounds. Prior to the IGY, Woollard's group at the University of Wisconsin had carried out a string of pendulum measurements from Fairbanks, Alaska, to Mexico City. During the IGY itself this was extended north to Point Barrow and the American drifting stations on the Arctic Ocean, and southward to Punta Arenas, at the southern tip of South America. Another north-south line was run from Hokkaido, the northernmost island of Japan, through Australia and New Zealand to McMurdo Sound, Antarctica.

While gravity measurements are useful to prospectors in that their short-range variations reflect changes in rock structure beneath the surface, on a broader scale they reveal the shape of the earth. If the world were all covered by dry land, it might be possible to survey it with sufficient accuracy to determine its shape. But since most of it is ocean, this has been impossible. When the IGY began, the relative positions of the continents had not been determined with precision because of the uncertainty regarding the earth's shape and the direction of gravity at any point. Surveyors sighting on sun, moon, and stars use a bubble level or plumb line to establish the horizontal, but because of irregularities in the earth's shape, in its density and other factors, the plumb bob does not necessarily point toward the earth's center;

likewise a level does not always indicate the true horizontal. These errors, though slight, are enough to limit the accuracy of position determinations made by observing celestial bodies.

In the 1920s Vening Meinesz began making gravity measurements at sea, carrying his delicate triple pendulums in a submarine. His group in the Netherlands continued this work into the IGY, but meanwhile a new gravimeter had been developed in Germany that could be used on the deck of a rolling ship. After modification by J. Lamar Worzel at the Lamont Geological Observatory, it was used during the IGY and instruments of this type, as well as a more recent airborne variety, ultimately should make possible the world-wide charting of gravity.[2]

Meanwhile, several other approaches were made to the problem of the earth's shape and the precise three-dimensional determination of locations on its surface. One of these employed a device invented by the director of the Paris Observatory, André L. Danjon, and known to the world's astronomers as the Danjon Impersonal Astrolabe. It measured the elevation of a star above the "horizontal" by a method that eliminated the human errors inherent in ordinary star sights. The sextant used by ship navigators is equipped with mirrors that can be swung until the image of a star is brought down to coincide with the horizon. This determines the elevation angle of the star at a moment determined by stop-watch and chronometer. In the Danjon Impersonal Astrolabe the horizontal is established by mirroring the star image in a pool of mercury (kept "level" by gravity). Another image of the same star is directed through a 60° prism and its elevation angle is measured automatically when the two images come into coincidence. This made it possible to determine latitude and longitude to within about five feet, apart from the error introduced by gravity variations. Assuming that the latter remained constant at a given location, such observations would be accurate enough to settle, ultimately, the long-standing question of continental drift.

Two other astronomical programs were independent of gravity. One of them employed a device (the dual-rate moon position camera) developed at the Naval Observatory in Washington by William Markowitz. In essence what it did was photograph the moon, at a given instant, against a background of stars. This made it possible to compute lines of position from the center of the earth, through the camera, past the edge of the moon, to known points in the heavens.

The problem was to obtain such photographs, since the brightness of the moon hides the stars and its motion against the starry background is quite rapid. These difficulties were overcome by an optical system that dimmed the moon's brilliance and halted its motion against the backdrop of stars sufficiently long for it to be photographed in its precise position relative to the stars at a known instant of time. A series of such observations made it possible, by rather complex computations, to determine the observatory's position with respect to the center of the earth, accurate to within 100 or 200 feet. In addition to the prototype at the Naval Observatory, cameras of this design were delivered to the observatories at Greenwich, Paris, and seventeen other points around the world.

The other position-determining program that was independent of gravity made use of a camera capable of photographing a fast-moving ping-pong ball at a range equivalent to the distance from Boston to Baltimore. Satellite pictures taken by this remarkable device, the Baker-Nunn camera, could be processed in much the same manner as the moon photos, to determine the observatory's position in terms of the earth's center.

The camera was designed to record stars and satellites so faint they would be invisible to the naked eye. To achieve adequate exposure times for such dim targets, it alternately swung with the swift motion of the satellite (comparable to that of a passing aircraft) and then slowed to the imperceptible pace of the stars. The camera operators required sufficient advance knowledge of the satellite orbit to allow them to aim the camera within three degrees of its path and set the tracking system to follow its flight. The camera recorded the time to within one-thousandth of a second. This was achieved by a rapidly rotating barrel that obscured the sky for an instant on each rotation, chopping each exposure into four segments. During one of these chops a stroboscopic flash illuminated a clock. The tracking system was capable of eliminating all but about 1 per cent of the satellite's motion and the movement that remained produced a stubby streak, cut into four parts. Sometimes, as in the picture of Vanguard I in the first group of photographs in this book, the barrel timer was not used.

A dozen of these cameras were installed for the IGY. The first was placed at Organ Pass, New Mexico, in November, 1957, and the others encircled the world in the lower latitudes from which the Vanguard satellites would be visible. Their locations were:

Olifantsfontein, South Africa	Shiraz, Iran
Woomera, Australia	Curaçao, N.W.I.
Cádiz, Spain	Hobe Sound, Florida
Tokyo, Japan	Villa Dolores, Argentina
Naini Tal, India	Haleakala, Hawaii
Arequipa, Peru	

Australia, India, and Japan assumed complete responsibility for operating the stations within their territory, while the other nations depended upon varying degrees of assistance from the United States. By a special communications network the Smithsonian Astrophysical Observatory in Cambridge, Massachusetts, notified each observatory of the proper camera settings for each visible pass.

The cameras obtained photographs of such tiny targets as the grapefruit-sized Vanguard I, although this satellite was far beyond the range of human vision. The Baker-Nunns were not the only cameras used in satellite observations. The Soviet Union had an extensive photography program (see map on page 71) and several countries used regular astronomical cameras. Likewise, amateurs in many parts of the world obtained pictures of the brighter passes. One of their methods simply involved jarring the camera in pace with radio time signals. The satellite path through the stars then appeared as a streak, broken by evenly-spaced wiggles representing moments in time.

No other observations, however, seem to have approached the high precision obtained by the Baker-Nunn cameras. Computations of position from their photographs proved to be complex and prolonged, and not until 1960 did some of the results begin to appear. Nevertheless, soon after the early satellites were launched, tracking data of sufficient accuracy for study of the earth's figure began to be issued by the Vanguard project's Minitrack system.

The determination of the earth's shape, from satellite observations, was based on the effectiveness of gravity in holding the vehicle in orbit. If the earth were a completely homogeneous mass, shaped purely by its own gravity and the centrifugal force of its rotation, its configuration could be described in simple mathematical terms. Because of its spin, the equatorial region should bulge slightly, causing the diameter at the equator to be roughly twenty-seven miles greater than it is from pole to pole and making a man heavier at the poles than he is in low latitudes. The shape of the earth conforms almost exactly to this pattern—but not quite.

Observation of the smallest of IGY satellites by the fence of Mini-track stations in North and South America showed the world to be slightly asymmetrical. This was the vehicle, Vanguard I, that also proved its worth by disclosing the day-to-day variations in density of gas at high elevations. Its perigee (low point of orbit) migrated slowly around the earth, taking some eighty-two days for a complete circuit. This was to be expected, but the perigee dipped lower when it was north of the equator than when it was to the south, indicating a lack of symmetry in the earth's shape.

John A. O'Keefe of the National Aeronautics and Space Administration and two colleagues calculated that, to account for the behavior of Vanguard I, there must be an excess of matter at the north end of

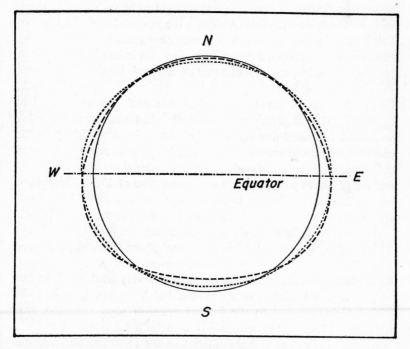

Our "pear-shaped" earth. The solid line is a perfect circle. The dotted line represents the traditional view of an earth symmetrically flattened at the poles. The dashed line shows the deviation from this pattern detected by studying the orbit of Vanguard I. The distortions are greatly exaggerated. Drawn to scale, all three circles would appear round.

the earth equivalent to a layer fifty feet thick and as large as the Atlantic Ocean, with a comparable deficiency of matter at the south end.[3] It was also estimated that there was a deficiency of about twenty-five feet in sea level in temperate northern latitudes and an equivalent excess in temperate southern latitudes. The combined effect of these distortions was a tendency toward a pear shape, although the digression from symmetry was small compared to the well-known polar flattening. Even the latter is so slight, in terms of the world's total size, that, if the earth were seen on the scale of a schoolroom globe, it would look perfectly round.

Nevertheless the discovery of this distortion, announced at the annual meeting of the American Physical Society in New York, January 28, 1959, raised fundamental problems with regard to the earth's interior. The fluidity of the earth was thought to be such that its shape must be highly symmetrical. Although the observed variations in surface level were small, they covered such large areas that vast amounts of material were involved. What kept the world from readjusting to its "proper" shape? Some suggested that the antarctic ice sheet had shrunk so fast that the crust of the earth had not yet had time to spring back. Others felt the asymmetry supported Meinesz' convection current hypothesis (described on page 370). Arthur L. Licht, one of O'Keefe's associates, estimated that six "cells" of circulating material within the earth's mantle could account for sags and bulges even more pronounced than those observed. In his calculation the material moved at about one and a half inches per year, with a turnover time of 175 million years, but the frictional resistance in the nonliquid mantle would be so massive, Licht said, that it was hard to see how such currents could flow.[4]

Asymmetry of the earth did not seem to account for all of the peculiarities of the Vanguard I orbit, and more refined calculations showed that still another perturbing influence was at work, namely sunlight. Light exerts pressure somewhat like that of a very weak wind. In our environment it is almost unobservable, but Vanguard I, in its swift orbital flight, exposed to the full spectrum of solar radiation, was sufficiently influenced by its pressure to suffer a detectable effect.[5]

Another indication that the interior of the earth did not conform to the symmetrical pattern shown in textbooks came from observations of Sputnik III. As noted in the discussion of Project Argus (Chapter 8), the intensity of the earth's magnetism, as observed on its surface, varies from place to place. It is weakest near Rio de Janeiro (less than .250 oersteds) and strongest in the vicinity of Antarctica south of New Zealand (more than .720 oersteds). However there are other anomalies, or marked irregularities, such as the low intensity near Capetown (less than .310 oersteds) and the Great Siberian Anomaly, with a high reading of more than .630 oersteds, centered near the mouth of the Lena River.

It was thought by many that these anomalies were due to deposits of magnetic minerals within the earth's crust. If so, their influence would decrease rapidly with elevation. However, the intensity of the Great Siberian Anomaly proved to be no more diluted, at the height of Sputnik III, than was the general magnetism of the earth, indicating that whatever caused it lay deep within our planet.[6]

It has been proposed that these anomalies may be manifestations of convection currents, not within the mantle, but deeper down in the liquid core, where some believe the flow of material acts like a dynamo, producing the chief component of the earth's magnetism. In any case the IGY left students of the earth with clues to formidable activity within its interior: earthquakes, volcanoes, island arcs, changing trenches, midocean ridges, the pearlike distortion of the earth's shape, oceanic basins, and the continents themselves. What was lacking was an adequate theory to account for them all.

CHAPTER 24
THE HARVEST

No one nation can determine adequately how deep the oceans flow, how high the air extends, how round the world is. Only together can the inhabitants of this planet learn its secrets and conquer its heartless inhospitality. The free exchange of data was, therefore, an essential ingredient of the IGY. One of the unfortunate aspects of the Second Polar Year had been the loss of a substantial portion of its results, partly through delays in their assembly and in part because of the destruction in World War II. It was to avoid a repetition of this calamity that three widely separated World Data Centers were provided for the IGY. Furthermore, delivery deadlines were set for the various types of data, taking into consideration problems of correction and analysis, as well as the delays inherent in the slow return of polar expeditions. The IGY Coordinator, Vice-Admiral Sir Archibald Day, prodded the various nations to keep up the flow and, although the schedules proved somewhat optimistic, the IGY harvest steadily accumulated at the Data Centers. The delays that did occur were generally of nonpolitical origin.

Particularly gratifying to western scientists was the extensive flow of material from the Soviet Union. Solar data from remote Soviet observatories sometimes reached the assembly point in Colorado before comparable observations from sites in the United States. There also was a full delivery of data in almost all the other IGY sciences. Harry Wexler of the Weather Bureau told Congress that the Soviet meteorological reports were "just as complete as the material we sent to them." [1] He said the Russians had gone a step further by sending their weather records for World War II. These had long been sought by the United States to complete a set of weather maps for the entire Northern Hemisphere from 1899 to the present.

It was almost as though the world of science had forgotten the Cold War—with one important exception: the exchange of data on rockets and satellites. The first Sputniks were launched by the Soviet Union's newest and most powerful weapon, its intercontinental ballistic missile. This meant that, while Soviet scientists were permitted to publish specific results of their space experiments, there were strict limitations on what they could say about the satellite-launching vehicle, including the final-stage rocket that went into orbit. Nor were they allowed, during the IGY, to make public the orbital elements—the mathematical characteristics of the orbit helpful to anyone who wished to aim a telescope or radar antenna in anticipation of a pass. Possibly this was because the military thought these elements could be used to run the orbit backward and pinpoint the launching site. Actually the location, near Kapustin Yar north of the Caspian Sea, seems to have been well monitored by the large American radar in Turkey.

What made matters more difficult was the Soviet security doctrine that apparently forbids anyone to admit that an item of information is secret. An effective way to keep a secret is to conceal its very existence, but this sometimes placed the Soviet scientists in embarrassing situations. Such a case was described in the American journal *Science* following the final CSAGI conference in Moscow in July–August, 1958. Some of the American delegates asked if they could visit the Soviet orbit-computing center that had been mentioned in a *Pravda* article on the launching of Sputnik III.

> The American scientists felt justified in seeking to make this visit [*Science* reported] since in September 1957 Soviet scientists had visited the Vanguard computing center. After some jockeying, arrangements for the visit were concluded. But when the appointed day arrived, the Americans found themselves inspecting not the orbit computing center but instead an institute for computer development.[2]

One of the sorriest products of Cold War thinking was the episode of the "stolen satellite." Orbital analyses of the Sputnik I rocket indicated that it would probably fall about December 1, 1957. The Smithsonian Astrophysical Observatory asked all of its Moonwatch stations and any other willing observers to keep a lookout for its fiery end. About one minute after its last expected pass over Alaska, a flaming object streaked across the sky. The Geophysical Institute at College, headquarters of the satellite watch in central Alaska, was deluged with phone calls. The local Army headquarters announced that the rocket had apparently fallen onto the Army reservation some 100 miles southeast of Fairbanks.

The more experienced observers at the Geophysical Institute quickly recognized that, by a remarkable coincidence, a fireball, or large meteor, had plunged into the earth's atmosphere at almost the exact moment the satellite was due to pass. Furthermore the large experimental radar at Stanford Research Institute, near Palo Alto, California, observed the rocket fly past after its supposed demise over Alaska. Nevertheless it was widely reported that the object had fallen on Alaska. The Russians said the United States, having found the fragments, was now trying to conceal the fact. On December 6 Premier Khrushchev was talking to a group of foreign correspondents at a reception in the Finnish Embassy. "We know it fell on the United States," he was quoted as saying, "but they do not want to give it back to us." [3]

In the days that followed, the Academy of Sciences of the USSR and the Soviet IGY Committee sent similar messages to their American counterparts:

> According to available data some not entirely burnt remnants of the first earth satellite rocket have been scattered along a line including Alaska and the west coast of North America [they said].

After citing the scientific importance of studying these fragments, the messages asked the scientists of America to forward data concerning the fall, as well as "the remnants which were found," to the Academy of Sciences in Moscow. Detlev W. Bronk, president of the National Academy of Sciences in Washington, replied that no evidence had been found to support the view that fragments had fallen on American soil. He said the Soviet request was being forwarded to those in the field, but added: "It will be helpful if you can provide data you mention as available to guide our further search." [4]

There were no further developments in the matter for several months. Then, in the June 27, 1958, issue of *Science,* Robert Jastrow and Isadore Harris, who were at that time with the Naval Research Laboratory in Washington, published a remarkable finding. The Sputnik I rocket had fallen in the Russians' own back yard. A final radar sighting by the Royal Radar Research Establishment at Malvern, England, had shown the burned-out rocket to be only seventy-one miles overhead—so low that it had clearly entered on the final dive of its re-entry into the atmosphere. Hence it must have fallen somewhere between western Siberia and China—most probably in Mongolia—Jastrow and Harris reported.[5] Their finding was thrust unavoidably before the Russians when it was presented a month later at the CSAGI conference in Moscow.

It was at this conference, held at Moscow State University from July 29 to August 9, 1958, that the relations between Soviet and American IGY scientists passed through their most difficult period. At one time leaders of the United States delegation even discussed the possibility of walking out or seeking to adjourn the meeting to another location. The chief problems were those of Chinese representation and satellite data exchange.

The Washington conference that ended with the launching of Sputnik I had produced a formula calling for the delivery of precise orbital information within five months and, within eight months, of "a complete tabulation" of data radioed from the satellite. Immediately after the launching of Sputnik I, Radio Moscow began broadcasting the times of expected passes over various cities. Likewise the British, at the Jodrell Bank radio telescope, found that by simply telephoning Moscow they could obtain short-term orbital predictions to enable them to aim their giant "dish." Nevertheless the American tracking system found it was getting little or no help from Moscow. In mid-October, 1957, shortly after Sputnik I went into orbit, CSAGI headquarters in Brussels asked the Soviet IGY committee for data and was told that Moscow hoped to send some in early November. On November 25 Ivan Bardin, head of the Soviet IGY program, sent to Brussels proposed codes for rapid transmission of orbital information, so that world-wide tracking and photography of the satellites could be more effective. This encouraged hope in the West that the Russians were prepared to exchange information and were simply impeded by their own tracking difficulties. American trackers had thought that modern computers would make it possible to work out orbit characteristics on the basis of a few sightings, but it took them almost a month to get good predictions on Sputnik I.

Actually the dearth of information from Moscow seems to have been due to a change in policy that followed the launching of the first two Sputniks. The entry of the world into the space age was so dramatic that it inspired radical changes in the thinking of both East and

West. The United States reacted by accelerating its missile program—a response which probably took Moscow by surprise. Political and military leaders in Moscow may have decided that the formula accepted by the Soviet scientists in Washington was an American trap, designed to capture military secrets or, at least, to obtain "something for nothing," since no American satellites had been launched.

The change in Soviet attitude came to light when Sir Archibald Day visited Moscow in January, 1958, in his role as IGY Coordinator. Following the Washington meeting, three months earlier, he had revised the rocket and satellite chapter of the *CSAGI Guide to IGY World Data Centers*—the rulebook on data exchange—embodying the modifications agreed upon at that conference. However, during his stay in Moscow, where he sat in on two sessions of the Soviet IGY Committee, he was presented with a proposed revision of his chapter. In contrast to his detailed provisions, it simply provided for direct exchanges between NIZMIR (the Institute of Terrestrial Magnetism, Ionosphere and Radio Propagation) in Moscow and each observing station. The latter would trade visual, optical, or radar data for orbital predictions. If and when the United States put up satellites, further exchanges could be arranged according to a similar plan, the Russians said.

This was quite unacceptable to the United States, but an attempt was made to incorporate some of the Soviet ideas in a new draft of Day's document. A requirement for one more item of information was added, namely the weight of all objects placed in orbit, since it had been found that the carrier rockets were better suited to air-drag studies than the satellites themselves. The United States National Committee for the IGY also insisted on retention of the provision calling for an exchange of all decoded and corrected data from each experiment.

Yevgeny K. Federov, chairman of the Soviet Working Group on Rockets and Satellites, replied that, in the view of his colleagues, "the publication of the detailed data about the methods and equipment used and of the results of observations in the usual routine adopted in all the scientific researches will provide every opportunity for any scientist to make use of the scientific information received with rockets and satellites." Some of the data called for in the American-sponsored draft, Federov added, "are not connected with geophysical researches."

He was, in effect, saying that the Soviet scientists intended to publish "detailed data" in their scientific journals, but could not commit themselves unequivocally to publish everything. The data "not connected with geophysical researches" was presumably that concerning the final-stage rocket, which appears to have been one of the medium-range Soviet missiles.

It was decided to let the matter ride until the Moscow conference, where a working group was formed to thrash out the problem. There both sides accepted a large portion of Sir Archibald's latest draft, including a number of relaxations in the reporting schedule originally agreed upon in Washington. Both the United States and the Soviet Union had found the latter impractical. Rocket-firing reports were called for "within four weeks if possible" (instead of within two weeks). Satellite launchings, with initial orbital data, were to be announced within twenty-four hours (instead of two hours). Preliminary reports on scientific experiments were to be published within "several weeks" after launching and full reports on both rocket and satellite experiments within a year "after the end of the experiment or investigation" (instead of eight months after launching or collection of bi-monthly data increments). A compromise also was reached on the identification of the launching site. Day, in his latest draft, had changed this, in an effort to satisfy the Russians, making it necessary only to disclose the point in space at which orbital velocity was first established. The Russians apparently thought the launching pad could still be pinpointed by backward computations from such data. Hence this was further modified to require simply that the time and place of one reference point in the orbit be given, so that other nations could figure out where to look for the vehicle. Such information was useful for crude, short-term predictions, but did not constitute the precise "orbital elements," which are computed after a satellite has been in flight for a considerable period.

Despite this progress, no agreement could be reached on the other data-exchange problems. Although it was agreed that the size and weight of the satellite itself should be announced, there was a stalemate with regard to the other objects. Hence both Soviet and United States comments were appended to this part of the conference resolution. The American one called flatly for the size and weight of all "significant objects" placed in orbit. Rather than unequivocally refusing such information, the Soviet delegation appended this statement: "Although the satellite is the primary object for scientific observations, information about the rocket carrier which is necessary to organize its observation should be given by the launching country in the form appropriate to that country."

Another provision called for transmission to the World Data Centers of "the observational data concerned, including those received by telemetry from scientific instruments carried in the satellite as well as those obtained by means of external observations." The material was to be fully corrected and processed, so that any outside scientist could use it. Appended to this section was a notation that "the U.S.S.R. propose to send data only on request in any particular case. The U.S.A. prefer the above wording which implies sending all data without any specific request." [6]

Thus, as noted afterwards by Homer E. Newell, Jr., soft-spoken scientist from the Naval Research Laboratory, who was substituting for Lloyd Berkner in the coordinating role of CSAGI Reporter for Rockets and Satellites, the Russians had refused to commit themselves to furnish orbital elements while their satellites were aloft and would not agree to an automatic dispatch of data to the World Data Centers.

> On the last point the U.S.S.R. provided no guarantee whatsoever that the rest of the world will ever see any of the desired data [he said]; the Soviets say that they intend to negotiate each request for information with the requestor. When it was pointed out that this procedure would not provide a means for scientists to know what data existed, the Soviets had no comment.

Newell defined data, in this sense, as including such information as antenna patterns and corrected readings from all satellite-borne instruments. These were needed by researchers in other countries, he said, "either for evaluating Soviet reports and papers or for carrying out researches of their own." His presentation to the full assembly of 400 delegates from 35 countries (including 53 from the United States and 179 from the USSR) brought into the open one of the few discords of the IGY.

> As acting reporter for rockets and satellites [he wrote later], I felt compelled to state in my report to the full assembly on the last day that the working group for rockets

and satellites had failed to achieve a satisfactory solution of the data exchange and world data centers problem.[7]

In fairness it should be pointed out that, in these negotiations, the Americans were at an advantage in that, apart from the greater openness of their rocket firings, the hardware used was largely nonmilitary. When, in 1959, as part of a military program, the first Discoverer satellites were placed in polar orbits traversing the USSR, the Russians were quick to point out that the United States was maintaining secrecy concerning much of that project (although it had nothing to do with the IGY or its successor).[8] Likewise, it should be noted, the Russians at the Moscow conference presented a number of papers on their IGY space program. The visiting Americans found the Russian results largely in line with their own and came home with armfuls of Soviet rocket and satellite reports.[9]

The second major problem before the Moscow meeting concerned the issuance of Soviet visas for the Nationalist Chinese delegates. Three months before the conference, reportedly with encouragement from Washington, the Chinese on Taiwan wrote IGY headquarters in Brussels inquiring as to the procedure for attending the Moscow conference. Within a few days they were sent the accreditation forms provided by the Academy of Sciences of the USSR and the filled-out forms were sent back to Belgium.

On July 31, 1958, the day after the conference opened in Moscow, the Nationalists sent the following message and at the same time released it to the press:

> Please forward greetings from Chinese National IGY committee to the fifth meeting CSAGI in Moscow, but we want put on record our disappointment over failure in processing necessary visa requirement for our delegates in time by Soviet government in contravention obligations of a host country according international practice.[10]

The Department of State in Washington, through its Moscow embassy, pressed the American scientists to demand a showdown at a plenary meeting and it was then that leaders of the delegation considered a walkout or demand for a change of conference site. The scientists found themselves being swept into the main stream of the

Cold War, the high ideals of IGY cooperation drifting out of sight. It turned out, however, that there was no clear evidence of the Chinese ever having made direct application for Soviet visas. They had been told by IGY headquarters to apply for them at a Soviet embassy, but this would have required them to embark on their journey before they knew whether or not they would be admitted. The Taiwan scientists probably thought it unlikely that Moscow would issue such visas after the mainland Chinese had withdrawn from the IGY in protest against the inclusion of Taiwan. Hence, although the CSAGI Bureau inquired of Bardin about the Chinese visas, no further action was taken during the Moscow conference, and it was agreed that the whole question of political nondiscrimination should be referred to the International Council of Scientific Unions (ICSU), sponsor of the IGY.

A further difficulty at Moscow was the censorship of news dispatches written by visiting science reporters. The meeting was attended by some thirty-eight correspondents from Soviet and foreign news media and this question arose almost at the outset, following the presentation of a paper by Y. Kawabata, chief of the Division of Observations in the Japanese Meteorological Agency. He reported on a study of rain samples whose radioactivity, he said, originated in four areas: Eniwetok, Nevada, eastern and western Siberia, and the Arctic area north of Siberia. The first two were, of course, the United States test sites for nuclear weapons; the others were obviously Soviet test sites. He said that owing to prevailing winds the largest increases in radioactivity in Japan came from the Soviet sites.

Roughly half of a proposed Columbia Broadcasting System broadcast, including all reference to this paper, was deleted by the Soviet censor and similar stories by United States correspondents were held up. Several correspondents wrote letters of protest to Sydney Chapman, head of CSAGI, arguing, for example, that in censoring reports on papers presented at the conference, the Soviet government, as host, was in effect censoring the scientific findings of the delegates.[11] When Hugh Odishaw brought up the Chinese question before the CSAGI Bureau, he also cited the reports of censorship and Beloussov, the Soviet member of the Bureau, must have acted swiftly, for from then on the correspondents reported no further problems with the censors. News stories that had been held up earlier were released.

Another question before the CSAGI Assembly in Moscow was whether or not to extend the IGY. Such a step had been proposed by the USSR on several grounds. A number of IGY tasks would not be completed by the end of the eighteen-month Year. Some of them, such as the study of Antarctica, had only just begun and (as noted earlier by the United States) there had been time for only a comparatively small return on the great investment required to set up stations in that region. Also the Russians argued that machinery was needed to provide for permanent international cooperation in geophysics and an extension of the IGY would allow time for such arrangements to be made. "From their position on this question of extending the IGY," Newell reported, "and from what individuals said in defense of that position, it appeared that the Soviet scientists need the IGY name and organization to help them maintain their position at home and their outside contacts and the freedom of intercourse that has been achieved so far. Apparently this need is a very urgent and demanding one in the opinion of the Soviet geophysicists and solar physicists." [12]

One difficulty was that many IGY committees, in asking for money, had told their governments the IGY was a one-time expenditure. They feared, therefore, that its extension would not be warmly received. All agreed, however, that much IGY work should be continued, particularly in solar observations and in the exploration of space, the oceans, and the Antarctic. It was even decided to enlarge the work in one area by conducting a World Magnetic Survey during the quiet part of the sunspot cycle in the mid-1960s, the last such survey having been in the 1920s. The limited continuation of the IGY was to be known as International Geophysical Cooperation–1959 (IGC–1959). Other resolutions adopted at Moscow looked toward the day when space near the earth would be congested with long-lived satellites, some with sun-powered radios crowding the frequencies available for communications. It was proposed that nations study means to pluck superannuated satellites from orbit and that some group be made responsible for coordinating the frequencies allocated to such space vehicles. As one of its last acts, the full CSAGI recommended that there be established a permanent committee "for international planning and coordination of scientific experiments and observations in both rockets and satellites."

Two months later the IGY's parent body, ICSU, held its General Assembly in Washington and endorsed a number of the steps taken in Moscow. It was recommended that a special committee be created to succeed CSAGI and place IGY cooperation on a permanent basis, leading to the formation, a year later, of the International Geophysics Committee or CIG (for Comité International de Geóphysique). At its organizational meeting this group proposed that the three great World Data Centers continue to be repositories for new results, with periodic review of the nature of the data to be interchanged. The committee also undertook to see that the many-volume summation of IGY results, the *Annals,* was brought to completion and the years 1960 and 1961 were designated the "IGY-IGC analysis and theoretical research period" to encourage swift processing of the mountainous material. Beloussov was named president of the committee, with scientists from Britain, France, the Netherlands, and the United States holding lesser offices, an arrangement indicative of the Soviet Union's new place in the scientific world.[13]

The ICSU General Assembly, in 1958, also provided for the continuation of the watch on the sun and the calling of Alerts and Special Observational Intervals when warranted. This program and the drafting of an annual calendar were assigned to an International Service for World Days, created under the International Scientific Radio Union. Another resolution dealt with the question of political nondiscrimination, in view of the difficulties over Nationalist China, but it cut two ways, for there was little enthusiasm in Washington for receiving scientific delegates from such states as Communist China (which belonged to at least one ICSU affiliate).

Perhaps the most historic action of this assembly was its creation of an agency to promote the international exploration of space. The IGY had broken the bonds that had tied man to the earth. The question now was whether those who sent vehicles into the outer void did so only on behalf of their own nation, or for the benefit of all mankind. The problem, however, was more difficult than that of the Antarctic, for space is the crossroads of those fearsome weapons, the intercontinental ballistic missiles. Even peaceful space vehicles are launched, as a rule, from military missile sites. Therefore the inhibitions that troubled the exchange of satellite data also impeded efforts to form the Committee on Space Research (COSPAR). Resolutions supporting such a move had been passed at the rocket and satellite conference in Washington and at the CSAGI meeting in Moscow.

The committee formed by ICSU at first was provisional, its task being "to provide the world scientific community with the means whereby it may exploit the possibilities of satellites and space probes of all kinds for scientific purposes, and exchange the resulting data on a cooperative basis." [14] The committee was to report on what steps could be taken to enable scientists in smaller countries to use their genius in devising experiments to be carried by the vehicles of large nations. It also was to keep in touch with space-control efforts in the United Nations. The committee was to be composed of representatives from countries engaged in launching rockets and satellites (at the outset Australia, Canada, France, Japan, the Soviet Union, United Kingdom, and United States), plus three representatives from countries engaged in tracking space vehicles, chosen on a rotational basis, and delegates from the nine international scientific unions concerned with space research.

When COSPAR held its initial meeting in London on November 14 and 15, 1958, two of Russia's leading space scientists came to represent their country. One, Leonid I. Sedov, was chairman of the Soviet Interdepartmental Commission on Interplanetary Communications, which —like the Space Science Board of the National Academy of Sciences in the United States—was responsible for dealing with groups abroad. The other representative was Anatoli Blagonravov, who had led the delegation at the Washington talks on rockets and satellites. To complete the committee roster, India, Peru, and the Union of South Africa were chosen as representatives of the tracking nations and H. C. van der Hulst of the Netherlands was elected president. COSPAR seemed off to an auspicious start, but shortly after this meeting the situation took a turn for the worse. The United Nations General Assembly, by a vote of 53 to 9 with 19 abstentions, created a Committee on the Peaceful Uses of Outer Space, despite Soviet protestations that it was loaded in favor of the West and that the USSR would therefore boycott the group.

It was then, apparently, that Moscow took another look at COSPAR and realized that, when the representative of the Academy of Sciences of the USSR sat down at the conference table, there would not be a single political ally among the eighteen others there. This was primarily because the representatives of the nine scientific unions were all from western countries and does not appear to have been intentional, particularly since it was evident that major decisions by the group would have little meaning unless the Russians concurred. Nevertheless Moscow decided the situation was unacceptable and when COSPAR held its next meeting, at The Hague in March, 1959, the

Soviet delegate, Yevgeny K. Federov (who served as one of the two vice-presidents, the other being an American), argued that the committee membership did not reflect the preeminent Soviet position in space research and included a multitude of scientific unions not one of which had ever fired a rocket. He proposed a revision that would have included virtually all European members of the Soviet Bloc.

Richard W. Porter, the United States representative, and other western scientists said membership could not be determined on political grounds, but they made it clear that they were willing to take any reasonable steps to meet the Soviet objections. A compromise plan was presented in which the president of COSPAR would be elected from an open slate, but in which other members of its ruling bureau would be chosen in equal numbers from slates presented by the two satellite-launching countries. This gave the Russians a considerable degree of parity and, after several months of boycott, the Soviet Union agreed to a modified version of this scheme that retained the unions within an executive council, but, on important budget and program matters, required concurrence by the inner bureau, where the two great powers were equally represented. The first meeting of the newly constituted COSPAR took place at Nice, France, in January, 1960. By this time a compromise had been achieved regarding membership in the UN space committee and at Nice further progress was made. The Soviet representatives agreed to furnish orbital elements for their satellites, after launching, so that scientists in all lands could compute when and where to look for them. They even said they would give advance notice of launchings where the orbit, power output, radio frequency or other observational characteristics were significantly different from those of previous satellites.[15] Thus, through patience, manifest good faith, and careful negotiation, these questions, which had caused a certain amount of discord during the IGY, seemed to have been resolved, although, by early 1961, some of the hoped-for data still had not been received in the West.

The other groups born of the IGY had a less stormy beginning. The fifteen members of SCOR, the Special Committee on Oceanic Research, who held their first meeting at Woods Hole in 1957, subsequently developed a plan for a concentrated attack, in 1960–64, on the least-known of great water areas, the Indian Ocean.

SCAR, the Special Committee on Antarctic Research, grew out of a United States proposal at the fourth IGY Antarctic Conference, held in Paris June 13–15, 1957, that the program in the South Polar region be continued after the IGY. After the formation of a continuing organization had been approved by ICSU, SCAR held its first meeting at The Hague from February 3–6, 1958. Besides the nations active in Antarctica, its membership included representatives from ICSU and five of the scientific unions. The post-IGY program, under SCAR, was hardly diminished from that of the IGY itself. Morton J. Rubin of the United States Weather Bureau followed Gordon Cartwright as the American at Mirny, but when it came to arrange for a successor to Rubin, there were difficulties. The Antarctic Weather Central, where a Soviet meteorologist had been stationed, was being shifted to Australia, since Little America henceforth was to be used only in summer, but the Russians wanted their man to be somewhere in Antarctica, where he could take part in scientific research. It was finally agreed that the Soviet representative would be at McMurdo Sound, and the exchange program was resumed for the winter of 1960.

The stark, perilous environment of Antartica had a remarkable effect in submerging political differences. The expeditions there were bound together by the presence of a common enemy. If the Australians at home were stirred to feelings of alarm at the nearness of the Russians, those in Antarctica saw a deeper significance in IGY activities there. Phillip Law, leader of Australian activities in that region and director of the Antarctic Division in Australia's Department of External Affairs, put it thus:

> The era of territorial competition of the first 50 years of this century has given way to an era of technological competition, in which nations use the arena afforded by Antarctica to demonstrate their technical and scientific skills. This is a healthy and productive form of competition, particularly when carried out in a spirit of friendliness and helpful co-operation, and I believe that the international amity and goodwill which have characterized the IGY in Antarctica will extend beyond scientific circles and contribute towards improved international relations in general and a broader understanding between all peoples.[16]

What Law had to say about the South Polar region was applicable, in large measure, to all IGY activities.

The most important specific product of the IGY, in Antarctica, was at first greeted glumly by many concerned with research in that region. This was the United States note, transmitted on May 2, 1958, to the eleven other nations taking part in the IGY antarctic program, proposing a treaty that would set the continent aside as an international laboratory. Political claims would, in effect, be shelved and all forms of military activity would be outlawed. The cool reception accorded this idea among some scientists was based on their conviction that, in contrast to space research, where military and political considerations had intruded, the cooperation in Antarctica rested on purely scientific foundations. Their reaction was that, if diplomats got into the act, this delicate situation might be upset.

An international approach to Antarctica had been discussed for a number of years. The United States had proposed it to the claimants in 1948, without favorable response. In 1956 an Indian suggestion that the United Nations Assembly deal with the problem was shelved to avoid controversy during the IGY effort. In March, 1957, when United States Secretary of State Dulles was in Australia for a SEATO meeting, the Australians pressed upon him their disquietude at having Soviet bases so near. A year later, in February, 1958, British Prime Minister Harold Macmillan visited Australia and again the matter was discussed. Walter Nash, Prime Minister of New Zealand, already had made statements in favor of an international solution, and at the conclusion of Macmillan's visit it was evident that the Commonwealth was prepared to back a plan in which control over Antarctica would be vested in a commission representing all the nations with interests there.

This idea was not welcomed in Latin America, but when the United States put forth its plan in May, all eleven recipients of the proposal agreed to join in preliminary talks. The participants—Argentina, Australia, Belgium, Britain, Chile, France, Japan, New Zealand, Norway, South Africa, the Soviet Union, and the United States—carried on secret negotiations in Washington for a year and a half before they found sufficiently broad areas of agreement to call a formal conference, the success being due in large measure to the patience and skill of Paul C. Daniels, representing the United States. The formal treaty conference opened in Washington on October 15, 1959, and culminated, on December 1, in the signing of an historic treaty setting aside one entire continent as a preserve for scientific research, immune from political and military strife. It included a free-wheeling inspection system that empowered any of the signatories to designate inspectors who could go anywhere they wished in the area—the first such inspection agreement achieved by the great powers. It also revived the principle of unanimity, which had fallen into disrepute during the Cold War as "the veto." Decisions of the Consultative Committee, which was to administer the treaty, had to be unanimous, but this did not affect the provision for freedom of inspection. It was also agreed that, while claims to antarctic territory were not directly affected, no future activities in that region could serve to strengthen those claims. It was clearly the hope of at least some signatories that this would lead to the "withering away" of the territorial rivalries.

Before putting their pens to the document, several of the signers pointed out that, contingent upon the treaty's ratification, it could serve as a precedent for the settlement of the more difficult problem of outer space.[17]

Looking back upon the IGY, there seems little doubt that it marked a major turning point in history. The common striving toward greater knowledge that it initiated did not halt on January 1, 1959. It was perpetuated in many organizations, such as SCOR, SCAR, COSPAR, and CIG. But it was the peaceful disposition of Antarctica, the emergence of the Soviet Union as a leader in science and technology and, above all, the initiation of space exploration that wrought fundamental changes in the world. The provincialism of the pre-Sputnik era was dead forever. Science and scientists came out of the IGY as a potent influence in world affairs. Russian academicians, many of them bearers of a venerable humanistic tradition, had re-established contact with the western world and had shown the extent—and limitations—of their influence on Soviet policy.

Important changes had taken place in the United States as well. The serene passage of Soviet Sputniks across American skies had precipitated a re-examination of the educational system and, in fact, of the entire American scale of values. Not that Americans had any cause to be ashamed of their scientific prowess. The United States rocket and satellite program had demonstrated that big vehicles are not necessarily the best. Such discoveries as the Van Allen radiation belts were the fruit of ingenious instrumentation and imaginative interpretation of the results. What was impressive about the work of the Russians, apart from their virtuoso performance with rockets, was the magnitude and sophistication of their scientific endeavors at so early a stage of their economic development.

One of the side effects of the IGY was to force the United States government to undertake a new function—that of large-scale exploration. It became necessary to form a new organ, the National Aeronautics and Space Administration, and to allocate to it an increasing share of the national budget. In its early stages it required about half a billion dollars per year, with a promise of far greater demands in the future. Development of the gargantuan Saturn rocket alone cost about a quarter of a billion per year. Furthermore, the atmosphere created by the IGY made it acceptable to Congress that the United States space program, as framed in the National Aeronautics and Space Act of 1958, be cast in an international mold.

The government found itself faced with new and difficult decisions. In view of the pressing needs for foreign aid, medical research, housing, education, and similar programs, how much should be allocated to space research? Though even a modest effort would be costly, the urge was irresistible. The IGY had given the world a peak beyond the enveloping atmosphere, a glimpse of the universe in its naked glory. We had seen dynamic events taking place in space, even in the immediate vicinity of the earth—radiation belts that wax and wane; lethal protons shot out by the sun and drawn toward the earth's poles; solar eruptions of hot, magnetized plasma that may hold clues to the harnessing of unlimited nuclear energy. Having had one look, we cannot close the door again. One of the characteristics of the human animal that has driven him across perilous oceans, up the highest mountains, and even to the poles is the spirit of adventure. It is not an impractical, useless element in man's character, for it has spread his species over the face of the earth; and the same spirit, applied to scientific inquiry, has been responsible for all of the discoveries that have made us "civilized."

Space, of course, offers more than a limitless field for exploration. Satellites can fulfill many roles—in communications, navigation, and weather observation—that can be achieved in no other way. If disarmament should at last be achieved, a bold program of space exploration would help avoid an economic crisis during the period of readjustment, particularly for those industries directly involved in the missile program.

From the administrative point of view the IGY had been a remarkable achievement in that, although it probably cost the participants about one billion dollars, the total expenditure for its international secretariat, for the CSAGI publications, and for the meetings was only about $250,000.[18] The IGY promoted a revival of science in former colonies (where observatories had closed when the colonists went home) and in other underdeveloped areas; it stimulated an interdisciplinary approach in which men trained in different, though related, fields worked together to resolve problems beyond the reach of any one of them. Finally, the IGY set in motion a number of research programs that became permanent. It seems likely that, as the world grows up economically, politically, and scientifically, there will be even more ambitious international scientific undertakings.

The IGY's construction of scientific bridges across political chasms coincided with a general growth of science's role in diplomacy, as well as in national policy-making. Specialists from East and West reached broad areas of agreement in the United Nations Scientific Committee on the Effects of Atomic Radiation, and scientists played a central role in the Geneva talks on a cessation of nuclear test explosions. Science had emerged as a potent force in world affairs, although it had become clear that it could not, with a wave of the hand, dispel deep-seated fears and distrust. Thus George B. Kistiakowsky, successor to Killian as President Eisenhower's science advisor, told the American Physical Society in 1960:

> The significance of international scientific activities to the relations between nations is perhaps the most important of the roles science and scientists can play in today's embittered and divided world—not a new role in the sense that international activities of science are part of the life-blood of science; but new in its potential impact on political relations.
>
> For science is today one of the few common languages of mankind; it can provide a basis for understanding and communication of ideas between people that is independent of political boundaries and of ideologies. Science also provides a sometimes unique opportunity for cooperative endeavors that can contribute in a major way to the reduction of tension between nations. . . .[19]

From the perspective of a few years, the difficulties concerning China and the exchange of satellite data loom small alongside the achievements of the IGY. In studying itself, the world has grown closer together. The immeasurable enlargement of man's horizons through IGY exploration of space, the atmosphere, the seas, the poles, and the earth's interior has stirred the layman as well as the scientist. We have begun to learn that hurricane, drought, and pestilence know no national frontiers and we have come a little closer to a cosmic view of our planet—a water-covered sphere, crusted here and there with continents upon which there is the fragile green hue of life.

NOTES

CHAPTER 2: EXPERIMENTS IN CONCERT

1. M. F. Maury, *The Physical Geography of the Sea* (New York: Harper, 1855), p. xiii. During the American Revolutionary War Benjamin Franklin had expressed a similar point of view when he asked that all United States men-of-war be told not to molest the ships of Captain James Cook's expedition.
2. Weyprecht's plan was first presented to the Academy of Sciences in Vienna in January, 1875. See *Annals of the International Geophysical Year* (New York: Pergamon Press, 1959), Vol. I, p. 6. The First Polar Year is also known as the First International Polar Year. To its contemporaries it was known by such titles as the Polar Year or the International Circumpolar Stations.
3. *Programme des Travaux d'une Expédition Polaire Internationale Proposée par le Comte Wilczek et Charles Weyprecht* (Vienna, 1877).
4. A. W. Greely, *Three Years of Arctic Service* (New York: Scribner, 1886), Vol. II, pp. 321–322. For additional details concerning the circumpolar stations, see Greely's *The Polar Regions in the Twentieth Century* (Boston: Little, Brown, 1928), pp. 208–219. A recent detailed treatment of the Lady Franklin Bay Expedition is Alden Todd's *Abandoned* (New York: McGraw-Hill, 1961).
5. V. Laursen (compiler), *Bibliography for the Second International Polar Year 1932–33*, Temporary Commission on the Liquidation of the Polar Year 1932–33 of the IMO (Copenhagen: 1951), p. 14.
6. The International Meteorological Organization consisted of two bodies: the Conference of Directors, which met about every six years, and the International Meteorological Committee, elected by the Conference of Directors to act on its behalf between Conference sessions.
7. International Meteorological Organization, *I^r Rapport de la Commission Internationale de l'Année Polaire 1932–33*, Secretariat Publication No. 6 (Leyden: 1930), pp. 17–22.
8. D. la Cour and J. M. Stagg, "The International Polar Year 1932–33," in IMO, *IIe Rapport de la Commission Internationale . . .*, Secretariat Publication No. 12 (Leyden: 1932), Appendix H-II, pp. 55, 54.
9. IMO, *Rapports des Présidents des Commissions . . .*, Secretariat Publication No. 3, Part 2 (Utrecht: 1930), Appendix T, p. 128. For further details on organization and planning, see the above and Laursen, *Bibliography. . . .*
10. IMO, Secretariat Publication No. 12, *op. cit.*, pp. 36–47.

11. The existence of an ionized region in the sky had been proposed as early as 1882 by the Scottish scientist Balfour Stewart.
12. IMO, Secretariat Publication No. 6, *op. cit.*, Appendix D, p. 57.
13. Hearings before the House Committee on Foreign Affairs, 72d Congress, First Session; January 26, 27, February 2, 1932.
14. Laursen, *Bibliography* . . . , p. 33.
15. IMO, Secretariat Publication No. 12, pp. 5–36.
16. Laursen, pp. 32–33.
17. J. A. Fleming and V. Laursen, "International Polar Year of 1932–1933," *Science*, CX (September 23, 1949), 308–309.
18. See for instance Dr. Joseph Kaplan's "The International Geophysical Year," an address at Wilson College, Chambersburg, Pa., October 25, 1955 (issued in mimeograph form by the National Academy of Sciences), p. 1.

CHAPTER 3: GLOBAL PLANS

1. *ICSU, A Brief Outline* (The Hague: ICSU Secretariat, 1958), p. 3.
2. *Ibid.*, p. 4.
3. For details on the steps taken in planning the IGY, see Walter Sullivan, "The International Geophysical Year," *International Conciliation* (Carnegie Endowment for International Peace, January 1959), pp. 269ff. Records of these and other pre-IGY meetings appear in *Annals of the IGY*, Vol. II.
4. V. S. Zaletaev, *Izvestia Akademii Nauk SSSR* (Ser. Geofiz. No. 7 [1957]), pp. 965–967. English translation by P. J. Hyde published by Pergamon Press for the American Geophysical Union, New York; p. 160.
5. *CSAGI Bulletin d'Information No. 4* (IUGG News Letter No. 9 [London, 1955]), pp. 54–55.
6. *CSAGI Bulletin d'Information No. 5* (IUGG News Letter No. 11 [London, 1955]), p. 60.
7. *Pravda*, November 28, 1953. Quoted in F. J. Krieger, *Behind the Sputniks, A Survey of Soviet Space Science* (Washington: Public Affairs Press, 1958), p. 3.
8. *Proceedings of the Eleventh General Assembly* (URSI Administrative Proceedings, Vol. X, Part 8 [Brussels, 1954]), p. 74.
9. *CSAGI Bulletin No. 4*, p. 179.
10. *CSAGI Bulletin No. 7* (1956), p. 68.
11. *CSAGI Bulletin No. 6* (1956), pp. 30–31.
12. *CSAGI Guide to IGY World Data Centers*, mimeographed draft of June 7, 1957, pp. 1–2; sec. 1, pp. 2–4.
13. *Ibid.*, p. 1.

CHAPTER 4: CHINA AND THE KICKOFF

1. This and subsequent quotations in the chapter are from unpublished CSAGI material. For a brief account of the Chinese question see

Sydney Chapman, *IGY: Year of Discovery* (Ann Arbor: University of Michigan Press, 1959), pp. 107–8.
2. *IGY News* [published by CSAGI], July 15, 1957.
3. Peking Hsin-hua news release, June 7, 1957; Lhasa Jih-pao, August 14, 1957; Shih-chia-chuang Jih-pao, September 6, 1957; *Soviet Bloc International Geophysical Year Information* (Washington: U.S. Department of Commerce, Office of Technical Services, issues of February 21 and March 7, 1958). These reports were in part confirmed in 1958 by the visit of Dr. J. Tuzo Wilson, president of IUGG.
4. See Astronomical Council, Academy of Sciences USSR, *Bulletin of the Optical Observation Stations, Artificial Earth Satellites*, No. 2 (Moscow: 1958), table 2.
5. *Illustrated* (London), July 27, 1957, pp. 26–27.
6. Kaplan, "The International Geophysical Year," *op. cit.*, p. 11.
7. "The International Geophysical Year," *USSR* No. 9 (1957), 39. Abridged from the magazine *Ogonyok*.

CHAPTER 5: MOSKVA—SPUTNIK

1. F. J. Krieger, *Behind the Sputniks, op. cit.*, p. 333.
2. *Ibid.*, p. 1. See also P. E. Cleator, "History," in D. R. Bates (ed.), *Space Research and Exploration* (New York: Sloane, 1958), p. 31.
3. "De Mundi Systemate: Opera Quae Existant Omnia," Part III of *Philosophia Naturalis Principia Mathematica* [translation] (London, 1782), Vol. III, pp. 180–181. The first edition (1687) contains the supporting mathematics but not this illustration; it was revised by Newton for his 1713 edition.
4. Cleator, pp. 31–40.
5. Krieger, pp. 1–2.
6. See, for example, Hanson Baldwin, "Soviet Air Strategy in the Second World War," in Asher Lee (ed.), *The Soviet Air and Rocket Forces* (New York: Praeger, 1959), p. 87.
7. Hearings on H.R. 11881, Select Committee on Astronautics and Space Exploration, 85th Congress, 2nd Session, April–May 1958, pp. 19–20. (Cited hereafter as *Astronautics Hearings*.) See also testimony of Lt. Gen. James M. Gavin, *ibid.*, p. 197.
8. As announced in 1957. See Krieger, pp. 334–335.
9. English translation in Krieger, p. 330.
10. *Pravda*, August 5, 1955. English translation in Krieger, pp. 330–331.
11. Quoted by Krieger, p. 6.
12. CSAGI Rocket and Satellite Conference (Washington, September 30–October 5, 1957) Document 5 (September 25, 1957), p. 7.
13. See *Pravda*, October 9, 1957. Translation in Krieger, p. 321.
14. See *Pravda* article (March 4, 1958) by Alla Genrikhovna Masevich, deputy chairman of the Astronomical Council of the Academy of Sciences of the USSR. Translation in *Soviet Bloc IGY Information* (March 28, 1958), pp. 3–4.
15. *Pravda*, October 9, 1957. Translation in Krieger, p. 321.

16. *Miscellaneous Information on the Artificial Earth Satellites* (Special Report No. 12, Optical Satellite Tracking Program, Smithsonian Institution Astrophysical Observatory, Cambridge, Mass., April 30, 1958) p. 22.
17. Text in Krieger, p. 325.
18. *Pravda,* November 13, 1957; published in English in *Soviet Writings on Earth Satellites and Space Travel* (New York: Citadel, 1958), pp. 166–179. According to the Harvard College Observatory's *Sky and Telescope* (January 1958, p. 129), the cone was made of a ceramic containing cobalt. Such substances are used on cones designed for re-entry into the atmosphere; therefore some suspected that recovery of the cone and whatever it may have contained had been planned. Roy Johnson, director of ARPA in the Department of Defense, testified on May 5, 1958 (Astronautics Hearings, p. 1200) that he believed recovery of the dog was intended but that the guidance equipment failed. He added that "We know they have had failures" since the launching of Sputnik II.
19. For an account of this experiment see *Iskusstvenniye Sputniki Zemli* (Moscow: Academy of Sciences USSR, 1958), Issue I, pp. 80–94.
20. The USSR said later that its combined weight was "over" 4000 kilograms (8818 lbs.); see *New Times,* No. 42 (October 1959), p. 8. This was stated in response to the orbiting by the United States of an Atlas missile with a burned-out weight of 3969 kg. (8750 lbs.).
21. *Soviet Writings . . . ,* p. 226.
22. *Ibid.*

CHAPTER 6: VANGUARD BRINGS UP THE REAR

1. *New York Times,* October 10, 1957, p. 14.
2. Astronautics Hearings, p. 1055.
3. *Annual Report,* Chap. 2; quoted in *New York Times,* May 11, 1958, p. 22.
4. See *First Report of the Secretary of Defense* (Washington: National Military Establishment, 1948), p. 129, and testimony of Rear Adm. John T. Hayward, Astronautics Hearings, p. 275.
5. *Life,* October 21, 1957, p. 22.
6. See Erik Bergaust and William Beller, *Satellite!* (New York: Hanover House, 1956), pp. 35–46.
7. Commander Hoover reported in a private communication after his retirement that NRL had been asked to submit a back-up program for Orbiter, based on the Viking, and had instead come up with its own satellite-launching proposal.
8. See *Project Vanguard, A Scientific Earth Satellite Program for the International Geophysical Year* (A Report . . . by Surveys and Investigations Staff), Part VI, p. 68. Hearings, House of Representatives, Committee on Appropriations, Subcommittee on Department of Defense Appropriations, 86th Congress, 1st Session. (Cited hereafter as

Project Vanguard.) See also testimony of Adm. Hayward, Astronautics Hearings, p. 293.

9. See Dr. Herbert F. York testimony, Astronautics Hearings, pp. 48–49 and transcript of Eisenhower press conference, *New York Times,* October 10, 1957, p. 14.
10. *New York Times,* July 30, 1955, p. 8.
11. *Project Vanguard,* p. 58. Further information on the work of the advisory group was furnished to the author by Dr. Stewart, Cmdr. Hoover, and other participants.
12. Astronautics Hearings, p. 74.
13. *Project Vanguard,* p. 59.
14. Astronautics Hearings, pp. 155–157.
15. *Ibid.,* pp. 18–19, 34. Maj. Gen. J. B. Medaris gave similar testimony (p. 149).
16. *Ibid.,* p. 183.
17. *Ibid.,* p. 64.
18. *Life,* October 21, 1957, pp. 23, 22.
19. *Project Vanguard,* p. 74.
20. *Ibid.,* pp. 78–79.
21. *Ibid.,* pp. 62, 75. See also Astronautics Hearings, p. 333.
22. "Summary Report on United States Satellite Program for the International Geophysical Year" presented at opening plenary session, CSAGI Rocket and Satellite Conference, Washington, D.C., September 30, 1957 (multigraphed text).
23. *New York Times,* October 10, 1957, p. 14.
24. Astronautics Hearings, p. 333.
25. *Project Vanguard,* p. 68.
26. *Ibid.,* p. 71.
27. *Ibid.,* p. 67.
28. *Ibid.,* pp. 55–56.
29. Department of Defense Press Release No. 588-58.
30. *Loc. cit.*
31. This includes the U.S. orbiting of an Atlas missile whose mission was essentially nonscientific.

CHAPTER 7: THE BELTS

1. Quoted in Carl Störmer, *The Polar Aurora* (London: Oxford, 1955), p. 5.
2. Carrington, *Geomagnetism,* p. 334; cited in Störmer, p. 205.
3. Störmer, pp. 205ff.
4. From Hermann Fritz, *Das Polarlicht* (Leipzig, 1881). Fritz published preliminary results in *Vierteljahrsschrift der Naturforschenden Gesellschaft,* XVII (Zurich, 1872), 338–372.
5. "Sur les Trajectoires des Corpuscules Electrisés dans l'Espace sous l'Action du Magnétisme Terrestre avec Application aux Aurores

Boréales," *Archives des Sciences Physiques et Naturelles*, 4ème Période, Vol. 24 (Geneva, 1907 [in four installments, published in the issues for July through October]). Illustrations shown here are from the October issue, pp. 334, 358. Störmer had put his students to work calculating great numbers of possible trajectories; by 1905 Miss Gudrun Ruud and Lars Vegard had stumbled upon those which became the basis for his entrapment theory (see Störmer, pp. 281–284). Vegard later became a leading authority on the aurora.

6. In 1906 Störmer suggested that world-wide magnetic pulsations might be caused by particles trapped in the earth's magnetic field, but what he had in mind were orbits weaving in and out around the earth's equatorial plane. See *Polar Aurora*, p. 387 and figures 162, 163, and 164.

7. L. Katz and N. C. Gerson (eds.), *Proceedings of the Conference on Ionospheric Physics, State College of Pennsylvania* (July 1950), Geophysical Research Paper No. 12 (Geophysics Research Directorate, Air Force Cambridge Research Center, April 1952), Part B, p. 38.

8. At first it was called the V-2 Upper Atmosphere Research Panel.

9. *Physical Review*, XCVII (January 1, 1955), 201–5. See also James A. Van Allen, "Radiation Belts around the Earth," *Scientific American*, CC (March 1959), 39–47, and *Bulletin of the American Physical Society*, Series II, I (April 26, 1956), 230.

10. Van Allen article in *Scientific American*, p. 42.

11. This paper, "Observation of High Intensity Radiation by Satellites 1958 Alpha and Gamma," was printed in *IGY Satellite Report Series No. 3: Some Preliminary Reports of Experiments in Satellites 1958 Alpha and 1958 Gamma* (Washington: National Academy of Sciences, 1958), pp. 73–92.

12. Van Allen credits S. B. Treiman of Princeton with having helped shape his thinking in this regard. Treiman had shown how cosmic-ray "splashes" could follow the earth's magnetic field to the opposite hemisphere (*Physical Review*, XCI [August 15, 1953], 957–959). See also Van Allen (ed.), *Scientific Uses of Earth Satellites* (Ann Arbor: University of Michigan Press, 1956), pp. 180–182.

13. Published in *Transactions, American Geophysical Union* (cited hereafter as AGU: *Transactions*), XXXVIII (April 1957), 175–190. An abstract of Singer's April 28 paper appears in *Bulletin of the American Physical Society*, Series II, I (April 26, 1956), 229.

14. From the paper presented by Van Allen, McIlwain, and Ludwig at the American Physical Society meeting in Chicago in November 1958; reprinted in *Journal of Geophysical Research*, LXIV (March 1959), 271–286.

15. *Loc. cit.*

16. See for example A. Ye. Chudakov and Ye. V. Gorchakov, "Terrestrial Corpuscular Radiation," *Priroda*, No. 8 (Moscow State University, August 1959), 86–89; translated in *Information on Soviet Bloc International Geophysical Cooperation-1959*, published by the

U.S. Department of Commerce, Office of Technical Services (Washington: September 25, 1959), p. 5.

17. Van Allen, "Radiation Belts of the Earth," AGU: *Transactions,* XLI (June 1960), 246–248; "The Geomagnetically Trapped Corpuscular Radiation," *Journal of Geophysical Research,* LXIV (November 1959), 1683–1689.

CHAPTER 8: ARGUS

1. P. J. Kellogg, E. P. Ney, and J. R. Winckler, "Geophysical Effects Associated with High-Altitude Explosions," *Nature,* CLXXXIII (February 7, 1959), 358–361.
2. Quoted by Sadami Matsushita in a paper presented at the annual meeting of the American Geophysical Union, May 5, 1959.
3. Atomic Energy Commission Release B-94, June 15, 1959.
4. A. L. Cullington, "A Man-made or Artificial Aurora," *Nature,* CLXXXII (November 15, 1958), 1365–1366.
5. *Ibid.* (December 6, 1958), 1598–1599. Actually, two scientists at the French IGY station in Adelie Land, Antarctica, believed they saw lithium emissions beginning in October 1957; see *Comptes Rendus hebdomadaires des Séances de L'Académie des Sciences, Paris,* CCXLVII (September 15, 1958), 806. They later proposed meteorites as the origin; see *ibid.* (September 22, 1958), 886.
6. " 'Corona' of the Earth," interview with Professors I. S. Shklovsky and V. I. Krasovsky, *Izvestia,* March 8, 1959, p. 6. Translated in *Soviet Bloc IGC-1959* (March 27, 1959) pp. 1ff. Article notes dissent by Vernov and Lebedinsky.
7. N. C. Christofilos, "Trapping and Lifetime of Charged Particles in the Geomagnetic Field" (printed for the U.S. Atomic Energy Commission by the University of California Radiation Laboratory, Livermore [UCRL-5407 (November 28, 1958)]), p. 4.
8. *Ibid.,* p. 6. The orbiting of an accelerator had already been proposed by Singer (see *Journal of the British Interplanetary Society,* November 1958).
9. *Science,* CXXVIII (December 26, 1958), 1601.
10. Department of Defense (Office of Public Information) minutes of press briefing on Project Argus, 19 March 1959, pp. 33–34.
11. "Symposium on Scientific Effects of Artificially Introduced Radiations at High Altitudes: Introductory Remarks," *Journal of Geophysical Research,* LXIV (August 1959), 866–867.
12. *Ibid.,* p. 870.
13. Philip Newman, "Optical, Electromagnetic, and Satellite Observations of High-Altitude Nuclear Detonations, Part I," *ibid.,* 926.
14. See "The Argus Experiment," National Academy of Sciences, IGY Bulletin (AGU: *Transactions,* XL [September 1959] 309).
15. Van Allen, McIlwain, and Ludwig, "Satellite Observations of Elec-

trons Artificially Injected into the Geomagnetic Field," *Journal of Geophysical Research,* LXIV (August 1959), 877, 890.

16. Peterson, *ibid.,* p. 936.
17. Allen, Beavers, Whitaker, Welch, and Walton, *ibid.,* 907.
18. "The Argus Experiment," p. 311. This presumably refers to thickness in terms of half the maximum intensity. Some injected radiation was detected by the Jason rockets as much as 400 miles north and south of the shell. Explorer IV, which pierced the shells at far higher elevations, showed an average thickness at half maximum intensity of about 90 kilometers (56 miles) for the first two shots and 150 kilometers (93 miles) for the third.
19. Paper by Carl McIlwain and Pamela Rothwell, to be published.
20. See W. K. Berthold, A. K. Harris, and H. J. Hope, *Journal of Geophysical Research,* LXV (February 1960), 613–618 and (August 1960), 2233–9; *New York Times,* November 3, 1959, p. 1; and H. A. Bomke *et al.,* "Global Hydromagnetic Wave Ducts in the Exosphere," in Letters to the Editors, *Nature,* CLXXXV (January 30, 1960), 299–300.
21. V. A. Troitskaya, "Effects in Earth Currents Caused by High-Altitude Atomic Explosions," *Izvestia Akademii Nauk SSSR,* Ser. Geofiz., No. 9 (1960), 1321–1327.
22. "Science in Outer Space," *The News in Engineering* (Ohio State University College of Engineering), XXXII (April 1960), 11.
23. "A Report Prepared under the Direction of the President's Science Advisory Committee and the IGY Committee of the National Academy of Sciences." Issued by The White House for publication March 26, 1959.

CHAPTER 9: ELECTRIC WINDS

1. S. Fred Singer, E. Maple, and W. A. Bowen, Jr., in *Journal of Geophysical Research,* LVI (June 1951), 265–281. For a study of Second Polar Year data, see preceding article by A. T. Price and G. A. Wilkins of the Imperial College of Science and Technology, London.
2. The indicator in this instrument consists of a number of protons that are oriented by a strong magnetic field. The magnets are periodically switched off, allowing the protons to precess around the natural magnetic field. Their precession frequency indicates the strength of the field and the precession also induces a weak signal at the same frequency in a suitably arranged coil, making it possible to measure the intensity.
3. Laurence J. Cahill, Jr., "Detection of an Electrical Current in the Ionosphere above Greenland," *Journal of Geophysical Research,* LXIV (October 1959), 1377–1380. The following January an Aerobee-Hi fired into an auroral display over Ft. Churchill detected another type of current, which had been postulated on the basis of

ground observations. Its elevation appeared to be 75 miles (L. H. Meredith, L. R. Davis, J. P. Heppner, and O. E. Berg, "Rocket Auroral Investigations," in *IGY Rocket Report Series No. 1: Experimental Results of the U.S. Rocket Program for the IGY to 1 July 1958*, IGY World Data Center A [Washington: National Academy of Sciences, 1958], pp. 169–178).

4. At Talara, Chiclayo, Chimbote, and Huancayo in Peru and at La Paz, Bolivia.

5. IGY Bulletins (AGU: *Transactions*, XL [September 1959], 273–277; *ibid.*, XXXIX [June 1958], 582–585; *ibid.*, XXXVIII [December 1957] 998–1000); *Journal of Geophysical Research*, LXIV (May 1959), 489–503.

6. M. P. Southworth, "Night-Time Equatorial Propagation at 50 Mc/s First Results from an IGY Amateur Observing Program," *Journal of Geophysical Research*, LXV (February 1960), 601–7.

7. Bateman *et al.*, "IGY Observations of F-Layer Scatter in the Far East," *ibid.*, LXIV (April 1959), 403–5.

8. IGY Bulletin (AGU: *Transactions*, XL [December 1959], 391–401). For North American rocket measurements see *ibid.*, XLI (March 1960), 113–118.

CHAPTER 10: FLARE PATROL

1. Dodson and Hedeman, "Survey of Number of Solar Flares Observed during the IGY," *Journal of Geophysical Research*, LXV (January 1960), 123–131.

2. "Fact Sheet on Project Sunflare II" (Washington: National Academy of Sciences, September 1959), p. 2.

3. IGY Bulletin (AGU: *Transactions*, XLI [March 1960], 95–98). See also *ibid.*, XXXIX (February 1958), 165–167, and two reports on the flare patrol by Friedman, Chubb, Kupperian, and Lindsay in *IGY Rocket Report Series No. 1*, pp. 179–185.

CHAPTER 11: ECLIPSE

1. Private communication from Talbot A. Chubb of NRL. In "Rocket Astronomy" [*Journal of Geophysical Research*, LXIV (November 1959), 1760], Friedman used 25 per cent, but he and his colleagues have revised the figure downward.

2. "Reports on IGY Solar Eclipse Expedition," IGY Bulletin (AGU: *Transactions*, XL [March 1959], 48). Although ionospheric transparency did not appear to increase, radio soundings showed a drop in critical frequencies of both the E and F-2 layers (see *ibid.*, p. 43).

3. A. P. Molchanov, Ch'eng Fang-yun, and N. N. Parisky, "Annular Eclipse of the Sun; Joint Expedition of Soviet and Chinese Scientists," *Vestnik Akademii Nauk SSSR*, No. 9 (September 1958), 66–71; translated in *Soviet Bloc IGY Information* (November 7, 1958), pp.

2–8. An account was published as well in *Acta Astronomica Sinica*, VII (June 1959), 7–9; translated in *Information on Soviet Bloc IGC-1959* (December 25, 1959), pp. 4–5.

CHAPTER 12: THE GREAT CLOUD

1. During the entire IGY there were twenty-one SWIs and forty Alerts. The February storm occurred during a two-and-a-half-month period of low magnetic activity in which no SWIs were called. From then on the standards were lowered and SWIs called more often. See exchange of memos between A. H. Shapley, CSAGI Reporter for World Days and Communications, and R. C. Moore, head of the IGY World Warning Agency (Circular Memorandum RWC-50, published as Item 98, *IGY News* [May 7, 1958], Section VI, pp. 183–184).
2. J. A. Lockwood, "Decrease of Cosmic-Ray Intensity on February 11, 1958," *Journal of Geophysical Research*, LXV (January 1960), 27–37.
3. V. L. Williams, "The Simultaneity of Sudden Commencements of Magnetic Storms," *ibid.*, 85–92.
4. *The New Yorker*, February 7, 1959, p. 64.
5. E. R. Manring and H. B. Pettit, "Photometric Observations of the 5577 A and 6300 A Emissions Made during the Aurora of February 10–11, 1958," *Journal of Geophysical Research*, LXIV (February 1959), 149–153.
6. IGY Bulletin (AGU: *Transactions*, XL [June 1959], 180).
7. Ten Chinese stations, probably part of the network set up for the IGY, reported on progress of this aurora. See *Information on Soviet Bloc IGC-1959* (May 8, 1959), p. 7.
8. Winckler *et al.*, "Auroral X-Rays, Cosmic Rays, and Related Phenomena during the Storm of February 10–11, 1958," *Journal of Geophysical Research*, LXIV (June 1959), 608. See also IGY Bulletin (AGU: *Transactions*, XXXIX [December 1958], 1225–1230).

CHAPTER 13: NATURE'S ATOM-SMASHERS

1. P. Freier, E. J. Lofgren, E. P. Ney, F. Oppenheimer, H. L. Bradt, and B. Peters, "Evidence for Heavy Nuclei in the Primary Cosmic Radiation," *Physical Review*, LXXIV (July 15, 1948), 213–217.
2. George C. Reid and Harold Leinbach, "Low-Energy Cosmic-Ray Events Associated with Solar Flares," *Journal of Geophysical Research*, LXIV (November 1959), 1801–1805. In these events the time interval between the flare and the blackout is too great for the protons to have traveled directly. Hence their route appears to be magnetically curved. At the Space Science Symposium held in Nice, France, January 11–15, 1960, Soviet scientists proposed that the protons are temporarily trapped in the gas cloud ejected by the flare.

3. Short-term cosmic-ray increases had previously been observed at balloon altitudes, but not correlated with polar blackouts. On August 9, 1957, a balloon flown by Singer's group at the University of Maryland observed an increase of 30 per cent at 25,000 feet, 19 minutes after a flare on the edge of the sun. It lasted about 2.7 minutes and was followed, 41 minutes later, by a second burst of two minutes' duration. Sputnik II observed what may have been a similar burst on November 7, 1957, when it was high above the atmosphere on a pass over the northern part of the Soviet Union. The increase was 50 per cent on both of the satellite's charged particle counters, although it was not detectable on the ground. See *Pravda* and *Izvestia* for March 26, 1958; *Doklady Akademii Nauk SSSR,* CXX (1958), 1231–1233. [Translations in *Soviet Bloc IGY Information* (April 18, 1958), pp. 2–5 and (October 10, 1958), pp. 1–3.]

4. W. O. Roberts, "Solar-Terrestrial Relationships," AGU: *Transactions,* XLI (June 1960), 230.

5. See Scott E. Forbush, "The U.S. Program for Cosmic Ray Investigations During the IGY," a paper presented at the National Academy of Sciences, June 22, 1957, p. 7. Issued by the U.S. National Committee for the IGY. (Mimeo.)

6. The device is a pile somewhat similar to that in a nuclear reactor except that, instead of containing radioactive fuel, it depends on incoming rays to produce the fissions. These strike lead in the pile, producing neutrons that are slowed sufficiently by paraffin to be detected by boron trifluoride proportional counters.

7. "Twenty-seven-Day Variations of Cosmic Ray Intensities in the Stratosphere," *Doklady Akademii Nauk SSSR,* CXXII (October 11, 1958), 788–791; translated in *Information on Soviet Bloc IGC-1959* (February 13, 1959), pp. 1–3. The balloons were apparently of rubber and did not hover. Rubber balloons were also used by several of the American projects. An account of cosmic-ray observations in Siberia is translated in *ibid.* (March 27, 1959), pp. 6–8. Twelve-hour and twenty-four-hour cycles were also observed. See Forbush and Venkatesan, *Journal of Geophysical Research,* LXV (August 1960), 2213–2226.

8. IGY Bulletin (AGU: *Transactions,* XLI [March 1960], 81–86); see also *Physical Review,* CXV (September 15, 1959), 1734–1741.

9. For Pioneer V results see R. L. Arnoldy, *et al., Journal of Geophysical Reseach,* LXV (September 1960), 3004–7. Aircraft study results by personal communication. For a somewhat similar survey the Royal Australian Air Force allocated a Lincoln bomber to make flights between Australia and Japan.

10. "Progress in Cosmic Ray Research Since 1947," *Journal of Geophysical Research,* LXIV (February 1959), 164. Nine years earlier Peters had been denied issuance of a requested passport as "contrary to the best interests of the United States," but the Department of State reversed its decision some months later, enabling him to join the staff

of the Tata Institute of Fundamental Research in Bombay. Peters was born in Poland and educated in Germany; he emigrated to the United States in 1934. He worked on projects sponsored by the Office of Naval Research and was a faculty member at the University of Rochester. He became involved in the American security travails of the postwar period, apparently because of earlier left-wing associations, and finally left the country.

11. Bruno Rossi, "High-Energy Cosmic Rays," *Scientific American,* CCI (November 1959), 135–146.

CHAPTER 14: NIGHT LIGHTS

1. "The Visual Auroral Program," IGY Bulletin (AGU: *Transactions,* XXXIX [June 1958], 600).
2. News Letter No. 24 (Ithaca, N.Y., August 23, 1959).
3. Ya. I. Feldschtein, "The Distribution of Auroras in the Circumpolar Region," *Izvestia Akademii Nauk SSSR,* Seriya Geofizicheskaya, No. 1 (January 1959), 170–171. Translated in *Information on Soviet Bloc IGC-1959* (February 20, 1959), pp. 8–11.
4. U.S. Visual Observations News Letter No. 26 (Ithaca, N.Y., October 23, 1959). Reference is to an aurora on September 3–4, 1959.
5. "A Monochromatic Low-Latitude Aurora," *Journal of Research of the National Bureau of Standards–D. Radio Propagation,* LXIII-D (November–December 1959), 297–301; see also LXIV-D (March–April 1960), 205–9. Roach reports in a private communication the triangulation of such an arc on November 27–28, 1959, showing it to be 250 miles high. Explorer VII detected incoming radiation from the outer Van Allen belt in association with this arc. See O'Brien, Van Allen, Roach and Gartlein in *Journal of Geophysical Research,* LXV (September 1960), 2759–2766.
6. "Comparison of Absolute Intensities of [OI] 5577 in the Auroral and Subauroral Zones," *ibid.,* LXIII-D (July–August 1959), 20; see also reports by Roach *et al., Journal of Geophysical Research,* LXV (May 1960), 1489–1511. D. Barbier continued to support different causes for the two forms of 5577 emission; see *Annales de Géophysique,* XVI (1960), 143–147.
7. "Excitation Mechanisms of the Oxygen 5577 Emission in the Upper Atmosphere," *Journal of Research . . .* LXIII-D (November–December 1959), 324.
8. Fesenkov's account appears in *Astronomichesky Zhurnal,* No. 2 (March–April 1958), 305–313; translated in *Soviet Bloc IGY Information* (August 8, 1958), pp. 10–25.
9. Molchanov *et al.,* "Annular Eclipse of the Sun; Joint Expedition of Soviet and Chinese Scientists," *Vestnik Akademii Nauk SSSR,* No. 9 (September 1958), 66–71; translated in *Soviet Bloc IGY Information* (November 7, 1958), pp. 7–8.
10. Reported by Blackwell at annual meeting of the National Academy

of Sciences, Washington, D.C., April 1960. See also his "The Zodiacal Light," *Scientific American,* CCIII (July 1960), 54–63.

11. I. V. Sokolov, "Methods of Scientific Motion Picture Investigation," *Priroda,* No. 3 (March 1959), 55–60; translated in *Information on Soviet Bloc IGC-1959* (May 1, 1959), pp. 13–14. See also *Vestnik Leningradskoga Universiteta, Seria Matematiki, Mekhaniki i Astronomi,* No. 19 (Issue 4, 1957), 184–187; translated in *Soviet Bloc IGY Information* (July 11, 1958), pp. 1–5.

CHAPTER 15: **THE OCEAN ABOVE**

1. For details on development of radiosondes see William H. Wenstrom, "Radiometeorography as Applied to Unmanned Balloons," *Monthly Weather Review,* LXII (July 1934), 221–226.

2. Report by John Poulos, quoted in *Review of the First Eleven Months of the IGY,* Hearings, Subcommittee of the House Committee on Appropriations, 85th Cong., 2nd Sess., June 1958, p. 38. (Cited hereafter as *IGY Hearings.*)

3. T. N. Krishnamurti, "A Vertical Cross Section Through the 'Polar-Night' Jet Stream," *Journal of Geophysical Research,* LXIV (November 1959), 1839.

4. IGY Bulletin (AGU: *Transactions,* XLI [June 1960], 384–388).

5. DOVAP (Doppler-Velocity-And-Position) tracking depends on a minimum of three ground stations that make continuous comparison between the radio frequency of signals received via two routes: one direct from a master transmitter on the ground, the other from the master transmitter via a relay in the vehicle aloft. The frequency of the relayed signal is modified by doppler effect (a frequency change resulting from the rocket's motion). Comparison of the doppler, as observed at each of the ground stations, makes it possible to pinpoint the rocket's position.

6. For accounts of this warming, see S. Teweles and F. G. Finger, "An Abrupt Change in Stratospheric Circulation Beginning in Mid-January 1958," *Monthly Weather Review,* LXXXVI (January 1958), 23–28; *IGY Rocket Report Series No. 1, op. cit.,* pp. 47–79; IGY Bulletins (AGU: *Transactions,* XXXIX [August 1958], 778–781, 789–794, and *ibid.,* XL [March 1959], 84–88); and H. P. Pogosjan, "Seasonal Peculiarities of the Temperature and Atmospheric Circulation Regimes in the Arctic and Antarctic," World Meteorological Organization Technical Note No. 28 (WMO No. 90, TP 37 [Geneva, 1959]), p. 8. On explosive warmings in general, see Sidney Teweles, "Some Variations in the Vertical Structure and Circulation of the Stratosphere," a paper presented at the IGY Symposium of the AAAS meeting in Washington, December 30, 1958; and Harry Wexler, "A Meteorologist Looks at the Upper Atmosphere," in Henry G. Houghton (ed.), *Atmospheric Explorations* (New York: Wiley & Technology Press, 1958), pp. 79–100.

7. "Rocket Grenade Measurements of Temperatures and Winds in the Mesosphere over Churchill, Canada," *Journal of Geophysical Research,* LXV (August 1960), 2307–2323.

8. H. E. Landsberg, "Trends in Climatology," *Science,* CXXVIII (October 3, 1958), 756.

9. J. K. Angell, "The Use of Transosonde Data as an Aid to Analysis and Forecasting during the Winter of 1958–1959," *Journal of Geophysical Research,* LXIV (November 1959), 1845–1853.

10. U.S. National Committee for the IGY, "U.S. Special Meteorological Studies for the IGY: A Preliminary Data Report," presented at the CSAGI Conference in Moscow, July–August 1958.

11. From Richard J. Reed, "The Circulation of the Stratosphere," a paper presented at 40th anniversary meeting of the American Meteorological Society, Boston, January 1960.

12. See IGY Bulletin (AGU: *Transactions* XLI [March 1960], 75–81); "Status Report, U.S. Meteorological Program for the IGY" prepared for the CSAGI meeting in Moscow, p. 7; and Landsberg, "Trends in Climatology," p. 750.

13. "Status of Special Studies in Meteorology," IGY Bulletin (AGU: *Transactions,* XL [March 1959], 60–62).

14. See IGY Bulletins (*Ibid.,* XXXIX [August 1958], 779–801, and *ibid.,* XL [March 1959], 62); also "Radiochemical Analysis of Fission Debris in the Air along the 80th Meridian, West," by L. B. Lockhart, Jr., *et al., Journal of Geophysical Research,* LXV (June 1960), 1711–1722. A report on 1959 observations by Lockhart *et. al.* appears in *ibid.* (December 1960), 3987–3997.

15. See articles by A. C. Chamberlain and J. Crabtree in *Quarterly Journal of the Royal Meteorological Society,* LXXXV (October 1959), 350–370.

16. "Electron Densities to 5 Earth Radii Deduced from Nose Whistlers, *Journal of Geophysical Research,* LXV, (September 1960), 2583.

17. The British-Australian program included the launching of three Skylark rockets from the Woomera range in Australia (November 1957, April and December 1958). The rockets fired grenades, released a sodium cloud and also metal foil ("window") which would be observed by radar to determine winds. On February 21, 1958, the Soviet Union fired its newly developed "Geophysical Rocket" to a height of 473 km., its loftiest probe of the IGY.

18. See *IGY Rocket Report Series No. 1,* especially pp. 1–5, 186–189, and IGY Bulletins (AGU: *Transactions,* XXXIX [August 1958], 789–794, and *ibid.,* XLI [March 1960], 95–98, 113–117).

19. Spread-F was also blamed for the nighttime scintillation of satellite radio signals. Such signals "twinkle" because of the unevenness of the atmosphere, much as stars do. Daytime scintillation was blamed on irregularities at a somewhat lower level. See *Journal of Geophysical Research,* LXIV (December 1959), 2232ff.

20. "Solar Effects on the Acceleration of Artificial Satellites," *Research*

in Space Science, Special Report No. 29 (Smithsonian Institution Astrophysical Observatory, September 21, 1959), p. 1.

CHAPTER 16: LIFE ADRIFT

1. During the 1951–52 period the Office of Naval Research also made some eight skiplane landings between Alaska and the Pole, but the total American coverage did not compare with the multitude of landings made by the Russians during the postwar period.
2. See Hunkins, "Some Features of Arctic Deep-Sea Sedimentation," in Vivian C. Bushnell (ed.), *Proceedings of the Second Annual Arctic Planning Session, October 1959,* GRD Research Notes No. 29 (Bedford, Mass.: Geophysics Research Directorate, Air Force Cambridge Research Center, December 1959), pp. 11–15. See also Hunkins, "Station Alpha Geophysical Investigations," in J. H. Hartshorn (ed.), *Proceedings of the First Annual Arctic Planning Session, November 1958,* GRD Research Notes No. 15 (April 1959), pp. 23–25. And see Thomas, "Lithology and Zoology of an Antarctic Ocean Bottom Core," in *Deep-Sea Research* (London: Pergamon Press, 1959), Vol. VI, pp. 5–15.
3. *New York Times,* April 20, 1958.
4. For a description of *Skate* surfacing and visit to Station Alpha, see Cmdr. James Calvert, *Surface at the Pole* (New York: McGraw-Hill, 1960), pp. 109–121.
5. Accounts of scientific studies at Station A appear in IGY Bulletins (AGU: *Transactions,* XXXIX [June 1958], 601–605; *ibid.* [December 1958], 1213–1215; and *ibid.,* XL [June 1959], 159–162).
6. Vivian C. Bushnell (ed.), *Scientific Studies at Fletcher's Ice Island, T-3 (1952–1955),* Geophysical Research Papers No. 63 (Bedford, Mass.: Geophysics Research Directorate, September 1959), Vol. I, p. 3.
7. "Build-up of Thick Floating Ice in the Arctic Areas" (GRD Research Notes No. 29), p. 41.
8. *Ibid.,* p. 39.
9. In mid-June the island drifted over the Lomonosov Ridge and American visitors to Russia that summer were told that a submarine volcanic eruption had jarred the station and overcome the men with sulfurous fumes. The ridge is known to be a source of earthquakes, but this report has not been substantiated, although the Russians subsequently published their discovery of volcanic material of seemingly recent origin on the ocean floor. "IGY in the Arctic— Volcanoes in the Arctic," *Nauka i Zhizn,* No. 1 (January 1959), 24–26; translated in *Information on Soviet Bloc IGC-1959* (April 17, 1959), pp. 16–18.
10. "A Year of Floating on the Arctic Ocean," *Fizkultura I Sport,* No. 1 (January 1959), 10–11; translated in *ibid.* (March 20, 1959), pp. 11–12.

11. Lucien Barnier, *Secrets of Soviet Science* (London: Allan Wingate, 1959), p. 83. He says the automatic weather stations weighed 400 pounds.

CHAPTER 17: HELICOPTERS AND REINDEER

1. Estimates by G. Avsyuk (quoted in *Pravda*, December 29, 1959, p. 6) and by Chapman (*IGY: Year of Discovery*, p. 28).
2. For report on the McCall Glacier Project see articles by Mason, Sater, and Keeler in *Arctic*, XII (June 1959), 77–97. The circumstances of Hubley's death were made public by the Air Force on November 2, 1957. See *New York Times*, November 3, p. 50.
3. "The Exceptional Advances of the Muldrow, Black Rapids, and Susitna Glaciers," *Journal of Geophysical Research*, LXV (November 1960), 3703–3712. See also Troy Péwé in *Bulletin of the Geological Society of America*, LXVIII (1957), 1908–9. Much of the advance was over moraine-covered ice.
4. "Distribution and variations of glaciers in the United States exclusive of Alaska," in *Proceedings* of the IUGG General Assembly, Helsinki, 1960 (in press).
5. Paper presented at the annual meeting of the American Geophysical Union in Washington, April 29, 1960.
6. See *Information on Soviet Bloc IGC-1959* (November 27, 1959), pp. 7–8, and IGY Information Bulletin No. 5 (Moscow, 1957), pp. 56–63.
7. Of the ten German participants, at least seven were from East Germany. See J. Toeppler, "Back From Pamir and Tien Shan," *Vermessungstechnik*, No. 1 (January 1959), 12; translated in *Information on Soviet Bloc IGC-1959* (March 13, 1959), p. 5.
8. Verbatim remarks recorded by Barnier, *Secrets of Soviet Science*, p. 82.
9. See Eugène Schreider, "The Abominable Snowman," *Discovery*, XXI (May 1960), 196–198. Among the accounts reviewed by the commission was that of a Soviet army doctor called in by local police to examine a man found naked in midwinter in the mountains of Daghestan. He was thought to be an enemy agent, but was covered with hair like that of a bear and apparently could not speak.
10. R. D. Zabirov, "The Present State of Central Asian Glaciers," IGY Information Bulletin No. 5 (Moscow, 1957), pp. 91–94. Translations of reports on the Fedchenko expedition appear in *Soviet Bloc IGY Information* for April 11 and October 10, 1958; *Information on Soviet Bloc IGC-1959* for October 30 and November 27, 1959; and in *IGY News* (January 7, 1958), Item 65, pp. 160–161.
11. See *Information on Soviet Bloc IGC-1959* for July 31 and October 23, 1959, and *Information on Soviet Bloc IGC-1960* for February 12, 1960. There are almost 300 glaciers in the Altai Mountains, close to the western junction of the USSR, China, and Mongolia, but most

IGY work was concentrated on the Great Aktru, the Little Aktru, and the Taldurinski glaciers.

12. N. A. Grave, "Preparation for Investigations in the Suntar-Khayata Mountain Region," IGY Information Bulletin No. 3 (Moscow, 1957), pp. 68–73; translated in *Soviet Bloc IGY Information* (February 21, 1958), pp. 11–16. See also Koreysha and Grave, "On the Progress of Researches in the Region of the Suntar-Khayata Range," *ibid.* No. 7 (Moscow, 1959), pp. 46–51. On Koryak survey, see *Information on Soviet Bloc IGC-1959* (March 13, 1959), p. 4.

13. For Franz Joseph studies see *Soviet Bloc IGY Information* (June 27, 1958), pp. 19–20; (July 4, 1958), pp. 19–20; and (April 4, 1958), pp. 19–20.

14. S. Manczarski, "Polish Balance Sheet of the Geophysical Year," *Zycie Warzawy* (Warsaw: July 26, 1958), p. 5; translated in *Soviet Bloc IGY Information* (October 17, 1958), p. 3.

15. *Discovery,* XIX (September 1958), 388.

CHAPTER 18: ANTARCTIC PREPARATIONS

1. *CSAGI Bulletin d'Information No. 5,* p. 61.
2. On the preceding March 28 the White House had announced that there would be three American bases, including one at or near the South Pole.
3. *CSAGI Bulletin d'Information No. 7,* p. 17.
4. For more details on these pre-IGY meetings, see Walter Sullivan, "The International Geophysical Year," *International Conciliation,* pp. 318–326.
5. *Operation Deepfreeze* (Operation Plan No. 1–55, Commander, U.S. Naval Support Force Antarctica), p. 2.
6. Among the books that have dealt with the establishment of IGY bases in Antarctica are Dufek's *Operation Deep Freeze* (New York: Harcourt, Brace, 1957), Paul Frazier's *Antarctic Assault* (New York: Dodd Mead, 1958), and two books by Sullivan: *Quest for a Continent* (New York: McGraw-Hill, 1957) and *White Land of Adventure* (New York: Whittlesey, 1957).
7. Named Williams Air Operating Facility in memory of Richard T. Williams, the Navy tractor driver who died during the initial unloading there.
8. Australian radar studies of meteor trails 50–60 miles above Mawson disclosed ionospheric winds blowing predominantly from the Antarctic coast toward the Pole. See Phillip Law, "The IGY in Antarctica," *Australian Journal of Science,* XXI (June 1959), 293. Some also attributed the nighttime persistence of ionization to the ultraviolet radiation detected by rockets, apparently coming from sunlit, neutral hydrogen in space.

9. A full account of the South Pole project appears in Siple's *90° South* (New York: Putnam, 1959).
10. Law, "The IGY in Antarctica," p. 285.
11. Based primarily on *ibid.,* p. 286. The eight U.S. stations include Wilkes Satellite Station, manned only part-time, and Hallett Station, manned jointly with New Zealand.

CHAPTER 19: CONTINENT OR ARCHIPELAGO?

1. Reported by Tass. See *New York Times,* August 31, 1957, p. 32.
2. In *90° South,* Siple terms this phenomenon the "Antarctic Hush" (pp. 153–154). The Russians attributed it to the collapse of layers four to eight inches thick at a depth of thirteen to sixteen feet, propagating in a wavelike manner over distances up to 300 miles or more: V. M. Kotlyakov, "Snow collapse in Antarctica," *Priroda,* No. 3 (March 1960), 110–111; translated in *Information on Soviet Bloc IGC-1960* (May 13, 1960), pp. 35–36.
3. For a discussion of polygons in Antarctica see the article by T. L. Péwé in *American Journal of Science,* CCLVII (October 1959), 545–552.
4. C. R. Bentley, A. P. Crary, N. A. Ostenso, and E. C. Thiel, "Structure of West Antarctica," *Science,* CXXXI (January 15, 1960), 131–136.
5. For accounts of traverses, see IGY Bulletins (AGU: *Transactions,* XXXVIII [August 1957], 612–617; *ibid.,* XXXIX [April 1958], 369–375, and [August 1958], 772–778; *ibid.,* XL [March 1959], 48–50, and [September 1959], 277–282, 311–315, and [December 1959], 423–426).
6. See IGY Bulletin (*Ibid.,* XXXIX [August 1958], 794–799).
7. See Henri Bader of SIPRE in IGY Bulletin (*Ibid.,* XXXIX [February 1958], 163).
8. The Soviet expedition reported boring to a depth of 1217 feet at Pionerskaya. See *Discovery,* XIX (August 1958), 345. For an account of the U.S. program, see IGY Bulletin (AGU: *Transactions,* XXXIX [October 1958], 1021–1023).
9. Vivian Fuchs and Edmund Hillary, *The Crossing of Antarctica* (Boston: Little, Brown, 1958), p. 264.
10. *Little America* (New York: Putnam, 1930), p. 130.
11. Cordon D. Cartwright with Beverly Smith, Jr., "I Lived with the Russians in Antarctica," *Saturday Evening Post,* October 18, 1958, p. 92.
12. *Loc. cit.*
13. *Vodny Transport,* April 26, 1958; from *Soviet Bloc IGY Information* (June 13, 1958), p. 23.
14. See photographs in Walter Sullivan, "Dry Valley," *Natural History,* LXVII (February 1958), 112–113. Péwé's study showed no change

for the past fifty years. See IGY Bulletin (AGU: *Transactions,* XLI [June 1960], 392).

15. P. A. Shumsky presented his views at a symposium on Antarctica during the IUGG General Assembly, Helsinki, 1960. For Mellor's analysis, see *Journal of Glaciology,* III (October 1959), 522–533. The views of Loewe are cited and referenced by Mellor.

16. *Sovietsky Flot,* April 9, 1959; translated in *Information on Soviet Bloc IGC-1959* (June 12, 1959), pp. 25–26. Shumsky likewise found Antarctica to be a continent. (See his article in *Journal of Glaciology,* III [October 1959] 455–457.) John Hollin and Willis L. Tressler reported that raised beaches at Wilkes Station showed a 100-foot rise in the land since ice retreated from the area about 12,000 years ago. See IGY Bulletin (AGU: *Transactions,* XLI [March 1960], 99).

17. See Kapitsa in *Informationy Bulleten, Sovietskoi Antarkticheskoi Expeditsii,* No. 19 (Leningrad: 1960), pp. 10–14. Crary's results were reported at the IUGG symposium on Antarctica mentioned above.

18. See *Information on Soviet Bloc IGC-1960* (March 18, 1960), p. 31, and (May 27, 1960), pp. 13–18.

19. The Soviet plan originally called for thirty shots in this area, leaving eight unaccounted for.

20. Report on Antarctic Geophysical Studies, *Priroda,* No. 7 (July 1958), 59–62; from *Soviet Bloc IGY Information* (August 29, 1958), pp. 19–20. The hypothesis was proposed by V. V. Shuleykin about 1951. See *Information on Soviet Bloc IGC-1960* (April 15, 1960), pp. 23–26.

21. See Korotkevich in *Izvestia Vsesoyuznogo Geograficheskogo Obshchestva,* XC (May–June 1958), 220–231; from *Soviet Bloc IGY Information* (October 24, 1958), p. 19. The absence of snow at this station made it impossible for skiplanes to land and a snow runway was marked out 12 kilometers away; a helicopter was used to ferry men and supplies the intervening distance.

22. Malcolm Mellor, "Ice Flow in Antarctica," *Journal of Glaciology,* III (March 1959), 337–384.

23. Law, *op. cit.,* p. 292. L. M. Gould gave similar testimony before Congress. See IGY Hearings, p. 51.

24. See Law, p. 287.

25. *Science,* CXXIX (February 20, 1959), 462–463.

CHAPTER 20: THE WATER PLANET

1. See John H. Ryther, "Potential Productivity of the Sea," *Science,* CXXX (September 11, 1959), 602–608.

2. *Time,* July 6, 1959, p. 51.

3. See Roger Revelle, "International Co-operation in the Marine Sciences," *ICSU Review,* I (January 1959), 36.

4. See Revelle testimony in IGY Hearings, p. 71.
5. *Ibid.*, p. 70.
6. *Ibid.*, p. 71.
7. *Ibid.*, pp. 70–71.
8. G. E. R. Deacon, "The Pinger," *Oceanus,* V (Summer and Autumn 1957), p. 14; also G. Wüst, "Stromgeschwindigkeiten und Strommenger in den Tiefen des Atlantischen Ozeans, unter besonderer Beruchsichtigung des Tiefen und Bodenwassers," *Wissenschaftliche Ergebnisse: Deutsche Atlantische Expedition . . . "Meteor" 1925/27,* (Berlin: 1957), Vol. VI, part 2, 6.
9. Further material on this project and Stommel's work appears in other articles in *Oceanus, op. cit.,* pp. 3–25. See also Robert Cowen, *Frontiers of the Sea; the Story of Oceanographic Exploration* (Garden City, N.Y.: Doubleday, 1960).
10. Data on these currents were taken from a paper presented by John A. Knauss of Scripps at the annual meeting of the National Academy of Sciences, April 27, 1959. See also IGY Bulletin (AGU: *Transactions,* XL [March 1959], 78–79).
11. H. Wexler "The Atlantic Convergence—or Divergence?" *The Rossby Memorial Volume* (New York: Oxford, 1959), pp. 107–120.
12. IGY Bulletin (AGU: *Transactions,* XL [June 1959], 167–170). For other Atlantic studies see *ibid.,* XXXVIII [December 1957], 1019–1021.
13. On the Pacific program see U.S. National Committee for the IGY, "Status Report, U.S. Oceanography Program for the IGY," presented at CSAGI meeting in Moscow, 1958.
14. See section by June Pattullo in *The Sea: Ideas and Observations,* to be published by Interscience.
15. IGY Bulletin (AGU: *Transactions,* XL [June 1959], 167–170). Laclavère told the CSAGI meeting in Moscow that IGY observations of long waves were only partly successful due to inexperience and uncertainty as to response of instruments to various wave types. The studies, he said, were a first step toward more refined measurements ("Report on the Oceanographic Programme of the IGY," Doc., 0.2–1). Other reports on the U.S. oceanographic program appear in IGY Bulletins (AGU: *Transactions,* XXXVIII [August 1957], 629–630; *ibid.,* XXXIX [February 1958], 184–185, and [October 1958], 1011–1017).

CHAPTER 21: THE DEEPEST DEPTHS

1. Birshteyn, Savilov, and Udintsev, "Trawling in the Maximum Depths of the World Oceans," *Priroda,* No. 3 (March 1958), 70–71; translated in *Soviet Bloc IGY Information* (May 16, 1958), pp. 16–18. See also L. A. Zenkevitch, "Certain Aspects of Ocean Depths Studies," paper presented at CSAGI meeting, Moscow, 1958.
2. Reported by F. F. Koczy of the University of Miami at a symposium on the deep sea during the annual meeting of the National Academy

of Sciences, April 27, 1959. At the same meeting Stommel gave 300 years as a minimum turnover time, based on his theoretical studies. Carbon-14 measurements by Ewing and his colleagues showed that North Atlantic deep water had been isolated from the atmosphere for an average of 650 years, whereas the figure for Antarctic bottom water was less than 350 years. See *Journal of Geophysical Research*, LXV (September 1960), 2903–2931.

3. IGY Bulletin (AGU: *Transactions*, XL [March 1959], 73–75).
4. The *Vityaz* reported recovering a 111.5-foot core. N. N. Suisnov, *Sovietskoye Expeditionnoye Sudno "Vityaz,"* (Moscow, 1959), p. 30.
5. IGY Hearings, p. 68.
6. *Ibid.*, p. 76. See also p. 64 and IGY Bulletins (AGU: *Transactions* XXXIX [February 1958], 159–162, and *ibid.*, XLI [March 1960], 109–110).
7. Most of the nodules are about the size of a billiard ball, although some reach two feet in diameter. It has been proposed that the minerals have been extracted from sea water by colonies of bacteria. After discovery of the nodules, American commercial interests investigated the feasibility of scraping them off the bottom, but apparently were not interested in such a high-risk venture. See *New York Times,* March 8, 1959, Financial Section p. 1.
8. L. A. Zenkevitch, "Oceans—The Storehouse of Mankind," *Izvestia* Sunday supplement, April 10–16, 1960. See *Information on Soviet Bloc IGC-1960* (June 3, 1960), pp. 20–21.

CHAPTER 22: THE WORLD TREMBLES

1. This account based on text issued to accompany a documentary film on this earthquake, shown at the CSAGI meeting in Moscow, July–August 1958, and on the account in *Izvestia Akademii Nauk SSSR, Seriya Geofizicheskaya,* No. 11 (1959), 1687–1689 (see *Information on Soviet Bloc IGC* [December 25, 1959], pp. 7–10, and [March 25, 1960], pp. 20–21).
2. Developed by Maurice Ewing and his former student Frank Press at the Lamont Geological Observatory.
3. IGY Bulletin (AGU: *Transactions, XXXIX [April 1958], 380–382).
4. L. T. Aldrich, M. N. Bass, M. A. Tuve, and G. W. Wetherill, "The Earth's Crust," *Year Book 58* (Washington: Carnegie Institution of Washington, 1959), p. 234.
5. IGY Bulletin (AGU: *Transactions, XXXIX [June 1958], 581). See also *ibid.*, XLI [June 1960], 354–355.
6. Aldrich *et al.*, "The Earth's Crust," p. 236.
7. IGY Bulletin (AGU: *Transactions, XLI [June 1960], 351–355). The Mexican data are subject to two interpretations. The one used in the illustration is that favored by the Wisconsin group.
8. *Bulletin of the Geological Society of America,* LXX (March 1959), 229–244.

9. Don Tocher and Don J. Miller, "Field Observations on Effects of Alaska Earthquake of 10 July 1958," *Science,* CXXIX (February 13, 1959), 394–395. See also articles by Miller, Tocher, *et al.,* in *Bulletin of the Seismological Society of America,* L (April 1960), 217–322.

10. Results of long-period seismic observations in this chapter are taken from Jack Oliver, "Long Period Waves and the Lᵍ Phase," draft article for *IGY Annals* (in press).

11. Hugo Benioff, "Circum-Pacific Tectonics," from "A Symposium on the Mechanics of Faulting, with Special Reference to the Fault-Plane Work," *Publications of the Dominion Observatory,* XX (Ottawa: 1958), 395–402.

12. *Discovery,* XIX (April 1958), 165.

13. *Information on Soviet Bloc IGC-1960* (March 18, 1960), pp. 22–29.

14. "Seismic Waves from High-Altitude Nuclear Explosions," by Paul Pomeroy and Jack Oliver, *Journal of Geophysical Research,* LXV (October 1960), 3445–3457.

CHAPTER 23: OUR PEARLIKE PLANET

1. One of the problems in observations of such precision is uncertainty with regard to the travel path (and hence travel time) of radio time signals.

2. See IGY Bulletins (AGU: *Transactions,* XXXVIII [August 1957], 624–625, and [October 1957], 830; *ibid.,* XXXIX [February 1958], 175–178, and [December 1958], 1205–1211.

3. John A. O'Keefe, Ann Eckels, and R. Kenneth Squires, *Science,* CXXIX (February 27, 1959), 565–566. See also the same authors' "The Gravitational Field of the Earth," *Astronomical Journal,* LXIV (September 1959), 245–253. Their calculations were partly disputed by W. A. Heiskanen. See "The latest Achievements of Physical Geodesy," *Journal of Geophysical Research,* LXV (September 1960), 2833–2836.

4. "Convection Currents in the Earth's Mantle," *Journal of Geophysical Research,* LXV (January 1960), 349–353. See also IGY Bulletin (AGU: *Transactions,* XL [June 1959], 172–173), and R. Jastrow, "Astrophysics Progress," *Missiles and Rockets,* V (July 20, 1959), 43–47.

5. P. Musen, R. Bryant, and A. Bailie, NASA, "Perturbations in Perigee Height of Vanguard I," *Science,* CXXXI (March 25, 1960), 935–936.

6. A. N. Nesmeyanov, "Our Knowledge of the Earth is Expanding," *Pravda,* July 1, 1959, p. 5; see *Information on Soviet Bloc IGC-1959* (July 24, 1959), pp. 2–3.

CHAPTER 24. THE HARVEST

1. IGY Hearings, p. 48.
2. *Science,* CXXVIII (November 21, 1958), 1249.
3. *New York Times,* December 7, 1957, p. 1.
4. IGY Bulletin (AGU: *Transactions* XXXIX [February 1958], 192–193).
5. *Science,* CXXVII (June 27, 1958), 1499–1500.
6. Resolutions of the Fifth CSAGI Assembly, Moscow (Document 170).
7. *Science,* CXXIX (January 9, 1959), 80.
8. Alla Masevich of the Soviet space program said in a Radio Moscow broadcast that the U.S. was not keeping its "side of the bargain" with regard to the Discoverer satellites. (See *New York Times,* November 2, 1959, p. 16.) Van Allen felt the exchange of space research data was equally inhibited on both sides by security restrictions (see "Science in Outer Space," *op. cit.,* pp. 10–11).
9. J. W. Townsend, Jr., "Soviet Papers Presented at the Rocket and Satellite Symposium," *Science,* CXXIX (January 9, 1959), p. 84.
10. *New York Times,* August 1, 1958, p. 23.
11. *Science,* CXXVIII (November 14, 1958), 1197–1198.
12. *Ibid.* (January 9, 1959), p. 80.
13. See Odishaw, "International Geophysics Committee," AGU: *Transactions,* XL (December 1959), 347–350.
14. *ICSU Review,* I (April 1959), 91.
15. Statement by A. W. Frutkin, director, Office of International Programs, NASA, before the Inter-American Defense Board, Washington, D.C., February 16, 1960 (NASA Release No. 60-124).
16. Law, "The IGY in Antarctica," *op. cit.,* p. 294.
17. For text of the Antarctic Treaty, see *The Conference on Antarctica,* Department of State Publication 7060, International Organization and Conference Series 13 (Washington, D.C.: September 1960), pp. 61–67. The United States ratified the Treaty on August 18, 1960. By early 1961 all but Argentina and Chile had ratified, although Australia had not yet deposited its instrument of ratification. All of the instruments must be deposited before the treaty comes into force.
18. This figure covers the period to the end of the IGY. The chief contributors were the United States ($75,000), the Soviet Union ($45,-000), Britain ($21,000), and Canada ($10,000). UNESCO gave $85,000 and ICSU $40,000. See Sydney Chapman, "The International Geophysical Year," AGU: *Transactions,* XL (June 1959), 118.
19. *Bulletin of the Atomic Scientists,* XVI (April 1960), 115.

INDEX

ABOUT THE AUTHOR

Walter Sullivan is the leading science writer of *The New York Times* and is the author of *Quest for a Continent* (the story of the four final American expeditions to the Antarctic) and *White Land of Adventure* (a junior book). He has followed the story of the IGY from its inception, a trail that has led around the world and earned for him the George Polk Memorial Award in journalism.

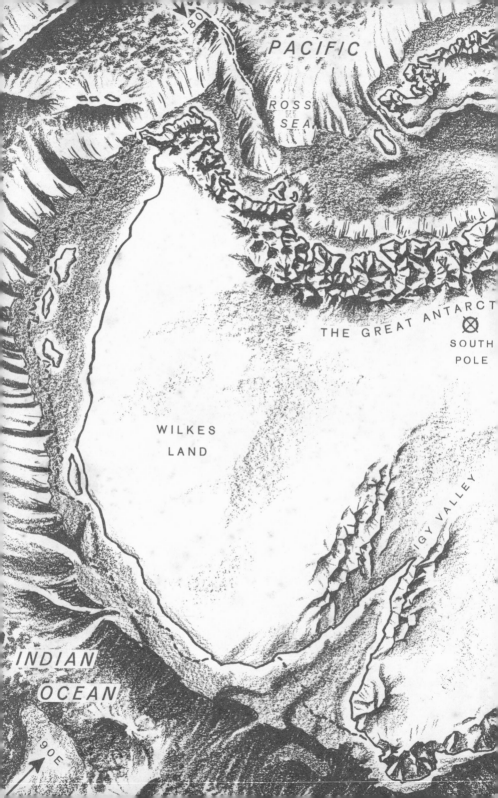